EUGENICS
AND THE
PROGRESSIVES

Donald K. Pickens

Vanderbilt University Press *1968*

To Mary Jo Pickens, loving wife and critic, this book is dedicated with love and deep appreciation.

ACKNOWLEDGMENTS

In THE evolution (no pun intended) of this book, many intellectual and personal debts have been created. The research grants from North Texas State University have aided immeasurably in completing this work. The interest of Dr. Hugh M. Ayer, Chairman of the Social Sciences, and Dr. Jack Scroggs, Director of the History Department at North Texas, have been most encouraging.

My gratitude goes to Dr. Donald J. Berthrong of the University of Oklahoma and Dr. David D. Van Tassel of The University of Texas for their patience and friendship in my professional training. Miss Karen Green and Mrs. William Land have typed the manuscript. I appreciate their fine job. Miss Green, as my secretary, has suffered from my bad jokes and typing but has responded with good humor in both instances.

My colleague, Dr. Donald E. Chipman, and his wife Doris, by their critical reading and commentary of the text, improved this volume. In taking time from his own research and productive career to read this manuscript, Don demonstrated the many virtues and kindnesses that make him a personal friend.

A different version of Chapter Six appeared in *Phylon,* XXVIII, number one (1967) as "The Sterilization Movement; The Search for Purity in Mind and State." The editors graciously allowed the material to appear in this book.

Mr. Robert P. Emmitt of Vanderbilt University Press, with his editorial guidance, gave both shape and substance to these pages and I am thankful.

To my wife, Mary Jo, the dedication is an inadequate summary of my indebtedness to her.

These people have given merit to this work; the residue of error and inadequacy is my own creation.

Denton, Texas   DONALD K. PICKENS
January 2, 1968

CONTENTS

INTRODUCTION

A. L. KROEBER, in 1917, published his now-famous article on "The Superorganic." Within the context of a skeptic antinaturalism, Kroeber criticized the basic naturalistic notion that society and nature were related parts of a continuous chain, the great chain of being. Kroeber did not deny man's animal origins and nature; yet he saw in human existence something else, a vital difference—civilization. Hereditary evolution, he believed, was organic, while social evolution, the process of civilization, was "not, or not necessarily tied up with hereditary agencies." [1] Civilization was the key distinction of kind, not degree, between man and animal.[2] After a brief discussion of cultural environment on the human organism, Kroeber classified the social insects as entirely instinctive creatures and therefore not capable of civilization,

1. A. L. Kroeber, "The Superorganic" *American Anthropologist* new series XIX (April-June 1917), 167. This article is reprinted in a collection of academic reprints entitled *Social Science Papers.*
2. *Ibid.,* p. 169.

the uniquely human enterprise. "Man is a social animal, thus, a social organism. He has organic constitution; but he has also civilization. To ignore one element is as short-sighted as to overlook the other; *to convert one into the other,* if each has its reality, is negation." [3] To convert one into the other was precisely the eugenist's major intellectual and ideological task. Kroeber maintained, however, that it was quite possible that civilization and heredity worked in

entirely separate ways, that therefore any outright substitution of one for the other in the explanation of human group phenomena is crass; and that the refusal to recognize at least the logical possibility of an explanation of human achievement totally different from the prevailing tendency toward a biological one, is an act of illiberality. [4]

Appropriately, Kroeber discussed Francis Galton, the intellectual founder of modern eugenics, in light of his thesis. Kroeber thought Galton and his followers failed to distinguish between the social and the organic. Though he acknowledged Galton's genius, Kroeber argued that the Englishman confused heredity as mental action with civilization, which is the result of mental exercise. Mentality was individual; civilization went beyond the individual. [5] A collection of individuals does not make a civilization, but within a collective history and language they do. Krobeber did not deny individual differences among men, but this organic factor (heredity) cannot be considered on the same level as civilization or the superorganic. The Galtonian eugenists believed the opposite. For them, modern man's failure to recognize the relationship spelled future genetic (and social) trouble for civilization. Kroeber believed in counter-distinction, that the social was a leap to a different plane. [6]

In summary, Kroeber concluded,

The mind and the body are but facets of the same organic material or activity; the social substance—or unsubstantial fabric, if one prefers the phrase,—the existence that we call civilization, transcends them utterly for

3. *Ibid.,* p. 180.

4. *Ibid.,* p. 184.

5. *Ibid.,* pp. 192–193. Years later Kroeber ranked Galton as an important figure in the history of psychology. See A. L. Kroeber, *An Anthropologist Looks At History,* p. 120.

6. Kroeber, "The Superorganic," p. 209.

all its being forever rooted in life. The processes of civilizational activity are almost unknown to us. The self-sufficient factors that govern their workings are unresolved. The forces and principles of mechanistic science can indeed analyze our civilization; but in so doing they destroy its essence, and leave us without understanding of the very thing which we seek. The historian as yet can do little but picture. He traces and he connects what seems far removed; he balances; he integrates; but he does not really explain, nor does he transmute phenomena into something else. His method is not science; but neither can the scientist deal with historical material and leave it civilization, nor anything resembling civilization, nor convert it wholly into concepts of life and leave nothing else to be done. What we all are able to do is to realize this gap, to be impressed by its abyss with reverence and humility, and to go our paths on its respective sides without self-deluding attempts to bridge the eternal chasm, or empty boasts that its span is achieved.[7]

This intellectual tension between Kroeber and Galton is the crux of modern man's dilemma: what is animal and what is cultural in human nature? Kroeber's essay was part of a twentieth-century critique of nineteenth-century naturalism. And yet, in our day of air and water pollution, of culturally creatured cancer (cigarette smoking), of drugs causing genetic mutation, of atomic fall-out, of rapid utilization and destruction of our earthly heritage, the American eugenists, despite their class and intellectual prejudices, still bear witness to the fact that men live in the world—both biologically and culturally. For after all, in a land of genetic eye trouble, the ophthalmologist is king, to paraphrase a cliché.[8]

The American eugenists from 1859 to 1930 were both creatures and creators of their intellectual history. It would be of little profit to use present-mindedness against the eugenists; rather, to understand the eugenists with their naturalistic Darwinian and sociological presuppositions as part of this problem of man's nature is the objective of this study.

7. *Ibid.*, pp. 212–213.
8. For a recent intellectual formulation of this problem see Frederick Sargent II, "The Adaptability of Man," *Medical Opinion and Review*, IV (March 1968), 38–51.

Beware of false prophets, which come to you in sheep's clothing, but inwardly they are ravening wolves.

Ye shall know them by their fruits. Do men gather grapes of thorns, or figs of thistles?

Even so every good tree bringeth forth good fruit; but a corrupt tree bringeth forth evil fruit.

A good tree cannot bring forth evil fruit, neither can a corrupt tree bring forth good fruit.

Every tree that bringeth not forth good fruit is hewn down, and cast into the fire.

Wherefore by their fruits ye shall know them.

Matt. 7:15–20

EUGENICS AND THE PROGRESSIVES

1

BACKGROUND TO EUGENICS: NATURE, MAN, AND HISTORY

The Problem: Its Nature and Organization

AMERICAN EUGENISTS, like some other progressives, had little faith in the innate ability of men to solve social problems democratically. Their belief in naturalism caused this distrust of democratic politics; for eugenists and many progressives recognized the animal origin of human nature and thereby assumed that for the majority of humans the benefits of civilization were only skin deep. Agitating for reform against the backdrop of Darwinian thought, the eugenists equated nature with society. Eugenists and large numbers of progressives thus viewed the class conflicts of the first thirty years of the twentieth century as examples of animal competition in nature. In consequence, the eugenists attempted to give a naturalistic justification for the divisions in United States society.

Eugenists, like other conservative members of the progressive crusade, used natural law, not as a means for establishing a democratic society in which all men realized an equitable situation in life, but to defend civilization from the menace of the biologically inadequate.

Charles Darwin's evolutionary theories, not John Locke's concepts of nature, provided the basis for their reforms. The eugenists also utilized pre-Darwinian concepts of economy in nature, the great chain of being theory, and teleology. Ideas drawn from nature, before and after Charles Darwin's explanation, helped justify the social affairs of men. Like many conservatives in the progressive camp, however, eugenists basically distrusted the cosmic forces of natural selection and survival of the fittest to solve society's problems; therefore, they hoped to "help" nature in reforming society in the name of an "objective" science—eugenics. Their goal was not to free man's innate rationality and goodness from the limitations of society but to control society more efficiently and effectively through the scientific manipulations of mankind's instincts.

In this way, eugenists appeared as progressives in their use of "science" in reform matters, and yet, worried about the growth of democracy in an urban and industrial America, they merely projected their class prejudices as objective laws of civilization and nature. The problem, therefore, is to explain how the development of biological science since the time of Darwin influenced the conservatives' response to an industrial America. For the conservatives during the progressive years, Sir Francis Galton's philosophy of eugenics provided a means of defending the status quo in the name of an apparent radicalism—eugenics. How this situation developed (the interaction of scientific and social thought) and its influence upon certain aspects of American life are important aspects of this study.

The body of this work investigates the nature of Galtonian eugenics in the United States during those years of its greatest influence, 1900–1929. Drawing heavily from naturalistic philosophy, Sir Francis Galton and his American followers, Charles Davenport, David Starr Jordan, Edward M. East and Harry H. Laughlin, constructed a philosophy for the eugenics movement. This movement had tremendous influence upon American social, political and academic life. Out of this movement came two major methods of achieving racial improvement—birth control and sterilization. Political theorists and politicians, such as Theodore Roosevelt, were sympathetic to the movement, since their progressive political theory had its roots in the same philosophy as eugenics—naturalism. Social scientists felt the impact of eugenics.

The concept of recapitulation became popular with the child psychologists. From the belief that behavior is innate, not learned, came the theory of instinct psychology. Some anthropologists adhered to the belief that civilization has weakened man and protected him from the natural law, survival of the fittest. The remedies which the movement offered for this corruption of man by civilization were threefold: to limit charity to those worth saving and, at the same time, to conserve natural resources, so that in the future they may be available for those humans worth saving, and to keep these superior creatures close to nature in order to keep them pure, that is, to allow Darwinian natural laws to function. Hence, these natural laws form a science that can effect the resurrection of natural man.

The Great Depression of 1929 and the rise of genetics marked the decline of eugenics as an organized movement and as a creed among intellectuals and social leaders. Environmentalism, based on fuller understanding of culture and individual development, contributed to the demise of Galtonian eugenics. Fascists with their programs of racial purity completed the process of disenchantment for Americans with racial reforms.

The Beginnings of Natural History to Darwin

Aristotle produced one of the first important theories about the relationship of the lower animals to man. This Greek philosopher arranged all animals in a single, graded scale according to their degree of perfection, with man at the top. This idea has come to be known as the great chain of being. All animals are not totally perfect, Aristotle concluded, but being related as they are, one species supplements another's imperfections.

John Ray (1627–1705), one of the great biologists of all time and pioneer in the systematic study of natural history, believed in Aristotle's theory and, in addition, expressed a concept of nature which dominated biological sciences for two hundred years: nature is static. All forms of life have remained the same since the moment of their creation. Ray's interest was not in the origin of animals, but in their purpose. He reasoned that, because God created the orders of nature, and since God is not wasteful, then there is a place for everything and everything should be in its place. Economy is the keynote of his theory—a concept which held sway over biology until the time of Darwin.[1] Ray also adhered to the ancient idea of the unity of form and function. Everything has a reason (teleology). Thus, God designed each detail of an animal's structure to perform a specific function in that particular animal's environment. Each species in this rational system is related to another species, and these related species exist harmoniously.

For many thinkers in natural history and science, a conflict developed between two theories of nature, both of which had a kinship with the great chain of being. One idea was that nature was simply an order of laws of motion and matter. The second concept was that nature was for the edification and enjoyment of mankind. God created each organic and inorganic item in nature and ordained that nature should then serve man. Isaac Newton (1642–1727), for example, found in his scientific experiments a concept of nature as a self-contained system of laws. This concept disturbed him, however, because he believed mechanical orientation discounted the value of God as a purposeful creator, and he could not accept a world without purpose.[2]

By the eighteenth century, some secular philosophers questioned the validity of a purposeful Deity as the major force in nature and the affairs of man. In fact, the course of such speculation has generally resulted in an advancement of the secular view of history. This secular view of nature paralleled developments in natural sciences. (Often in the past, the ideas about the operation of nature and history were the same).[3]

Some men, by the nineteenth century, discounted God as a vital force in history and nature, as the ultimate cause. Men began searching for immediate and less remote causes in explaining nature and their own past behavior. By the middle of the century, in the emerging view, History replaced God. History, viewed as progress,

1. Arthur O. Lovejoy, *The Great Chain of Being, A Study in the History of an Idea,* pp. 58–59, 81, 189–195, 211, 227, 231, 242. John C. Greene, *The Death of Adam, Evolution and Its Impact on Western Thought,* pp. 14–15, 136–137. Hereafter cited as Greene, *The Death of Adam.*

2. *Ibid.,* p. 23.

3. See Hans Loweth, *The Meaning in History,* and R. G. Collingwood, *The Idea of History* and his *The Idea of Nature.*

now explained the mysteries of human affairs. Faith in history, in man's past achievements and future greatness, replaced the total dependence on God in human existence and experience. Progress solved all problems.[4]

Although to twentieth-century man progress implied movement toward new and better forms of experience, this is not what nineteenth-century man meant. The vision embodied in the word *progress* was actually the restoration of a noble state that mankind for various reasons had lost. At one time, the theory explained, mankind lived in an early paradise. In a primitive existence, man had known the true values of life as only nature could reveal them. In Christian terms this past condition was the Garden of Eden. Even secular philosophers, for example, Karl Marx in the nineteenth century, felt that man could return to the natural goodness of life by discovering the laws of society. Progress was a return to a natural way of life if mankind followed certain natural and objective values. In varied forms this basic concept shaped much of the philosophical speculations of the eighteenth and nineteenth centuries.[5] Revolutionaries and reactionaries invoked the theory in defense of their philosophies and programs.

Like so much of the discussion and debate over the destiny of man, the theory of a primitive paradise suggested a particular interpretation of human nature. In that Golden Age when man was attuned to nature, he was a noble savage. Not the victim of civilization's corruption and artificial conceits, the noble savage lived in primeval innocence. His natural self (later termed "instincts") was his only guide to moral conduct. Civilization was alien to instinctual behavior. Man, being an animal, was happier in a savage existence.[6]

By the time of the nineteenth century, these concepts of human nature and the natural mode of existence contributed to the scientific and political discussions of the day. The rapid development of urban society with its working classes and fear of revolution forced the romantic love of nature into a new phase. Love of nature became an

4. Ernest Lee Tuveson, *Millennium and Utopia, A Study in the Background of the Idea of Progress*, p. 201. Hereafter cited as Tuveson, *Millennium and Utopia*.
5. *Ibid.*, pp. 146–147.
6. Hoxie N. Fairchild, *The Noble Savage, A Study in Romantic Naturalism*, pp. 2, 8. Tuveson, *Millennium and Utopia*, pp. 191–192.

expression of nostalgia for the English and American middle classes of a lost world of peace and friendship, of quiet minds and healthy bodies.[7] Even after Darwin's *The Origin of Species* was published in 1859, this romantic belief in a perfect past existence endured. In fact, the faith now had scientific support.

This lost world was the childhood of the race, when emotions were noble because they were natural. Romantics believed in the natural goodness of man and the spontaneous development of moral sentiments until civilization corrupted them by divorcing man from nature. Many Darwinists accepted this notion, albeit garbed in scientific terminology. The romantic and the naturalist in the nineteenth century saw absolute laws at work in nature and society. The romantic found innate goodness in the human heart, and the naturalist believed race wisdom, or instincts, made man good.[8]

Man was virtuous living close to nature. Civilized man was corrupt. Supporters of the idea of progress believed in a future perfection through a process of complexity while extolling primitivism based on simplicity and natural affection. No contradiction existed. History contained two processes. The decay of antediluvian thought and the advance in understanding nature were two simultaneous processes. In the latter process, progress by reversion to natural values was possible.[9] Only an elite comprehended these developments and thereby obtained a harmonious relationship with nature. The Social Darwinists, particularly the American eugenists, subscribed to this thesis. For them, the laws of nature provided right and natural conduct for society.

Progress, therefore, was part of the cosmic system. Although decay was operative in nature and man, the end result of such decay was improvement of the world. God, in theological terms, established a scheme of improvement in which the individual was free to determine his own speed and skill in self-advancement. This laissez-faire concept was important in religion for the development of the doctrine of free

7. Walter E. Houghton, *The Victorian Frame of Mind, 1830–1870*, pp. 55, 79, 85–86.

8. *Ibid.*, pp. 267, 345.

9. Lois Whitney, *Primitivism and the Idea of Progress*, p. 1. Tuveson, *Millennium and Utopia*, p. 167.

will and in economic theory for the creation of capitalist dogma. By this theory the individual proved his worth, either to find salvation in religion or to secure material advantage in society.[10] Later, Darwinists provided a naturalistic rationale for both natural and social competition.

In the nineteenth century many groups with contradictory programs, such as the Marxists and the positivists, held a common belief that history, that is, nature, was leading to an end, to an "historic" or concluding event. Historical analysis was a method of understanding the future which was implicit in the nature of things—human life and the world.[11] The various parts of mankind's experiences and existence were signposts to a consumation combining the past and the present in a future realization. If one understood the process of nature and history and adapted human life to it, the future indeed was optimistic.

After 1845, the biological, physical, and social sciences advanced with great strides. Development in anthropology, physics, biology, statistics, and sociology gave new life to the idea of progress.[12] The sciences appeared to uncover the innermost secrets of nature and man. The great thinkers of the nineteenth century did not hesitate to apply their concepts to all fields of knowledge. If Charles Darwin was slow in applying his theories for universal explanation, his disciples quickly invoked his name in such enterprises.

For example, Darwinists used natural selection, a key Darwinian concept in biology, in explaining the rise and fall of human civilization. The Darwinists were eager to show how the innately superior people could win in the competition of life and thereby produce more gifted offspring than the inferior element in society. Unfortunately, from the Social Darwinian viewpoint, modern society often inhibited the beneficial action of natural selection.[13] Modern societies unjustly and dangerously ignored nature's laws. This "interference" caused the growth of modern eugenics.

For years, the proponents of the great chain of being theory searched for missing links in nature and society. Charles Darwin

10. *Ibid.*, pp. 14, 148.
11. *Ibid.*, p. 75.
12. Philip P. Wiener, *Evolution and the Founders of Pragmatism*, p. 8.
13. Greene, *The Death of Adam*, pp. 326–327.

(1809–1882) attempted to prove that man was organically related to all living creatures. In *The Origin of Species* (1859), he disproved that life existed within a static framework. Since natural selection operated in opportunistic fashion, that is, without a preconceived plan on the part of the Deity, it offered an alternative to the necessity of teleology. Consequently, by the end of the nineteenth century most biological scientists had eliminated teleology in favor of natural selection in biological speculation.[14]

Despite the fact that American eugenists claimed to be in the Darwinian tradition, that is, working with man's animal origins, they distrusted the unlimited effect of natural selection. This distrust stemmed from their fear of democracy; thus they artificially coupled their own class prejudices and teleology, with natural selection. Eugenics, as a creed, often drew on pre-Darwinian notions of romanticism and teleology.[15]

The Effects of Darwinian Biological Evolution on Social Theory

The course of nineteenth-century thought underlined the unity of social and biological evolution. Social evolutionists such as Auguste Comte (1798–1857), the founder of modern sociology, saw mankind's development along evolutionary lines. Herbert Spencer, the great systematic speculator, linked social evolution with organic change. With Charles Darwin's *The Origin of Species* it became clear to thinkers of the day that human social progress and biological progress (evolution) were the same process.[16]

Although Darwin refuted the old Biblical concept of nature as being static, he did not greatly modify the acceptance of the great chain of being concept in Victorian scientific circles. *Progress* became equated with *change*, but this change was linear. Even without a fossil record, many of Darwin's contemporaries saw the white man as the top link

14. Conway Zirkle, "Natural Selection before *The Origin of Species*," *Proceedings of the American Philosophical Society*, LXXXIV (April 1941), 84.
15. Modern biologists since the growth of genetics reject a simple identification of the idea of progress with biological facts. Garrett Hardin, *Nature and Man's Fate*, p. 70.
16. Greene, *The Death of Adam*, p. 220.

in the chain with gradations down to the Negro leading toward the ape. For many nineteenth-century scientists the Negro and other non-white people were living fossils, both culturally and physically.[17] British imperialists in Africa and Asia subscribed to this anthropological assumption of superiority. The present relationship of the races demonstrated man's past development. Hence, the Negro would improve, but so would the already superior white man, and at the same rate.

Evolutionism in the nineteenth century was the hallmark of scientific investigations. As a generalization, evolutionism entered every area of investigation from biology to sociology, from cosmology to philosophy of history. Although evolution was a scientific premise developed only for biology,[18] combatants generally ignored this fact in their controversies over Darwin's theories. The Victorian scholarly urge was the discovery of universal laws and understanding thereby all aspects of the processes governing life on the planet. Consequently, the natural sciences provided analogies for nineteenth-century social science.

Social Darwinists like Herbert Spencer and William Graham Sumner believed that the findings of natural scientists provided proper guides for the scientific construction of society.[19] Eternal laws governed both social attitudes and nature. Improvement or progress was possible, but always within the limits nature established. The inferior were inferior, not because of some sociological or man-made arrangement, but because they were born that way.

Auguste Comte paved the way for the Social Darwinians when he stressed the importance of scientific laws in the development of human society. He attempted through his philosophy an understanding of the affairs of men based on the scientific method. This philosophy he termed "positivism." According to Comte, societies developed by stages as they increased in scientific knowledge. As a result of the

17. Gardiner Murphy, *Historical Introduction to Modern Psychology,* revised edition, p. 351. Loren Eiseley, *Darwin's Century, Evolution and the Men Who Discovered It,* p. 264.

18. Wiener, *Evolution and the Founders of Pragmatism,* p. 6.

19. Merle Curti, "Human Nature in American Thought: Retreat from Reason in the Age of Science," *Political Science Quarterly,* LXVIII (December 1953), 494. L. L. Bernard, *Origins of American Sociology, The Social Science Movement in the United States,* pp. 717–718.

impact of Darwin's evolutionary concepts, positivism lost its preciseness and became a loose definition for evaluating human behavior.

The rationalistic or intellectual orientation of positivism changed.
Darwin's biological terms, "heredity" and "environment," replaced
human "free will" as the major determinants in human behavior. The
struggle for existence replaced intellectual development as an explanation for social changes. Finally, the optimism of Comtian positivism
succumbed to the scientific fatalism of Social Darwinism. Instead of
crediting men with reason and logic, many late-nineteenth- and early-
twentieth-century social philosophers accepted "blood wisdom": heredity dictated men's actions. Comtian intellectualism gave way to
naturalistic antiintellectualism.[20]

By the last decade of the nineteenth century, social scientists began
investigating irrational sources for human behavior. They investigated
the nonlogical, the uncivilized, and the inexplicable in the human
animal. Instinct psychology, among other intellectual disciplines, developed from this interest. The objective was not to free mankind from
this original irrationality (even if that were possible); it was an attempt to find a more scientific basis for social control through the
careful manipulation of man's nature.[21]

This objective indicated the conservative's historic distrust of human
nature. Early-twentieth-century American eugenists adhered to the
basic conservative concern with social control. They utilized two
themes from progressive social science in their reforms—irrationalism
and extreme practicalism. Nineteenth-century social philosophy inspired them. These social thinkers considered history a vast impersonal
process understood and guided by science. Eugenists repeatedly
prided themselves as sound students of human nature because their
philosophy never deviated from the rigidity of man's true nature, that
is, man is a savage animal.

In fact, the twentieth-century eugenists accepted the laissez-faire
aspect of nineteenth-century biological thought, the "survival of the
fittest." Eugenists concluded that the strong (the biological good or
elite) must control society and the state by adjusting the environment

20. H. Stuart Hughes, *Consciousness and Society, The Reorientation of European Social Thought, 1890–1930*, pp. 36–39, 17.
21. *Ibid.*, pp. 35–36.

to eliminate the "bad" hereditary element and leaving the "good" in total freedom.[22] In democratic and humanitarian societies the biologically inadequate endured at great public expense and unnecessarily burdened the naturally superior class. The eugenists therefore attacked modern government as being too soft toward the unfortunate. They asserted that the welfare programs of the state ignored the natural law of the survival of the fittest. According to eugenic dogma, society must emulate nature for the future health of the race.

Naturalism in America: The Product of Social Darwinism

The concern for the racial quality of the American population is of long duration. Parson Weems, George Washington's famed biographer, believed, "My friends, 'tis population, 'tis population *alone*, that can save our bacon. List, then ye Bachelors and ye Maidens fair, if truly ye do love your dear:

> "O list with rapture to the decree,
> Which *thus* in genesis you may see:
> Marry, and raise up soldiers, might and main,
> Then laugh ye may, at England, France, and Spain."[23]

Theodore Roosevelt, more than one hundred years later, matched Weems's concern for a large population as the basis for a militant foreign policy. Even before the birth of Darwinian naturalism, the assumption of race and nation as a single unit existed. Modern thought often is only an ancient idea in fashionable terminology.

The eighteenth-century concept of equality of men rested on the scientific evidence of the day. In theologically oriented biology the Creator designed all men. In morphology the similarity of all men's bodies underlined a theme of equality, while rationalist philosophy generally stressed the importance of environment in guiding mankind's intellectual and physical development.[24] Indeed, the Declaration of Independence expressed the political aspect of this equality.

22. Crane Brinton, *A History of Western Morals*, p. 344.
23. Sidney Ditzion, *Marriage, Morals and Sex in America, A History of Ideas*, pp. 62–63.
24. William Stanton, *The Leopard's Spots, Scientific Attitudes toward Race in America, 1815–1859*, p. 11.

The Origin of Species directly challenged the rationalistic world view of the eighteenth century. Although many evolutionary concepts predated Darwin's research, his philosophy provided a convenient target for the ideological reaction to the growth of scientific naturalism. In the United States the controversy first centered around the religious significance of Darwin's theories with the racial implications gaining in importance as the century passed. The rise of Social Darwinism added a political-economic dimension to the spreading debate over the validity of Darwinian biology.[25]

The controversy also had a fashionable side, with "modern" scientists and intellectuals adhering to Darwinian analysis while "old-fashioned" scholars held fast to traditional biological dogma. The death in 1873 of famed Harvard biologist and opponent of Darwin, Louis Agassiz, marked the end of absolute rejection of the theory of evolution.[26]

Many of Agassiz's generation feared the religious implications of Darwinism rather than any revolutionary effect on natural sciences. The free-thought movement now had scientific evidence, so it seemed, to invalidate the theological case for design and creation in nature.[27] Using these new Darwinian laws, men could fashion a new world devoid of theological ornamentation.

As the controversy became racial in content, the debate affected the climate of opinion. Well-meaning reformers, such as Frank Parsons, accepted the belief of Anglo-Saxon superiority. Like the biologists of his time, Parsons thought that babies inherited their parents' acquired characteristics. This theory explained the innate superiority of Western Europeans. In his scheme to create the co-operative commonwealth, he wanted the proper stock in the utopia.[28] Likewise, Frank Lester Ward, a pioneer American sociologist, accepted the naturalistic assumptions of Western Europeans' racial superiority.

The implications of evolutionary thought affected both philosophical conservatives and liberals. The Darwinian classified both biological

25. Gertrude Himmelfarb, *Darwin and the Darwinian Revolution*, p. 290.

26. Bert J. Loewenberg, "The Controversy over Evolution in New England, 1859–1873," *New England Quarterly*, VIII (June 1935), 233.

27. Sidney Warren, *American Free Thought, 1860–1914*, pp. 46–47, 96–97.

28. Arthur Mann, *Yankee Reformers in the Urban Age*, p. 142.

behavior and social conduct as matters of inherited instincts. William James, E. L. Thorndike, and other psychologists saw human psychology as a study in instincts. Hence, the march of Darwinian biology carried the day in other sciences, both social and natural. Any program of social reform and amelioration, accordingly, had to take into account the natural instincts of man. To oppose human instincts was destructive of the innate wisdom in natural selection and the struggle for existence. American eugenists worked for their program in accord with the theory of instincts, and they constantly criticized American society for ignoring human instincts in the arrangement of the nation's institutions.

Although it was the major cause, Charles Darwin's thought was not the only influence in fostering American naturalism. For example, Hegel, the German philosopher of the dialectic, contributed to American naturalism in conjunction with Darwinian evolution. Darwin stressed the biological aspect, while Hegel contributed the metaphysical ideas, but both philosophers gave emphasis to the group over the individual's welfare. In fact, the welfare of the individual was determined by the larger group, be it named species or state. The nature of this group determined the nature of the individual.[29] American eugenists drew this hypothesis of group determinism in their racial program.

The progressives were naturalistic in their belief in evolution and yet held on to traditional religious sentiments. American reforms of the late nineteenth century and early twentieth had a dual character of hope and protest. Drawing on the materialism of evolutionary speculation and the moral fervor of Christian faith, conservatives protested change, while liberals looked with hope toward the future. Both the conservatives and liberals within the progressive ideology wanted laws to eliminate their respective enemies. In the religious movement of progressivism, the evangelicals wanted laws restricting the evil of drink, dance, and secular literature, while the social gospelers wanted legislative restrictions on the evils of American capitalism. The former wanted reforms only to conserve the status quo; the latter desired

29. David F. Bowers, ed., "Hegel, Darwin and the American Tradition," *Foreign Influences in America,* pp. 158–159.

modifications of society to solve new problems.[30] Within secular progressivism, the eugenists represented the attitudes of the evangelicals —the desire to save the old way of life. To be sure, the eugenists were naturalists, but on occasion they could match the emotional heights of any fundamental evangelical. The eugenists considered themselves to be missionaries rescuing America from racial sin.

This cross-fertilization in attitudes between evangelicalism and naturalism continued into the twentieth century. For example, the Reverend Warren A. Chandler used naturalism coupled with Christian teleology in urging an expansive foreign policy for the United States. He believed the country followed the will of God (and nature) by extending American interests in the Far East. America, as the home of the pure Anglo-Saxon, had a mission in the world. History and nature dictated this duty.[31]

In addition to these developments in popular religious sentiment, naturalism also affected the institutional growth of hereditary organizations, membership based on ancestry. Sparked by Sir Francis Galton's *Hereditary Genius* particularly, and by Social Darwinism generally, Americans in the last two decades of the nineteenth century sought personal assurance of their racial purity. America was great because its people were superior, and they were superior because they were Anglo-Saxon. Thus reasoned the patriotic American. This type of individual wanted to maintain national racial purity as national insurance in a world of innate inferiors. By 1900, seventy hereditary organizations existed, thirty-five of them having started in the previous decade. John Fiske, the leading philosopher of Social Darwinism, and David Starr Jordan, zoologist and eugenist, were active in hereditary organizations.[32]

The reason for this rush to establish ancestral purity existed in the course of American history. Post-Appomattox America experienced an acceleration of industrialization. The emerging machine economy

30. William G. McLaughlin, Jr., *Modern Revivalism, Charles Grandison Finney to Billy Graham* (New York, 1959), pp. 345–346.

31. *Ibid.*, p. 354.

32. Wallace E. Davies, *Patriotism on Parade, The Story of Veteran's and Hereditary Organizations in America, 1783–1900*, pp. 44, 48, 80, 229–230. Hereafter cited as Davies, *Patriotism on Parade.*

with its emphasis on bigness and urban living eroded the older order of America where, at least ideally, the better people controlled an aristocratic-agrarian social order. New England particularly saw the rise of vast industrial complex with "strange" directors who were not part of the Brahmin class. Men like Henry Adams and George Cabot Lodge felt that the world of history had pushed a kinder way of life aside in preference for a new industrial order marked by money-making, corruption, and the vaulting ambitions of undesirable immigrant groups.[33]

Nationalism sharpened the social problems of an industrialized America. By the close of the Spanish-American War nationalism grew into an irrational patriotism which, on occasion, found expression as ideological censorship and at other times as a wish to keep America racially pure. One result of this latter desire was the eugenics movement. In either manifestation, the theme was control which forced the individual—in mind and body—into a given value system. For eugenists the biologically inferior people in the nation's life were un-American because of their racial origin.

By 1899, one naturalist called for racial improvement to insure social progress. According to this naturalistic prophet, only by promoting the mental and physical health of those groups that were capable of this improvement would America advance to new greatness in the coming century.[34]

Naturalists (particularly the eugenists) saw the problem of creating American character as a matter of combining heredity with national pride. Superior forefathers had released congenital character in the nation's blood stream. Therefore, national character was innately exclusive, despite any good intentions from lesser folk to be good Americans. Biological facts, it seemed, prevented them from good citizenship.[35] The old-line Americans who accepted each other in the

33. *Ibid.*, pp. 353, 358. Van Wyck Brooks, *New England: Indian Summer, 1865–1915.* Barbara M. Solomon, *Ancestors and Immigrants, A Changing New England Tradition.*

34. Frank A. Fetter, "Social Progress and Race Degeneration," *Forum*, XXVIII (October 1899), 239.

35. David M. Potter, *People of Plenty, Economic Abundance and the American Character*, p. 25.

patriotic and hereditary organizations used this concept of national character to agitate for immigration restriction.

Progressivism: The Political Outgrowth of Naturalism

The first two decades of the twentieth century saw the flowering of a host of reform movements collectively called progressivism. Reformers in this era received the name of progressives, a term lacking ideological exactness. Despite the fact that progressivism possessed a varied ideological content, the sociological bases for the movements were remarkably clear.

The progressive was generally a self-made man with an Ivy League education. Professionally a lawyer, he exhibited a class-awareness of his place in the social order and, because of the aliens in the city, tended to romanticize America's agrarian past with its cult of the strong man. Being middle class, he feared the uncontrolled power of the upper class, while distrusting the democratic aspirations of the working class. Sociological changes during the expansion of the city left the middle-class reformer with a sense of lost status. Stressing spiritual values in opposition to the materialistic ethics of urban America, the progressive's language of reform used moral rather than economic terms. At the same time, this same moralizing reformer subscribed to racism in one of its varied forms. Both the conservative and the reformer in this age of naturalism found value in generalizing about the racial nature of the American population.[36] Most progressives found their strong man in Theodore Roosevelt, and the more naturalistic and conservative progressives found merit in eugenic schemes for saving the racial character of the American population.

This racial concern was a major plant of progressivism. A revolution in biological sciences coming from Charles Darwin's concepts provided the tap root. Other themes of the era were Puritan moral activism and Quaker humanitarian principles. Pragmatism was the background for interaction of these themes. American eugenists of this period naturally stressed the biological basis of reform, since that thesis was the most conservative of the three and because it worked within the limits of

36. George Mowry, *The Era of Theodore Roosevelt,* pp. 85–105.

human nature. Likewise, the progressive inherited from the nineteenth century the fear of savage human nature.[37] The appeal of the eugenic programs rested on this legacy from the past.

Although elements of the progressive ideology provided inspiration and practical guidance for later reform periods such as that of the New Deal, the creed also contained attitudes alien to the reforms of later generations. For example, the progressive assumed, often uncritically, the intrinsic inferiority of the Negro in the United States. The emerging caste system of Negro segregation gained legislative sanction during the progressive years.[38] All too often the progressive creed expressed only the hopes of white, middle-class Americans.

It was not surprising, therefore, to find American scientists in this age of urbanism and reform asserting the organic inadequacy of the Negro and claiming that all he wanted was food, drink, and sexual freedom. If a Negro did improve his lot in society, the reason, from the eugenic point of view, was the presence of "white blood" in the Negro. Accordingly, the mulatto had superior intelligence and as a result was discontent with the ways of the pure Negro.[39] This theme in progressivism will be developed in connection with the eugenics movement. As Robert H. Walcott, a typical progressive journalist, stated in 1914,

Mankind is emancipating itself from the blind obedience to what has been conceived to be natural and therefore divine law, and no longer looks upon itself as hedged about by divinely appointed limitations. We have harnessed the forces of nature and they answer to our bidding. We are now beginning to exert a certain control, as yet feeble, over the forces that operate in living matter, and to see that we hold in our hands the power to mould even our own destiny.[40]

37. Otis Pease, ed., *The Progressive Years, The Spirit and Achievement of American Reform*, p. 8. Henry May, *The End of American Innocence*, p. 333.

38. C. Vann Woodward, *The Strange Career of Jim Crow*, new and revised edition, pp. 49–95.

39. Herbert J. Webber, "Eugenics from the Point of View of the Geneticist," *Eugenics: Twelve University Lectures*, p. 43. Victor C. Vaughan, "Eugenics from the Point of View of the Physician," *Ibid.*, p. 46. Samuel J. Holmes, *Studies in Evolution and Eugenics*, p. 222. For an analysis of popular and scientific anti-Negro thought see I. A. Newby, *Jim Crow's Defense: Anti-Negro Thought In America, 1900–1930*.

40. Robert H. Walcott, "Eugenics as Viewed by the Zoologist," *Eugenics: Twelve University Lectures*, p. 16.

Although a eugenist spoke those words, the sentiment was indicative of the progressive optimism. Herbert Croly, a progressive journalist, for example, could have just as well written the passage. From 1900 to the close of World War I reformers of all types were certain that nature and society, united, told the history of progress and national well-being. In nature and society, man, through his discovery of the laws of behavior, was poised on the threshold of utopia. Conservative and liberal progressives asserted that this utopia was their goal.

The method for the realization of shaping the future through using the present-day knowledge of nature and society necessitated the abandonment of laissez faire and the natural-rights philosophy. Liberal intellectuals rejected laissez-faire economic policy as being dated in a pragmatic age of industrialization.[41] Many conservatives, including eugenists, rejected the dogma in order to save America from socialism and the rise of the mediocre man with his innate biological character. Thus Irving Fisher, Yale conservative and student of eugenics, urged programs to prevent the extremism of socialism or the total disregard of the nation's problems. American eugenics, as a conservative-progressive reform, claimed Fisher was the medication for America's ills.

Both eugenists and liberal progressives agreed that "the days of laissez faire have gone forever. There is no longer any field of human activity into which it is not acceptable as both the right and the duty of the state to intervene, by investigation and by remedial action." [42] Reformers accepted the technique. The issue debated in twentieth-century reform was the nature of the "remedial action" necessary for national progress, within society or the race.

Recent historical scholarship has shown the absence of any systematic concern for the civil rights of individual Americans during the progressive era. One possible reason for this absence was the sociological nature of progressive reform. Another important factor was the attack which liberals led against natural-rights philosophy and the

41. Morton White, *American Social Thought,* revised edition, *passim.*
42. Irving Fisher, "Why Has the Doctrine of Laissez-Faire Been Abandoned?" *Proceedings of the American Association for the Advancement of Science,* LVI–LVII (1906–1907), 591. S. N. D. North, "Seventy-five Years of Progress in Statistics: The Outlook for the Future," *The History of Statistics,* John Koren, ed., p. 21.

eighteenth-century rationalism which gave birth to it in United States history. Liberal reformers, in their rush to correct the evils of capitalism, rejected the natural-rights thesis as mere economic rationalization preventing necessary state and national reform. They seemed to have forgotten that the American tradition of civil liberties came from Thomas Jefferson's natural-rights philosophy. In throwing out the dirty bath water of capitalism, progressives ignored the civil liberties baby.

Conservative progressives, including the eugenists, were quite aware of the natural-rights origin of American civil liberties. A. B. Wolfe, a typical eugenist of the period, wrote in 1921, "We are specifically the victims of a social inheritance of political and economic individualism carried over from the eighteenth-century revolt, when the emphasis was on individual rights rather than where it must now be put, upon social function." [43] Naturalism was the cause of this change in social thought. In nature the organism, by its inborn abilities, by being stronger than the rest, created its own "natural rights" in the struggle for existence. The eugenist wanted this to be the arrangement in human society.

This misguided humanitarianism created social trouble by protecting the weak and inferior from their true natural destiny. In 1915, G. H. Parker, Harvard biologist, therefore reasoned, "If society protects them [the weak and inferior] against the attacks of unkind nature, it is entirely within the rights of society to see that their numbers shall not increase. Such growth," he concluded, "may well be the very undoing of society itself." [44] Later this sentiment gained legal sanction in the decision of the *State Board of Eugenics* v. *Troutman* (1931) 299 Pac. 668 (Idaho). "If there be any natural right for natively mental defectives to beget children, that right must give way to the police power of the state in protecting the common welfare, so far as it can be protected, against the hereditary type of feeblemindedness." [45]

43. A. B. Wolfe, "Eugenics and Special Attitudes," *Eugenics in Race and State, Scientific Papers at the Second International Congress of Eugenics Held at the American Museum of Natural History, September 22–28, 1921.*

44. G. H. Parker, "The Eugenics Movement as a Public Service," *Science,* n.s. XLI (March 5, 1915), 344.

45. Cited by J. H. Landman, *Human Sterilization, The History of the Sexual Sterilization,* p. 110.

The state, accordingly, was a super organism protecting and advancing its own existence against smaller organisms who collectively were quite dangerous.

More than a generation of eugenic agitation rested behind that legal decision with its emphasis on the higher collectivity—the race. A double reason existed for this concern for eugenic correction of the American population. Eugenics improved the race and, thereby, the state; and secondly, by restricting the birth of mental and moral defectives, it relieved the state of a great and unnecessary burden of taxation, support of public charitable institutions.[46] These sentiments echoed thoroughout the Galtonian eugenic era in the United States.

Since Sir Francis Galton came from the middle class, the sociological origin of American progressivism, his scientific concepts gave support to the progressive desire to effect a scientific adjustment of society in the name of the laws of nature. Galton's social origin determined his attitudes toward society and scientific speculations. In science and sociology, Galton inspired American eugenists.

46. "The Bureau of Analysis and Investigation: Its Purpose and Field," *Eugenics and Social Welfare Bulletin #1 State of New York State Board of Charities, Department of State and Alien Poor* (Albany, 1912), pp. 2–3.

2

FRANCIS GALTON:
CONSERVATIVE
AS PHILOSOPHER
OF NATURALISM

THE IDEAS of Sir Francis Galton (1822–1911) were important to American eugenics; by using his naturalistic thought many American conservatives accepted progressivism. Both Galton's life and thought demonstrated the importance of naturalism for the Anglo-American reformers wanting realistic reforms based on human nature. Even when later scientific developments rejected Galton's hereditary theories, people still supported his eugenics because of the social values in his scientific theories.

Galton was a fine example of the Victorian gentleman of leisure, letters, and science, having both economic security and intellectual curiosity. From his Quaker and businessman father, he inherited a sizable fortune which allowed him to drop his medical studies and develop his interest in exploration and scientific investigations. After a tour of Europe he explored Africa in 1840, covering areas never seen by a white man. Married at thirty, he then limited his travel to yearly trips to the Continent. Ironically, Galton, a biological scientist, experienced a childless marriage.

Despite a precocious childhood, Galton found his formal education dull and of little value. By his own efforts he developed mathematical and scientific interests. He enjoyed counting items and attempted on many occasions to reduce human behavior to statistical analysis. In fact, possibly Galton's most enduring contribution to science was his use of median, percentiles, and his invention of the correlation coefficient for statistics in 1852. Galton was a pioneer in the study of weather, fingerprints, composite photography, mental measurement, and number and word associations. In addition, he conducted psychological experiments in hearing and vision. Even without his particular formulation of eugenics, Galton had earned a permanent position in the history of science.[1]

Like his cousin, Charles Darwin, Francis Galton had a retiring personality augmented, however, by creative imagination. Galton was more active in public affairs than his famed kinsman and showed an interest in the fate of his ideas and means by which they might endure. In 1901 Galton and his student and later biographer, Karl Pearson, established *Biometrika*, a quarterly journal devoted to statistical analysis of biological problems. In 1908 Galton founded the Eugenics Education Society for the development of popular interest in eugenics and related problems. The Society published the *Eugenics Review* which became the most widely read of the eugenic journals, and it had branches throughout the British Empire. In his will, Galton provided £ 45,000 for a eugenics laboratory connected with the University of London. The Galton Laboratory investigated the scientific basis for eugenics, while the Eugenics Education Society agitated for public support of the Galtonian creed. In addition, this will established a chair in Eugenics at London University.[2]

Galton's first contribution to heredity came in 1870 with the publication of *Hereditary Genius, An Inquiry into Its Laws and Conse-*

1. Karl Pearson, *The Life, Letters and Labours of Francis Galton*, 3 volumes. Hereafter cited as Pearson, *Galton*. See also Garrett Hardin, *Nature and Man's Fate*. Details of Galton's various activities will be discussed when related directly to eugenics and the development of related intellectual disciplines in the United States. Additional biographical information may be found in C. P. Blacker, *Eugenics: Galton and After* (London, 1952).

2. H. S. Jennings, "Eugenics," *Encyclopedia of Social Sciences*, V, 618. (no author), "The Galton Chair of Eugenics," *Science*, n.s. XXXIII (March, 31, 1911), 480–481.

quences, an explanation of how superiority existed among only certain families. Like other scientists of his day, Galton saw inheritance as the key to evolution.[3] He sought a theory of heredity to provide an objective understanding of the biological reasons why certain individuals and groups prevailed in the struggle for existence. In the naturalist tradition, Galton held that distribution of mental capabilities followed what is now known as the bell-shaped curve. He wrote,

This is what I am driving at, that analogy clearly shows there must be a fairly average mental capacity in the inhabitants of the British Isles, and that the deviations from that average—upwards toward genius, and downwards toward stupidity—must follow the law that governs deviations from all true averages.[4]

According to this eugenic creed, an increase in stupidity in human population was dangerous. Galton, however, was optimistic, feeling that the gifted, regardless of circumstances, would succeed. In 1870 he stated, "I have shown reason to believe that few who possess these very high abilities can fail in achieving eminence." [5] The existence of a hierarchy was objective verification of organic differences among men and races.

He felt that the intervals between the grades of ability were the same in all races.[6] Taken together, however, the various races were not equal, but natural selection developed their fitness for living.[7] The races were placed in static system, a scale of nature or chain of being. In the development of races, man's nature did not keep pace with his physical and psychic progress. Men were animals whose instincts failed them in new circumstances.

The reason for this failure was in the nature of a given race. Culture changed too quickly for a race to respond morally to the new situation. This moral lag was important because only heredity provided any growth, according to Galton, which unfortunately was slow and non-

3. Edwin G. Conklin, "The Mutation Theory from the Standpoint of Cytology," *Science,* n.s. XXI (April 7, 1905), 525–529.

4. Francis Galton, *Hereditary Genius, An Inquiry into Its Laws and Consequences,* pp. 349–350. Hereafter cited as Galton, *Hereditary Genius.*

5. *Ibid.,* p. 32.

6. Francis Galton, *Inquiries into Human Faculty and Its Development.* Hereafter cited as Galton, *Inquiries into Human Faculty.*

7. Galton, *Hereditary Genius,* pp. 337–338.

teleological in form and direction. Man was only recently civilized after hundreds of years of barbarism. Ancestral habits influenced the nature of contemporary races. The Negro's inferiority resulted from his nature being inadequate for his moral needs.[8] Galton's racial attitude furnished justification for atavism and for seeing the nonwhite peoples as moral fossils in human evolution. In the early twentieth century many eugenists and progressives in the United States accepted this type of racism.

In addition, Galton saw the impact of nurture in shaping the climate of opinion and creating the difference between Englishmen and foreigners; but environment did not create the difference between individuals of the same class.[9] Galton did not explore the scope of nurture, but stressed the hereditary aspects of human existence and society.

Galton's coworker, Karl Pearson, believed that Sir Francis's *Hereditary Genius* contained indications of Galton's later law of Ancestral Heredity—the influence of an individual ancestor in the nth generation diminished in geometrical progression. Pearson claimed it was the starting place of the statistical or quantitative theory of heredity.

In 1883 Galton published *Inquiries into Human Faculty and Its Development*. Although human heredity was his lifework, Galton's formulations were unclear. His explanation of heredity ranged from acceptance of the inheritance of acquired characteristics, a theory stressing environmental influences, to strict hereditary determinism. In *Inquiries,* Galton used these two extremes in his own particular theory of the Law of Ancestral Inheritance. Karl Pearson expressed the belief that Galton saw the difference between barbarous and civilized man in the inheritance of mental and *moral* characteristics.[10] For Francis Galton, the assumption of the inheritance of morality was at least a tacit acceptance of a form of environmentalism. Pearson also thought Galton held to the continuity of the germ-plasm theory.[11]

The Law of Ancestral Inheritance was Galton's term for statistical analysis of inheritance. The law was based on the assumption that

8. *Ibid.*, p. 336.
9. Galton, *Inquiries into Human Faculty*, pp. 11, 23.
10. Pearson, *Galton*, II, 371–372.
11. *Ibid.*, p. 49. Pearson, *Galton*, II, 86.

two parents contributed one fourth to the nature of the offspring, the four grandparents one eighth, great-grandparents one sixteenth, and so on, until the hereditary influence reached zero.[12] "The child inherits partly from his parents, partly from his ancestry. Speaking generally, the farther his genealogy goes back, the more numerous and varied will his ancestors become, until they cease to differ from any numerous sample taken at haphazard from the race at large."[13] He suggested in 1885 an alternative theory which faintly anticipated later genetic thought.

There can be no doubt that heredity proceeds to a considerable extent, perhaps principally, in a piecemeal or piebald fashion, causing the person of the child to be to that extent a mosaic of independent ancestral heritage, one part coming with more or less variation from this progenitor, and another from that. To express this aspect of inheritance, where particle proceeds from particle, we may conveniently describe it as particular.[14]

Karl Pearson, long after Galton's death, used this theory even after the majority of biological scientists accepted the Mendelian hypothesis. For reasons noted in Chapter Three, American eugenists in the twentieth century did not, however, use Galton's theory; the spirit of the theory, the fatalism of heredity, motivated them to reduce the fertility of the biologically unfit. His theory also lent itself to historical and mathematical methods which gave eugenic investigations the appearance of making genealogy a science. Many eugenists in the United States of old American stock appreciated such "scientific" investigations.

By 1909, this possibility provided a basis for Galton's eugenics. In that year he collected his *Essays in Eugenics.* "Eugenics co-operates with the workings of nature by securing that humanity shall be represented by the fittest races. What nature does blindly, slowly, and ruthlessly, man may do providently, quickly, and kindly." For mankind it was a moral and biological necessity despite ignorance of any ulti-

12. Karl Pearson, "On the Law of Ancestral Heredity," *Science,* n.s. VII (March 11, 1898), 337–339.
13. Francis Galton, "Types and Their Inheritance," *Science,* VI (September 25, 1885), 270–271.
14. *Ibid.,* p. 273. For examples of Galton's influences, see anonymous, "Malthus and His Work," *Science,* VI (August 28, 1885), 165–167, in which Galton's contributions in this field are discussed.

mate destiny. Eugenics would "represent each class or sect by its best specimens, that done, to leave them to work out their common civilization in their own way." [15] This process fixed the environment in behalf of the social and biological fittest.

The object of eugenics, therefore, was for superior people to maintain a statistical advantage over inferior elements of the population. In regard to Malthusianism, Galton, once more like his American counterparts, felt that the prudential check (voluntary family limitation) was prejudicial to the better classes of citizens; even the misery-check, such as death from war or starvation, would not cover all causes of racial decay, for an inferior race simply became listless and apathetic in the presence of a superior one.[16]

Galton rejected unrestricted birth control because of his belief in the differential fertility of social classes. Like Theodore Roosevelt, Galton felt that if a race restricted its fertility without regard to other nations, race suicide would result. Therefore, both intelligent men and women must exercise racial wisdom by selecting superior mates and having more children.[17] The racially healthy family was the cornerstone of national welfare.

Although Galton wrote very little about socialism, he thought socialist reconstruction inadequate if the new society did not improve the race. The average citizen's moral and intellectual incompetence caused

15. Francis Galton, "Eugenics: Its Definition, Scope and Aims," *Essays in Eugenics,* pp. 36–37, 42–43.

16. Galton, *Hereditary Genius,* p. 320. For a comparison of Malthus's population theories with later theories, see Thomas Malthus, Julian Huxley, Frederick Osborn, *Three Essays on Population.* It might be noted that Malthus' theory—an important part of classical capitalistic theory—came from natural history. See Gertrude Himmelfarb, *Darwin and the Darwinian Revolution,* pp. 157–158. It is fitting therefore that a little known population essay of Ben Franklin influenced the shaping of Malthus's ideas. See Conway Zirkle, "Natural Selection before *The Origin of Species,*" *Proceedings of the American Philosophical Society,* LXXXIV (April, 1941), 71–123.

17. Pearson, *Galton,* II, p. 111, quotes Galton. This belief was shared by the neo-Malthusians in England and the United States who greatly contributed to the birth-control movement. See the chapter on Margaret Sanger for a fuller discussion. As late as 1924, Galton's major British disciple, Karl Pearson, believed that birth control was dangerous from the eugenic standpoint because it tended, he maintained, to increase the unintelligent caste of the community at the expense of the intelligent." See Pearson, *Galton,* II, 80, 110n.

the failure of socialism, not the innate merits or demerits of the ideology.[18] The worst characteristic of mediocre people was their contented mediocre intellectual and moral standards. Galton longed, as progressive Americans did, for a great-man theory of history. He bemoaned the lack of living men to point to as fine examples. All men in a mediocrity were at nearly the same, undesirable, average level, except for variety in physical faculties. With men of peculiar abilities there could be a special justification for division of labor, with each man working to his fullest extent in his particular talent. Biological realities for Galton dictated the necessity of a closed society.[19]

Any plan or action improving man's nature by making it more vigorous matched universal law and order. Like the progressive prophets of doom, Galton claimed the average citizen was too inferior for the daily common work of modern civilization. Civilized man had gained great powers in technology and manual efforts, but his wits and morals did not follow this progress sufficiently to enable him to conduct himself in accordance with the plan of the cosmos and society.[20] Again, the average citizen was too base for the everyday work of the modern world. Danger went with progress, for man's technical knowledge exceeded his moral development. Society, therefore, stood on the brink of self-destruction. Galton and many American progressives believed that physical improvement was a necessity for better individual and social morality despite any technological advancements of society.

Eugenics was central to Galton's theology. He felt that eugenics had the characteristics of a religious creed. In order to be effective, racial improvement must have religious sanction and be closely observed like any religious practice. Galton sought the conversion of controlled evolution into a religious precept and a practical philosophy of life. In the "logical" application of evolution to betterment of race, society would seek a higher morality based on rational religion using the laws of nature.[21] He criticized the Roman Catholic concept of chastity for its antieugenic impact on society.

18. *Ibid.*, IIIA, 90–91. Blacker, *Eugenics: Galton and After*, p. 94.
19. Pearson, *Galton*, II, 385, 743, 85.
20. *Ibid.*, IIIA, 91.
21. *Ibid.*, II, 267.

Thus, as she—to repeat my expression—brutalized human nature by her system of celibacy applied to the gentle, she demoralised it by her system of persecution of the intelligent, the sincere, and the free. It is enough to make the blood boil to think of the blind folly that has caused the foremost nations of struggling humanity to be heirs of such hateful ancestry and that has so bred our instincts as to keep them in an unnecessarily long continued antagonism with the essential requirements of a steadily advancing civilization.[22]

Accordingly, charity and religion must be made scientific by following the dictates of controlled evolution—eugenics. For Galton, the mission of charity was to "help the strong rather than the weak; and the man of to-morrow rather than the man of to-day; let knowledge and foresight control the blind emotions and impetuous instincts wherewith Nature, red-clawed, drives man, mindless and stupefied, down her own evolutionary paths." [23] Emotional humanitarianism was unscientific in its opposition to human nature and evolution; it was not the best basis for charitable institutions. Once again, Galton anticipated future progressive attitudes when he wrote that social agencies unwisely encouraged the multiplication of the unfit by their antieugenic sentimentality.[24] Galton's attitude, that philanthropy which ignored the quality of future offspring was deterimental to public welfare, found acceptance in the early decades of twentieth-century America. For Galton, eugenics was scientific philanthropy.[25] To realize racial improvement, Galton, for example, suggested low-cost housing for exceptionally healthy couples.[26] Based on racial consideration, reform was important in the realization of Galton's good society.

Charles Darwin's intellectual effect on Galton was of a mixed nature. In regard to inheritance, the cornerstone of Galton's system, Sir Francis took too seriously Darwin's adaptation of the inheritance

22. Galton, *Hereditary Genius*, pp. 358–359.

23. Pearson, *Galton*, III A, 435.

24. Galton, *Hereditary Genius*, pp. 352–353.

25. Galton, "Eugenics as a Factor in Religion," *Essays in Eugenics*, p. 70.

26. Galton, "The Possible Improvement of the Human Breed under the Existing Conditions of Law and Sentiment," *Essays in Eugenics*, pp. 24–25.

of acquired characteristics—pangenesis.[27] Galton felt that pangenesis for good or ill was a great service to those who are interested in heredity. He was certain that a man's character "is wholly formed through those gemmules that have succeeded in attaching themselves; the remainder that have been overpowered by their antagonists, count for nothing." As if clear of self-doubt, Galton concluded that, "Pangenesis brings all the influences that bear on heredity into a form that is appropriate for the grasp of mathematical analysis." [28]

As a philosopher of naturalism, Galton anticipated some of the later elements in American progressivism and eugenics. Later chapters will indicate that Galton's views influenced development in several academic disciplines used to support the eugenic creed. In his way, Galton contributed greatly to the progressive ideology. In accord with many such progressives as William Allen White and Herbert Croly, he believed that the instincts of egoism and altruism governed human behavior. According to Galton, criminal activity indicated an imbalance between the two forces, despite the fact that Richard Dugdale's work stressed the environmental source of criminality.[29]

Like Ernest Hooton, the Harvard anthropologist, Galton felt that the criminal was different, physically and morally, from the law-abiding person. The family was important for both social and biological reasons. A person was his ancestry. Fifteen years before the start of American progressivism, Galton stressed the eugenic importance of a person's hereditary background. "His vigour, his character, and his diseases are principally derived from theirs; sometimes his faculties are blends of ancestral qualities; but more frequently they are mosaics, patches of resemblance to one or other of them showing now here and

27. Pearson, *Galton*, II, 169–170. Pangenesis held that all parts of the body threw off particles called pangenes which were the hereditary parts of egg and sperm. Modified by environmental conditions that affected the entire body, they were constant. It was a backdoor acceptance of inheritance of acquired characteristics. The theory as expressed in The Variation of Animals and Plants under Domestication was to replace Darwin's theory of blending inheritance which Fleming Jenkin, Darwin's contemporary and critic, had rejected. The ultimate answer was Mendelian genetics. Hardin, *Nature and Man's Fate*, pp. 107, 109; Loren Eiseley, *Darwin's Century, Evolution and the Men Who Discovered It.* Hereafter cited as Eiseley, *Darwin's Century.*

28. Galton, *Hereditary Genius*, pp. 364, 367, 373.

29. Galton, *Inquiries into Human Faculty*, pp. 62–63, 125.

now there." [30] Eugenics was, therefore, scientific genealogy by assisting the direction of human evolution toward efficiency and more effective social control which were twin values of American progressives.

The men in politics and academic disciplines, in progressivism and eugenics, shared a common effort of having a more efficient nation and more stable social order. In this way, these men were conservative, for their naturalistic assumptions made them the exponents of limited economic system of a closed society. They were men of little hope. Galton anticipated these sentiments with his desire that society control the biological composition of its individual members.[31] Like some American progressives, Galton was not ultimately concerned with individual welfare or happiness per se, but rather with the influence of individuals on the structure of society.

Both Galtonian thought and aspects of American progressivism contained Hegelian philosophy. "A society," Galton wrote in 1909 and again during progressive reforms, "may be considered as a highly complex organism, with a consciousness of its own, caring only for itself, establishing regulations and customs for its collective advantage, and creating a code of opinions to subserve that end." [32] Old fashioned laissez-faire individualism in politics and in social science was finished.

Sophisticated conservatives such as Herbert Croly, Theodore Roosevelt, and Margaret Sanger spoke the language of liberal reforms in support of conservative and limited objectives. Like Sir Francis, they used the naturalistic sciences to maintain the conservative institutions and such attitudes as the family, marriage, national and racial loyalty. Their prime concern was society's welfare, and improvement in an individual's physical and moral conditions was only a means of advancing national interests. In words similar to Roosevelt's New Nationalism and to Herbert Croly's book, *The Promise of American Life*, Galton wrote, "Public opinion is commonly far in advance of private morality, because society as a whole keenly appreciates acts that tend

30. *Ibid.*, pp. 43–44.
31. *Ibid.*, pp. 1–2.
32. Galton, "Probability, the Foundation of Eugenics," *Essays in Eugenics*, p. 94.

to its advantage, and condemns those that do not." [33] In his essay, "Probability, the Foundation of Eugenics," Galton suggested a theory of behaviorism in the shaping of the social order.[34] In this emphasis on society as an organism, Galton and later American progressives tried to bury class conflicts in a conservative adaptation of the collective will.

Francis Galton and many progressives had the same concept of the ideal society. Economically the good society was not costly. Little of its income should be from inheritance. Most of the income should be from professional sources. Marriage and the family life were important social institutions in his scheme, each child being given the opportunity to prove his merit. The weak would be given homes in celibate monasteries or sisterhoods. Outstanding and intelligent immigrants and refugees from other places would be encouraged and their descendants naturalized.[35]

Galton's ideal society was closely allied to various social and political reforms in the progressive era, such as immigration restriction, birth-control movement, child welfare, and conservation. He was not always enthusiastic about some of these movements—for example, the birth control movement—but this movement expressed many of his aspirations.

The parallel lines of thought in Galton's philosophy and progressivism found a common origin in the mutual distrust of urbanization. Emotionally and sociologically kin to the landed aristocracy, Galton, like the American progressives who accepted the agrarian myth, saw towns as a menace to rural youth's vigor. Notice he wrote the difference between Northumberland peasant women and the unhappy, miserable look of the masses, especially women, in the streets in London and in other purely English towns. Galton felt that the latter group's environment created their misery and was crushing their spirits as well as any ability to be happy.[36] Similar to the reaction of American progressives, Galton noted the effect of this environment but never clearly understood the full implications of urbanization.

33. *Ibid.*, p. 97.
34. *Ibid.*, pp. 107–108.
35. Galton, *Hereditary Genius*, p. 362.
36. *Ibid.*, p. 340.

Like his American ideological cousin, he was part of a neophysiocratic tradition. The first paper Galton read before the Statistical Society of London, "The Relative Supplies from Town and Country Families to the Population of Future Generations," assured that urban population decayed and yet the cities attracted most energetic human beings. The city's lure accordingly was a racial poison. Many American progressives shared Galton's belief that cities were a great threat to high civilizations, for they observed the gradually declined urban birth rate.[37]

During his scientific career, Francis Galton had a respectable reputation in the United States. In 1886 the *Popular Science Monthly* published a highly laudatory feature article on him. Even the pioneer supporter of Mendel's ideas, W. E. Castle, praised Galton's work in heredity while censuring his followers for ignoring Mendel's message. During his lifetime Galton corresponded with a number of American scientists—one of whom was Henry P. Bowditch—for information on racial types. In fact, Galton used the pages of *Science*, a leading popular scientific weekly, soliciting hereditary information. As might be expected, the leading American authority on eugenics, Charles B. Davenport, corresponded regularly with Sir Francis in regard to the progress of eugenics in the United States.[38] Davenport fully represented Galton's social philosophy in America.

Despite the fact that America had greater opportunities for the masses, the nation had fewer eminent men of letters and science than did England, according to Galton's standards. Galton made this observation based on correspondence and books. He never visited the United States. In 1889 Sir Francis rejected an opportunity to lecture in America because of ill health. Three years later, however, his chief

---

37. Pearson, *Galton*, II, 123. Galton, "The Possible Improvement of the Human Breed under Existing Conditions of Law and Sentiment," *Essays in Eugenics*, p. 27.

38. "Sketch of Francis Galton," *Popular Science Monthly*, XXIX (May, 1886), 117–121. W. E. Castle, Review of William Bateson, *Mendel's Principles of Heredity* (New York: G. P. Putnam's Son, 1909), *Science*, n.s. XXX (October 8, 1909), 481–482. Helen Walker, *Studies in the History of Statistical Method*, pp. 101–102. "Regression and Organic Stability," *Science*, n.s. I (May 3, 1895), 498–499. Pearson, *Galton*, III B, 613.

British disciple, Karl Pearson, came to this country as a lecturer on heredity and variation.[39]

Generally speaking, American reviewers praised Galton's books. Characteristically, one reviewer emphasized the racial meaning of Galton's law. The *Inquiries into Human Faculty and Its Development* (1883) gained approval of readers for urging free social competition with proper segregation methods for the unfit, thereby insuring superior people's ultimate victory in the struggle for existence. In fact, this segregation found the basis for a new scientific charity. As for the destinies of Indians and Negroes, the reviewer rejoiced, "Galton's law is squarely across their path, and the sooner they die quietly out the better and to assist them to multiply becomes as wrong as keeping the filthy and effete Turk in Europe for the sake of enfeebling Russia." Any effort of kindly attention to those minority groups failed because the effort ran counter to racial law. Based on its "common sense" appeal, the reviewer took comfort in the fact that the harshness of Galton's law was recognized, for only the victor race would remain after the utter destruction of the remaining segments of mankind.[40] Despite an occasional criticism, two other journals, *The Nation* and *Science*, had praise for the *Inquiries into Human Faculty and Its Development*. Even in view of this criticism, the critic admired Galton's methodology for stressing the hereditary value of family histories.[41]

An anonymous writer endorsed *Natural Inheritance* (1889) for its originality in the utilization of statistics as a means for social and racial improvement. In like manner, *The Nation* found Galton's statistical techniques praiseworthy.[42]

Some reviewers, however, expressed criticism of Galton's conclusions about heredity. One such writer, in discussing *Hereditary Genius*, criticized family histories and the hereditary nature of genius; the

39. *Ibid.*, II, 92n, III B, 509, III A, 243.
40. Henry W. Holland, "Heredity," *The Atlantic Monthly*, LII (October 1883), 447–452.
41. "Galton's Development of the Human Faculty," *The Nation*, XXXVI (June 14, 1883), 512–513. "The Study of Heredity," *Science*, III (June 13, 1884), 734–735.
42. *Science*, XIII (April 5, 1889), 260–267. *The Nation*, XLIX (September 5, 1889), 198.

reviewer's explanation for genius came from environmental sources.[43] The book critic for *The Catholic World* denounced Galton's materialism for ignoring the interaction of body and soul. Mere heredity based on naturalistic assumptions, the Roman Catholic argued, was not the source of genius, "for the superiority of the blood depends originally and continuously on the soul, its original endowments, and its peculiar training or culture through several generations."[44] The emphasis on soul was not an effective antidote to Galtonian thought in the science of heredity grounded in Darwinian evolutionary theories.

In 1911, after Sir Francis's death, Karl Pearson wrote in an article soliciting funds for the laboratory, "In examining the correspondence of the late Sir Francis Galton I find very many appreciative letters concerning his work from Americans distinguished in science or social activities." As inspiration, Galton's eugenic theories found a kinder reception in the United States. After 1900, Galton's influence in the United States increased.[45] Progressivism provided congenial ideological support to Sir Francis Galton's social philosophy. Scientific and popular thought on human heredity in the United States provided the background for Galtonian influences on some American progressives. The task now is to trace the origins and organizational responses to Galton's eugenic philosophy.

43. M. E. Caw, "Genius and Heredity," *The Popular Science Monthly* XXIV (December 1883), 191–195.

44. *The Catholic World*, XI (November 1870), 731–732.

45. Pearson, "The Francis Galton Laboratory for National Eugenics," *Science*, n.s. XXXIV (December 8, 1911;, 799-800 Pearson, *Galton*, III A, 235. Nicholas Partore, *The Nature-Nurture Controversy* (New York, 1949), p. 25. Barbara M. Solomon, *Ancestors and Immigrants, A Changing New England Tradition*, pp. 145–146.

3

EUGENICS
IN THE
UNITED STATES:
ORIGIN AND
ORGANIZATION

The Nineteenth Century

SIR FRANCIS GALTON conceived of eugenics as a social science based on human heredity and Darwinian evolution. In nineteenth-century America the most widely known and respected hereditary concept was that of acquired characteristics. Both democratic and aristocratic interpretations were given to this concept. The democratic interpretation stated that if a characteristic acquired by a person during his lifetime was transmittable to his offspring, then environmental experiences had hereditary value. Thus, accordingly, all conditions that improved the individual improved his progeny and thereby his species. In addition the biological equality of all men was possible by this interpretation, since a humanitarian concern about raising the environment of biologically inferior to that of superior individuals in time made the inadequate people the equals of the biologically superior people. In a society such as the United States, this environmentalism appealed to reformers who wanted biological and sociological equality for all citizens. Education also played a large part in this transformation toward hereditary sameness.[1]

1. Alfred Wallace, "Human Progress: Past and Future," *The Arena*, V (January 1892), 159.

For this reason, Lester Frank Ward, the father of American sociology, rejected later theories of inheritances. He believed that "strengthening the faculties of the mind, through their lifelong exercises in special fields, is permanently preserved to the race by the hereditary transmission to posterity of the acquired increment." [2] Because of his democratic faith in the possibility of innate improvement in mankind, Ward distrusted any concept offering any hereditary exclusiveness for part of the American population.

The adherents to the "aristocratic" interpretation believed that natural selection meant that the fit survive, having overcome environmental obstacles by better adaptation. For the scientists using this method, aristocratic selection involved complex mathematics, since it was an observable fact in the United States that the "misfit" outbred the "fit." The result among conservative Darwinists was the popularity of Sir Francis Galton's law of ancestral regression.[3] Under the guidance of Karl Pearson, the eugenics movement in England used this method. Until the discovery and spread of Gregor Mendel's ideas in the United States, biologists in this country subscribed to the inheritance of acquired characteristics with an aristocratic orientation.

Respectable biological scientists such as Edward Drinker Cope (1840–1897), president of the American Association for the Advancement of Science in 1896, and Alpheus Hyatt of the American Academy of Arts and Sciences utilized the inheritance of acquired character in both their scientific work and their comments on human affairs. Scientists and men of letters used the theory to explain the white man's innate superiority over his dark-skinned rival.[4] Instincts played a major role in the maintenance of this superiority.

2. John C. Burnham, *Lester Frank Ward in American Thought*, p. 3. Lester F. Ward, "The Transmission of Culture," *Forum*, XI (May 1891), 319.

3. Conway Zirkle, "Commentary on the Papers of J. Walter Wilson and John C. Greene," *Critical Problem in the History of Science: Proceedings of the Institute for the History of Science at the University of Wisconsin*, September 1–11, 1957, Marshall Clagett, ed., pp. 463–464.

4. Henry F. Osborn, "Biographical Memoir of Edward Drinker Cope, 1840–1897," *National Academy of Sciences of the United States of America, Biographical Memoirs*, XIII (Third Memoir, 1929), 168; John A. Ryden, "Proofs of the Effects of Habitual Use in the Modification of an Animal Organization," *Proceedings of the American Philosophical Society*, XXVI (1889), 529; Ryden, "A Dy-

Thus, the scientific community of the nineteenth century contained both environmentalists and hereditarians. The former group stressed education and differences in opportunity and the plasticity of human nature; the latter element emphasized innate character, differential fecundity among the social classes, genetic determinism; and was pessimistic about improvement in human nature. In social thought, the environmentalists were philosophical democrats, while the hereditarians questioned the biological validity of a democratic society. Both groups of thinkers, however, assumed cultural change by genetic means, not by a cultural process.[5] Race played a large role in cultural advancement.

By 1870, natural selection and the inheritance of acquired characters had become the complete explanation of human heredity for both schools of thought. The only inadequacy of the explanation was that, whereas natural selection was a known process, the inheritance of acquired characters was mere speculation.[6] Thirty years later during the early stages of Mendelian controversy in the United States and England, pioneer geneticists rejected any effect of natural selection in human heredity because of its long-time connection with the disreputable theory of acquired chacteristics. In time, geneticists restored natural selection to a place of prime importance in heredity.

In the biological thought of the last century, "types" of organisms expressed the process of evolution and natural selection. These biologists believed that everything in nature was good or bad, useful or detrimental for man's welfare. They saw race as being part of type analysis. Accordingly, every representative of a race has the typical features of that race and is different from all other racial representa-

---

namical Hypothesis of Inheritance," *Science*, n.s. I (May 31, 1895), 597–605; Alpheus Hyatt, "Phylogeny of an Acquired Characteristic," *Proceedings of the American Philosophical Society*, XXXII (May 22–26, 1893), 349–647; Edward D. Cope, *The Primary Factors of Organic Evolution*, pp. 528–532; Edward J. Pfeifer, "The Reception of Darwinism in the United States, 1859–1880," unpublished dissertation (Brown University, 1957), pp. 160–171. Philip Wiener, *Evolution and the Founders of Pragmatism*, p. 284. Conway Zirkle, *Evolution, Marxian Biology and the Social Scene*, p. 339.

5. Nicholas Pastore, *The Nature-Nurture Controversy*.

6. Zirkle, Evolution, *Marxian Biology and the Social Scene*, pp. 79–80.

tives by the characteristics "typical" for the given race. Nineteenth-
and twentieth-century racists shared that theoretical assumption.[7]

Eugenists in the early twentieth century assumed the possibility
of individual perfection of mankind. By 1930, however, geneticists destroyed that eugenic aspiration. The latter theorists of natural selection
made no distinction between genetically and environmentally determined variation. In rejecting or selecting an organism, "Nature is not
concerned with the origin of its adaptation. Divested from environmental 'luck' the organism can only transmit its hereditary capabilities.
Perfection in a species, therefore, is not possible, but exists only as a
statistical character of a given population." [8]

During the nineteenth century in the United States, the hereditarians and the environmentalists, despite their scientific differences,
shared the common hopes of using biological science to improve
human society. In fact, for both groups there existed a mutual influence of scientific thought on social reform.

America, in the years following the Civil War, experienced great
changes, in society with the rise of the city and in science with the
growth of naturalism. Social and natural scientists began seeking
natural causes for human behavior and not supernatural explanations.
Thus, the moral code, for example, originated in nature, not in some
heavenly dispensation. Nature was the standard and judge of mankind's conduct and ethical judgments. Agnostics in the United States
and England, drawing on naturalism for intellectual justification, were
still solicitous of supernatural morality because of its great value as
social control.[9] Understandably then, Sir Francis Galton wanted eugenics accepted as a religious practice because of its merits for social

7. Louis Agassiz, "Evolution and Permanence of Type," *The Atlantic Monthly*,
XXXIII (January 1874), 98; Bert J. Loewenberg, "The Reaction of American
Scientists to Darwinism," *American Historical Review*, XXXVIII (July 1933),
693.

8. Garrett Hardin, *Nature and Man's Fate*, p. 63.

9. Bert J. Loewenberg, "The Impact of the Doctrine of Evolution on American
Thought, 1859–1900," unpublished dissertation (Harvard University, 1934), *passim*. For an excellent general discussion, see Stow Person, *American Minds*, pp.
217–345; Gertrude Himmelfarb, *Darwin and the Darwinian Revolution*, pp. 382,
388.

control. In like manner, American eugenists repeated the element of social control in their eugenic program.

During this era many scientists believed that science provided the basis for ethics and public policies. Professor E. W. Morse, the president of the American Association for the Advancement of Science, in 1887 echoed the sentiment of his generation in stating,

if the cause of degradation and ignorance, of poverty, of contagious disease, or of any of the miseries which make a nation wretched, can be pointed out by scientific methods, then it is the stern duty of science to step in and at least show the reasons, even if the remedy is not at once forth coming.

Anticipating eugenic opinion, he concluded that,

the men who would be reformers and agitators, and who by their earnestness and devotion get the attention of multitudes, are unfit for their work if they show the ignorance, as most of them do, of the doctrines of natural selection.[10]

Scholars sharing Morse's conviction joined the Social Science movement to reform scientifically American life and morals by following nature's laws. The context for these reformers was naturalism. By discovering the materialistic causes and effects of human behavior, they were sure that a natural order existed and their task was one of restoration—of returning society to the ways of nature. In the early twentieth century, American eugenists and many progressives continued the intellectual task of fusing nature and society through science.[11]

From the end of the Civil War to World War I, change, progress, and improvement were parts of the litany of American life as the forces of industrialization molded the social order. In economics, the temper of the times was growth and consolidation as new industries developed and became parts of an expanding industrial complex. Technology—applied science—in conjunction with vast natural resources and a tolerant public policy changed American society far greater than any political revolution.

Despite the hymns of progress sung by the leaders of American

10. E. W. Morse, "What American Zoologists Have Done for Evolution," *Science*, X (August 12, 1887), 73–76.

11. Zirkle, *Evolution, Marxian Biology and the Social Scene*, pp. 126–127.

science and industry, many citizens distrusted the future. Having no feudal past, Americans lacked the traditional bounds for the social classes. The ideas of the open society and individual mobility marked social philosophy in the United States. Yet, in the rush of change and conflict, Americans sought some means to distinguish members in the social order. Money was the answer. Wealth and leisure made a gentleman of anyone. Therefore, the ethical question for wealthy Americans of the nineteenth century was one of justification. Why were they rich? Dismissing luck as being alien to their success, Americans saw in heredity the reason for their cultural well-being. "Good blood and breeding" told the story of their innate superiority and reason for victory in the sociological struggle for riches. The successful Americans of the post–Civil War industrial order believed their status in the society indicated their biological superiority. "Nature" had justified the ways of society.

As a result of this new industrialization, then, Americans experienced individual mobility, new wealth, and a tremendous increase in the middle class. From 1900 to 1920, the progressives within the eugenics movement saw this failure of the better sociobiological classes to control the expanding numbers of the innately inadequate masses as the American tragedy. Such eugenists as Charles Davenport, leader of the American cause, held little hope for the society unless the country adopted eugenic programs. Having been taught the naturalistic ethics of the nineteenth century, the American urban middle class reformer became alarmed.

In the last few decades of the nineteenth century, scientists began questioning the validity of the old explanation of heredity. August Weismann (1834–1913), a German biologist, led the first serious attack on the inheritance of acquired character. Essentially, Weismann maintained that a basic difference existed between germ and body cells. He stressed the direct lineage of germ cells because the development of the germ cells and of the body cells occurred independently. The German biologist was not the first to suggest that distinction existed, but in nineteenth-century America the hereditary controversy centered around his experiments. Although a naturalist, Weismann rejected the idea that character acquired by the disuse and use of bodily organs could possibly be inherited. Rather, he identified germ plasm with chromosomes and what he termed "ids" (now called "genes"). Weismann's theory of particular inheritance strengthened the weakest element in the Darwinian system—the mechanism of heredity. In opposition to the theory of acquired characters, the advocators of particular inheritance "insisted that no characters acquired by body cells during the life of experience of an organism could be transmitted to future members of the species." The assumption was that the germ plasm rigidly determined individual and racial features, regardless of environmental influences or activities of individuals and races. Pioneer geneticists at first upheld this hereditary determinism which American eugenists utilized in their propaganda. The increasing acceptance among biological scientists of particular inheritance marked the decline of older theories of inheritance.[12]

Weismann's experiments were quite simple in conception and execution. For more than a year he removed the tails from white mice and found that five generations of mutated mice failed to show that any future mouse generation inherited their "taillessness." Noting the limited number of generations used, the German scientist still discarded the theory of acquired characteristics as false because it implied that "mutilation was immediately noticeable in the next generation." [13]

12. August Weismann, *Essays upon Heredity*, second edition, 2 volumes, E. B. Poulton, Sehnar Schouland, Arthur E. Shipley, translators. The essays are the same as when they were first published. For the 1883 essay, "On Heredity," see Volume I, pp. 71–106. Unless otherwise noted, any reference to Weismann's writings may be found in these two volumes. Henry S. Wilhams, "On the Genetic Energy of Organisms," *Science*, n.s. VIII (May 27, 1898), 730; Daniel G. Brinton, "The Factors of Heredity and Environment in Man," *American Anthropoligist*, XI (September 1898), 275–276; Edwin G. Conklin, "The World's Debt to Darwin," *Proceedings of the American Philosophical Society*, XLVIII (February 23, 1909), 1. Zirkle, *Evolution, Marxian Biology and the Social Scene*, pp. 122–123. A. E. E. McKenzie, *The Major Achievements of Science*, p. 263; C. D. Darlington, "Purpose and Particles in the Study of Heredity," *Science, Medicine, and History, Essays on the Evolution of Scientific Thought Written in Honor of Charles Singer*, ed. E. Ashworth Underwood, II, 478; Auguste Weinstein, "August Weismann 1834-1914)," *Encyclopedia of Social Science*, XV, 392. Persons, *American Minds*, p. 280. Loren Eiseley, *Darwin's Century, Evolution and the Men Who Discovered It*. pp. 219–220. Hereafter cited as Eiseley, *Darwin's Century*. For an engaging view of Weismann as man and scientist, see Alexander Petrunkevitch, "August Weismann, Personal Reminiscences," *Journal of the History of Medicine and Allied Sciences*, VXIII (January 1963), 20–35.
13. "Inheritance of Ingiunes," *Science*, XIV (August 9, 1889) 93–94.

Within six months after he published his results, American scientists were taking sides in the heredity controversy. Reviewers of Weismann's books quickly noted that particular inheritance discredited older theories of heredity.[14]

The advocates of acquired character still maintained during the last decade of the nineteenth century that a connection existed between body cells and germ plasm. They used Galton's theories of inheritance in an attempt to deny the validity of particular inheritance. The defenders of the inheritance of acquired character criticized August Weismann's conclusion by shifting the argument from inheritance per se to natural selection.[15]

This controversy over the mechanism of heredity indicated the importance of the biological view of human behavior in reform matters. Students of both Weismann and the inheritance of acquired character were materialists and racists. The individual's health was national health. The sum of individual inheritance was race inheritance—the material basis for future national development. Citing the work of Sir Francis Galton, George Preston stated in 1886 that enlightened public opinion could destroy the hereditary diseases of consumption and insanity. Using the analogy of selected breeding of lower animals, he concluded that human reproduction held the same possibilities.[16]

Articles in scientific and nonscientific magazines discussed the racial effect of artificial selection on mankind and upon marriage as a social

14. For example, see the news item "Health Matters," *Science,* XIV (November 29, 1889), 365–366. "Weismann on Heredity," *The Nation,* L (May 1, 1890), 357–358; Grant Allen, "The New Theory of Heredity," *The Review of Reviews,* I (June 1890), 537–538.

15. Such was the argument in Andrew Wilson, "What Is Inheritance?" *Harper's New Monthly Magazine,* LXXXIII (August 1891), 360–361; Manley Miles, "Heredity of Acquired Characters," *Proceedings of the American Association for the Advancement of Science,* XLI (August 1892), 208; unsigned review of Henry B. Orr, *A Theory of Development and Heredity* (New York: Macmillan, 1893) in *Science,* XXIII (December 15, 1893), 332. Henry F. Osborn, "The Present Problem of Heredity," *The Atlantic Monthly,* LXVII (March 1891), 355–357. Th. Eimer, *On Orthogenesis and the Importance of Natural Selection in Species-Formation,* p. 2.

16. George Preston, "Hereditary Diseases and Race-Culture," *The Popular Science Monthly,* XXIX (May 1886), 640–641.

institution. The latter consideration about the effect of artificial selection on marriage revealed a problem for nineteenth-century reformers. Marriage was a sacred trust for many Americans. Romantic love gave a basis to the trust. Consequently, a materialistic analysis of family life, such as Alexander Graham Bell's discussion of the racial implications of deaf-mute marriage, upset American romanticists. Bell rejected with finality a union of two mutes since—in his opinion—the offspring would share the parental handicap.[17] This dialectic between the material and romantic aspects of sex and marriage was in the foreground of the progressive birth-control movement.

The effect of American scientists' interest in heredity gave a hereditary bias to the solution of all social problems, including crime and drunkenness. In 1893 William Brewer, president of A.A.A.S., offered a grand scheme to end such problems by expressing in positive or creative terms the scientific breeding of man. He reasoned that science—biological, economic, and social—had knowledge for the controlled and eugenic creation of man.[18] Three years later, S. Millington Miller expressed a standard attitude of twentieth-century eugenists in demanding legislation forbidding the marriage of alcoholics. Miller demanded, "What humanity needs in many directions is prevention. They need to be prevented from reaching that condition where treatment is necessary. Prevention is the sphere and jurisdiction of government and law." [19]

By the end of the century, the conservative acceptance of man's irrationality and stupidity replaced the traditional liberal trust in human rationality in the name of a higher collectivity, a greater social control—the blood of the nation. This change in basic assumption

17. "How Mankind Might Be Improved," *The Review of Reviews,* II (July 1890), 32; "Artificial Selection and the Marriage Problem," *The Review of Reviews,* IV (November 1891), 457–458. Alexander Graham Bell, "Marriage," *Science,* XVII (March 20, 1891), 160–163; for an article on the marriage controversy, see Philip G. Gillett, "Deaf-Mutes; Their Intermarriage and Offspring," *Science,* XVII (January 30, 1891), 57–60; Henry May, *The End of American Innocence,* p. 340.

18. A. M. Holmes, "Heredity and Environment," *The Arena,* IX (April 1894), 576–580. William H. Brewer, "The Mutual Relations of Science and Stock Breeding," *Science,* XXII (September 29, 1893), 169–170.

19. S. Millington Miller, "The Ascent of Man," *Arena,* XII (March 1896), 134.

about human nature underlined progressive social thought and reform, since it provided a connecting link between conservative social attitudes and the desirability of certain eugenic reforms, such as birth control and sterilization.

The nineteenth century "lunatic fringe" of naturalistic reform only indirectly influenced later *organized* eugenics in the twentieth century.[20] Although these people did not materially contribute to theories of heredity, early twentieth-century reformers shared their optimism for eugenic enterprises. These Bohemians of the nineteenth century linked their eugenic opinions to other causes, such as free love and birth control, as methods of freeing the masses. In progressive America the objective changed because the philosophers of eugenics emphasized the creed's importance as social control.

The nineteenth century closed in violence. It was the time of the Pullman and Homestead strikes, the Haymarket Riot, the Indian wars, and the continuing appearance of Southern Europeans in the United States. For Americans in a naturalist age, the conflicts—many of which were examples of class struggles—appeared as racial strifes, of competition among alien biological groups. Americans under the spell of social Darwinism saw these industrial struggles as examples of the natural and animal competition.

Although the scientific interpretation of heredity changed in the twentieth century, American reformers still used instincts and other naturalistic causes to understand human nature. American progressives in the new age of reconstruction, 1900–1920, still believed the racial ideals of the last century. Their vision of American life and human nature allowed them no alternative.

The Twentieth Century

An Augustinian monk, Johann Mendel (1822–1884), studied the genetic nature of sweet peas, and from this humble enterprise, in time, came genetics—the modern science of heredity. Born in Moravia, Mendel came from circumstances of stark poverty. In 1843 he took the name of Gregor when he entered an Augustinian monastery. Despite

---

20. Sidney Ditzion, *Marriage, Morals and Sex in America, A History of Ideas,* pp. 128–325. Hereafter cited as Ditzion, *Marriage, Morals and Sex.*

his failure in the examination for certification, Mendel spent a number of years as a teacher of biology. Later, he was abbot of his monastery, and as such his time for hereditary investigations was limited. In 1865 he read his now famous paper on sweet peas before the Brünn Society for the Study of Natural Science. The response was silence. He died never knowing the wonderous impact of his efforts.[21]

Despite the fact that some of his concepts were already known,[22] Mendel's achievement still ranks as a major intellectual accomplishment in the history of science. In essence, Mendel discovered genes. "Roughly speaking, genes are material particles found in the nuclei of cells—particles whose chemical interaction determines how the organism reacts to the environment, particles that are passed on from parents to offspring in regular, predictable ways."[23] To be sure, geneticists have greatly increased knowledge about human heredity. The definition, nevertheless, gives the core of the science.

Mendel recognized that heredity was particular, that "factors" controlling height, for example, do not blend but retain their individuality from generation to generation. He refuted reversion to ancestral types, Francis Galton's favorite theory. Mendel showed that heredity is sometimes the unchanged work of recessive (hidden) genes, and their effect is known when they are paired together, instead of with dominant genes. Thus "dominance," "segregation," and "recombination" eventually became common terms in genetics.[24] In this regard, August Weismann was a true pioneer in genetic investigations.

Interestingly, three corn-breeders in the United States during the decade of the 1880s reported "Mendelian" ratios, but they lacked the insight or imagination to recognize the significance of their experi-

21. The standard biography is Hugo Itis, *Life of Mendel*. For an informative discussion of why Mendel's work was ignored until 1900, see Bentley Glass, "The Long Neglect of a Scientific Discovery: Mendel's Laws of Inheritance," *Studies in Intellectual History*, pp. 148–160. Garrett Hardin, *Nature and Man's Fate*, pp. 116–117, believes that since Mendel was intellectually isolated in the understanding or appreciation of his discovery, Mendel was unappreciated by fellow scientists.

22. Zirkle, "Gregor Mendel and His Precursors," *Isis*, XLII (June 1951), 103.

23. Hardin, *Nature and Man's Fate*, p. 117.

24. McKenzie, *Major Achievements in Science*, I, 258–259.

ments and nothing came of this discovery.[25] No doubt the stronghold that the theory of inheritance of acquired characteristics had on nineteenth-century scientists prevented any further experimental activities.

In 1900, William Bateson of England, Hugo de Vries of Holland, K. Correns of Germany, and E. Tschermak of Austria independently rediscovered the work of Gregor Mendel. Despite the preparatory work of Weismann, the impact of this rediscovery caused confusion among scientists. Some scientists mistook hereditary traits for traits acquired from the prenatal and preconceptual environments.[26] Advocators of earlier theories of inheritance still defended their particular concepts.

William Bateson's scientific career revealed this struggle between different schools of hereditary thought. Although his terminology caused some needless questions, the important aspect of his career for American eugenics was his intellectual conflict with Karl Pearson. Bateson's criticism of Pearson's investigations led to the establishment of *Biometrika*, devoted to Galtonian analysis. Once editor of the magazine, Pearson—using Galton's theory of inheritance—sharply criticized Bateson's suggestion for racial improvement. The controversy spread to the United States. Bateson supported Charles Davenport's investigations into particular inheritance. In fact, Davenport's use of modern theory and Pearson's dogmatic assertation of Galton's views on heredity provided the theoretical differences between American and English eugenic movements.[27]

Nevertheless, Karl Pearson, as an avid naturalist and American

25. Zirkle, "The Knowledge of Heredity before 1900," *Genetics in the 20th Century*, p. 50.

26. McKenzie, *Major Achievements in Science*, I, 256. One of the scientists—Hugo de Vries—discovered Mendel by means of a bibliography compiled by Liberty Hyde Bailey; see Zirkle, *Evolution, Marxian Biology and the Social Scene*, pp. 190–191. L. L. Bernard, *Instinct, A Study in Social Psychology*, pp. 15–16. Hereafter cited as Barnard, *Instinct*.

27. W. E. Castle, "The Beginnings of Mendelism in America," *Genetics in the 20th Century*, p. 59. For a discussion of his analysis of Mendel, see William Bateson, *Mendel's Principles of Heredity*. The standard biography is Beatrice Bateson, *William Bateson F.R.S.* William Bateson, "Facts Limited the Theory of Heredity," *Science*, n.s. XXVI (November 15, 1907), 660. James A. Field, "The Progress of Eugenics," *The Quarterly Journal of Economics*, XVI (November 1911), 32–33.

eugenist, shared the same philosophical convictions. He, like them, saw society as survival of the fittest, of race against race. Despite methodological differences, American eugenic progressives and Pearson held the same bloody and optimistic view of progress.

The path of progress is strewn with the wreck of nations; traces are everywhere to be seen of the headtombs of inferior races, and of the victims who found not the narrow way to the greater perfection. Yet these dead people are, in very truth, the stepping stones on which mankind has risen to the higher intellectual and deeper emotional life of today.[28]

English and American eugenists wanted progress insurance by having society follow the eugenic dogma.

Meanwhile, in 1903, a Harvard biologist, William E. Castle, began explaining Mendel's theories to the American public. Other scientists followed with additional evidence in support of Mendel's work. Wilhelm Johannsen (1857–1927), a Danish botanist, was one of those scientists spreading Mendel's message throughout the scientific community. His studies demonstrated that phenotypic characters without a genetic basis would not yield hereditary change. In brief, his results indicated environmental variations were not transmitted to the offspring. By 1905, American scientists and the educated public in general increasingly accepted the Mendelian law of heredity, the mutation theory of evolution, the inability of selection to build up species from fluctuations, and the chromosomal mechanism of sex determination.[29]

American eugenists utilized the new theories as an explanation for the existence of habitual criminals, the feebleminded, and the hopeless pauper by stressing hereditary inevitability in their offspring.[30]

28. Karl Pearson, *National Life from the Standpoint of Science*, pp. 46, 64.
29. W. E. Castle, "Mendel's Law of Heredity," *Science*, n.s. XVIII (September 25, 1903), 396–406. McKenzie, *Major Achievements in Science*, I, 255–256; Eiseley, *Darwin's Century*, pp. 228–229. Edwin A. Conklin, "Penrose Memorial Lecture, A Generation of Progress in the Study of Evolution," *Proceedings of the American Philosophical Society*, LXXIV (April 20, 1934), 137–158. There were exceptions to this general acceptance; see, for an example, O. F. Cook, "Transmission Inheritance Distinct from Expression Inheritance," *Science*, n.s. XXV (June 7, 1907), 911–912.
30. William Whetham and Catherine D. Whetham, *The Family and the Nation, A Study in National Inheritance and Social Responsibility*, p. 212; A. J. Rosauoff, "Heredity in Insanity," *Science*, n.s. XXXIII (April 7, 1911), 537–538.

With Calvinistic certainty, philosophers of eugenics preached naturalistic predestination. Mendel's analysis, not the statistical method of
Francis Galton and Karl Pearson, provided the hereditary determinism
desired by American eugenists. Ironically, Galton's *ideals* and philosophy still shaped American eugenic thought. Despite being Galton's
friend and admirer, Charles Davenport still used Mendel's conclusions
in his work. Eugenics based on Galtonian hereditary theories declined
in importance. Under Davenport's guidance, American eugenists used
Mendel's concepts to advance Sir Francis Galton's social philosophy.

In 1918 Ronald Fisher, a British biological statistician, demonstrated
that biometrics—the Galton-Pearson method of hereditary analysis—
must follow Mendelian inheritance. In fact, biometrics could show
by partition of continuous variation that Mendelian dominance was
recognizable. The letter of Galtonian thought died, but the spirit endured. Mendelian concepts strengthened the American eugenist's al-
legiance to hereditary determinism. At the same time, the rapid cultural and economic changes in American life caused no little concern
in the ranks of the middle-class eugenists. In fact, the extremely
wealthy eugenists saw their superiority forever present in their biological natures. Eugenists and other individuals affected by nineteenth-century naturalism saw mass man and corresponding upper-
class sterility as indices of race suicide. Theodore Roosevelt's agitation
for a greater American birth rate expressed this concern for reformers
in the years before the first World War. Eugenists, using programs of
education and state action, gave the eugenic creed the appearance of a
typical progressive reform. This reform, it might be added, was economical by keeping the biocultural unfit off welfare rolls and thus reducing taxes. Eugenists defended the status quo by sterilization,
immigrant restriction, and birth control for those cultural groups not
racially capable of being good Americans.[31]

This naturalistic concern for the proper racial composition of the
United States on the part of middle-class reformers soon had organiza-

---

31. Kenneth Mather, "The Progress and Prospect of Biometrical Genetics,"
Genetics in the 20th Century, pp. 113–114. Ironically enough, Fisher at this time
held the chair that Galton had created to further his work. Higham, *Strangers in
the Land*, pp. 150–153.

tional expression. Alexander G. Bell, a pioneer in the American eugenic cause, established in 1877 the Volta Bureau for the study of hereditary deafness. Thirteen years later he founded the American Association to Promote the Teaching of Speech to the Deaf. Bell combined the two organizations in 1908. At the height of the progressive movement in 1914, he started the Genealogical Record Office, but the Great Depression in 1929 ended its activities.[32] Many eugenic organizations suffered a similar fate in the New Deal years.

In 1902 Andrew Carnegie established the Carnegie Institution of Washington which, in turn, two years later set up the Station for Experimental Evolution at Cold Spring Harbor, Long Island. Charles B. Davenport was the director of the Station. While head of the Station, Davenport created his own private institute—the Eugenics Record Office—in 1910, through the gifts of money and eighty acres with buildings from Mrs. E. H. Harriman. Conflicting explanations exist for her generous gift. Davenport claimed that Mrs. Harriman's experience with race horses taught her to appreciate the attempt of applying good breeding principles to men. David Starr Jordan, however, thought that Mrs. Harriman's daughter, Mrs. Charles Cary Rumesey, having studied heredity at Columbia University, persuaded her mother to endow the project under Davenport's direction.[33] Either explanation indicates the American patrician class's interest in heredity and its social consequences.

In 1921, the Station for Experimental Evolution absorbed the Eugenic Record Office to form the Department of Genetics for the Carnegie Institution of Washington. This merger resulted from Mrs. Harriman's transfer of the Eugenics Record Office to the Carnegie Institution in 1918. Maintained as a subsection of the Department of

32. Bell recognized hereditary deafness. He founded in 1890 the American Association to Promote the Teaching of Speech to the Deaf. S. Wayne Evans, *Organized Eugenics*, p. 52; James A. Field, "The Progress of Eugenics," *The Quarterly Journal of Economics*, XVI (November 1911), 35.

33. The rich contributed to the eugenic cause. Mark Haller, "American Eugenics, Heredity and Social Thought 1870–1930," unpublished doctoral dissertation (University of Wisconsin, 1959). Hereafter cited as Haller, "American Eugenics." David Starr Jordan, *The Days of a Man, Being Memoirs of a Naturalist, Teacher and Minor Prophet of Democracy*, II, 297–298.

Genetics, the Eugenics Record Office in 1939 became, because of change in the climate of opinion, the Genetics Record Office.[34]

Meanwhile, eugenists found other organizational means for spreading the eugenic gospel among the American people. In St. Louis on December 29, 1903, the Association of American Agricultural Colleges and Experimental Stations created the American Breeders Association to further the practical side of heredity. Firmly in the naturalist tradition, the A.B.A. soon applied hereditary concepts to mankind. At the 1908 meeting, Alexander Graham Bell and David Starr Jordan read papers on eugenics. The number of such papers increased at the next year's conference. With this increase of interest in eugenics, C. B. Davenport urged that the eugenics committee of the organization be changed to a third section of the Association, along with the Plant and Animal Sections. The Association members voted 499 to 6 for the change in organizational structure.[35]

The Eugenics Section set up various subcommittees. With D. S. Jordan as Chairman and Davenport as Secretary, the Eugenic Section began a campaign of making the American Breeders Association a greater and more complete instrument for eugenics propaganda. Committees were needed, Davenport urged, for investigation, education, and legislation. The legislative program included sterilization of idiots, imbeciles, and dangerous criminals.[36] Such harsh measures were necessary to save mankind from "vice, imbecility, and suffering."

Within the entire organization eugenists reached success when in 1913 the American Breeders Association became the American Genetic Association. The reason given at the time of the change was that "the steady growth of eugenics and the full recognition to this new and

34. *Scientific and Technical Societies*, fifth edition, pp. 121–122; Evans, *Organized Eugenics*, p. 43.

35. *Scientific and Technical Societies*, sixth edition, p. 56; Castle, "The Beginnings of Mendelism in America," pp. 64–65; *American Breeders Magazine*, I (First Quarter, 1910), 64–65.

36. *American Breeders Magazine*, I (Third Quarter, 1910), 235–236. Arthur E. Fink, *Causes of Crime, Biological Theories in the United States, 1800-1915*, pp. 204–205; hereafter cited as Fink, *Causes of Crime*. Stanley P. Davies, *The Mentally Retarded in Society*, p. 50; Charles B. Davenport, "Report of Committee on Eugenics," *The American Breeders Magazine*, I (Second Quarter, 1911), 126–129.

important science by the association has made a change of name desirable." [37] The *A.B.A. Magazine* became *The Journal of Heredity* with Paul Popenoe as the new editor. The magazine continued to carry articles on plant and animal heredity, although human inheritance covered more pages.[38]

Despite the fact that Mendel's theory of inheritance replaced Galton's, Galton's influence on American eugenists was still strong in terms of their basic philosophy, that is, race and ancestor worship. In other words, the "how" might have been changed, but the aristocratic spirit of inheritance of characters was still the same. In 1918 the Galton Society was created in New York. Charles Davenport served as the first president of the group, limited in membership to twenty-five fellows. Davenport, Madison Grant, Henry F. Osborn, and Edward L. Thorndike were among the charter fellows. Earnest A. Hooten later joined the society which held the American elite of the eugenic leadership. Regularly meeting at the American Museum of Natural History, they chiefly promoted the study of physical and mental hereditary characters and their eugenics or dysgenic impact on the nation's population. To this objective, the Society issued as its official organ the *Eugenical News*. For some time the Galtonians operated the Galton Publishing Company.[39] This organization worked closely with other individuals and groups dedicated to racial improvement.

The last major eugenic organization was the American Eugenics Society, Inc., incorporated in 1926 as the successor to the Eugenics Committee of the United States and the Eugenic Society of the United States. The A.E.S, Inc., still functions today. In 1931 the organization consciously equated the eugenic ideal with democratic principles. With the Great Depression a reality, the American Eugenics Society denounced false claims of class superiority and wanted equal opportunity to demonstrate intrinsic merit.[40] Organized eugenics, however,

37. *American Breeders Magazine,* IV (Fourth Quarter, 1913), 177.
38. *Ibid.,* IV (Second Quarter, 1913), 126–127.
39. "Current Notes," *American Journal of Physical Anthropology,* I (April-June 1918), 264.
40. *Scientific and Technical Societies of the United States and Canada,* sixth edition, p. 53. C. B. Davenport, H. H. Laughlin, David Starr Jordan, Edward M. East, Paul Popenoe, Gifford Pinchot, E. S. Gosney, Edward Thorndike, William McDougall, Earnest Hooton, E. A. Ross, J. M. Cattell, and others were active

by the time of the New Deal ceased to maintain the interest created
during the earlier reform era.

The American eugenists supported the only two international congresses of eugenics. These meetings took place in London in 1912 and
in New York City in 1921. In 1931, world federation meetings were
also conducted.[41]

Since the decade of the thirties, hosts of small organizations devoted
to eugenics have come into existence. Generally speaking, the purely
genetic societies grew into substantial bodies devoted to scientific
investigations without any pernicious racism in their endeavors. As
genetics became a science, the mortality of eugenic organizations
increased with the passing years.[42]

We see, then, that Galton's naturalism supplied important basic
philosophy for American reformers, regardless of his inheritance theories. American eugenists, discussed in the next chapter, had their
own variations for the eugenic creed, although Galton's work supplied
the key ideas for eugenics and the Americans remained true to his
basic creed of conservatism.

---

in the eugenics movement. See Evans, *Organized Eugenics*, pp. 56–57. This
concern for equality to prove natural inequality was in keeping with the political
philosophy of the nineteenth century and its anti–natural rights assumption. Alan
Grimes, *American Political Thought*, p. 29. Accordingly, eugenics was the sociobiological recognition of this given condition.

41. Raymond Pearl, "The First International Eugenics Congress," *Science*,
n.s. XXXVI (September 27, 1912), 395–396; "The International Eugenics Congress," *Science*, n.s. XXXIV (October 13, 1911), 483; Harry Laughlin, "Historical
Background of the Third International Congress of Eugenics," *Decade of Progress
in Eugenics*, pp. 1–17.

42. For a brief history of genetics, see Ernest B. Babcock, *The Development
of Fundamental Conception in the Science of Genetics*. For the various titles, see
*Summarized Proceedings and Directory, 1940–1948; American Association for
the Advancement of Science; Scientific and Technical Societies*, fourth and sixth
editions; Wilbur Rich, *American Foundations and Their Field*, sixth and seventh
editions; Lawrence Snyder, "Old and New Pathways in Human Genetics," *Genetics in the 20th Century*, pp. 370–371; Higham, *Strangers in the Land*, pp. 273–
276.

4

THE
EUGENIC
CREED

DURING THE first thirty years of the twentieth century, reputable men of science in the United States formulated the eugenic creed. Charles Davenport, David Starr Jordan, Edward M. East, and Harry H. Laughlin were the major architects of American eugenics. Their scientific interests and personal attitudes contributed to an ideology of controlled and directed evolution, grounded in scientific naturalism. The common denominator among these men's theories was the supreme importance of heredity in man and his civilization: that the unfit must be eliminated or at least limited in number and the fit encouraged to increase their numbers, an objective achieved through a scientific knowledge and social application of heredity.

Eugenists, although Darwinists, distrusted the nebulously unscientific aspect of natural selection. They generally felt that a "good man" (of sound heredity) could overcome any disadvantage in his socioeconomic environment and win the positions of status and power in the social order. The problem was that inferiors threatened to outbreed good men. Sociologically, success "sterilized" the successful. Thus, the very people who should have more children did not. Consequently, eugenists believed (although some admitted this was only speculation) [1] that the long-run effect would be swamping of the social order in a sea of stupidity.

As proposed by such men as Samuel J. Holmes, a University of California biologist, the task was to control natural selection, consciously and institutionally directing biological evolution toward a predetermined goal. This controlled evolution would produce the new nation which held all the virtues of rural nineteenth-century Americans.[2] Ironically, despite their modernity, eugenists looked backward for the racial models in tomorrow's America.

Without doubt, the most outstanding scientific supporter of this creed in the United States was Charles Benedict Davenport (1886–1944). Davenport was to American eugenics what Sir Francis Galton was to the British. He not only wrote on the subject, he also provided organizational leadership. In fact, this strong leadership was probably a most important factor in the lack of ideological infighting among the disciples of the creed which, of course, strengthened the movement.

Davenport came from a Brooklyn middle-class background with its own classical economic virtues and Puritan morality. Despite a busy boyhood of work and scientific interests, Davenport was a lonely man, always uneasy in a crowd. He disliked argument—especially about his scientific contributions and theories.[3] He was graduated from Harvard in 1889. After serving as a biology professor at the University of Chicago, he persuaded the Carnegie Institution to establish a biological department. In 1904 Davenport became director of the Station for Experimental Evolution at Cold Spring Harbor, Long Island. The Eugenics Record Office was established at Cold Spring in 1900. Davenport remained director of both scholarly organizations until his retirement in 1934. After retirement he continued his many interests in human and animal evolution. His bibliography indicates a wide interest in biological investigations. The central theme of his scholarly interests was the overriding importance of heredity

1. Samuel J. Holmes, *Studies in Evolution and Eugenics*, pp. 75–77. See also Holmes, *The Eugenic Predicament*, pp. 90, x, 148–149.
2. See, for example, *Ibid.*, pp. 102, 176, 77.
3. Unless otherwise noted, the biographical data and opinions came from Oscar Riddle, "Charles Benedict Davenport," *National Academy Biographical Memoirs*, XXV, 75–109. This biography also included a bibliography of Davenport's writings.

in man's development. Heredity—or race, the collective means of inheritance—was the key.

Despite a large bibliography on eugenics, Davenport often reiterated the same message. Writing in 1904 or 1940, he still held to Galtonian eugenics, although he utilized Mendelian concepts.[4] Whatever the area of human behavior under study, Davenport constantly expressed his racist-eugenic ideals. He believed that members of other races were, in effect, members of different elementary species. Mental, moral, and intellectual aspects of racial development maintained these differences. According to Davenport, racial hybrids never utilized their native endowments.[5] He also believed man's general reactions, whether violent or repressed, were a product of his hereditary temperament. Thus he wrote, "a hyberdized people are a badly put together people and a dissatisfied, restless, ineffective people."[6] Racial intermarriage led only to "disharmony of physical, mental, and temperamental qualities and this means also disharmony with environment." Race mixing was, therefore, socially evil, for it resulted in a "clash of instincts in groups with unlike temperament and mores. The present safe course is to pursue the idea of race homogeneity. For man is an animal and permanent racial progress in eugenics must be based on the laws of biology."[7]

For purposes of social policy, Davenport viewed race and heredity as the same expression of biological determinism. With this hereditary emphasis, instinct psychology was a necessary intellectual complement to Galtonian eugenics. In the light of this philosophy, it almost seems redundant to note that Davenport favored segregation. He considered it a scientific social policy, necessary for social stability and order.

4. As noted, this practice brought into the conflict Karl Pearson and his school of thought. See Charles B. Davenport, "A Reply to Dr. Heron's Strictures," *Science*, n.s. XXXVIII (November 28, 1913), 773–774.

5. Charles B. Davenport, "The Presidential Address: The Development of Eugenics," *Decade of Progress in Eugenics*, p. 22. Charles B. Davenport and Morris Steggerda, *Race Crossing in Jamaica*, p. 477.

6. Davenport, "The Effects of Race Intermingling," *Proceedings of the American Philosophical Society*, LVI (April 13, 1917), 367; see also his "The Mean Stature of American Males," *Quarterly Publication of the American Statistical Association*, XVII (December, 1920), 487.

7. Davenport, "The Presidential Address: The Development of Eugenics," *Decade of Progress in Eugenics*, p. 22.

Another method of racial purity he suggested was immigration restriction. Although he based his racial studies on Mendelian concepts, Davenport suggested that geographical factors might influence body build.[8]

Militant nationalism augmented the eugenics program—limitation of the unfit and increase of the fit. With more biologically fit individuals, the nation would be improved and, therefore, able to fulfill imperialist aspirations. The key to reform was good blood. Social reconstruction based on eugenic concepts would be realistic, for only the biologically best provided permanent advancement.

In the years before World War I, American women agitated for the franchise. With increased job opportunities as a result of the industrial revolution—for example, as typists—the new woman challenged the historic attitude of her assumed natural inferiority and dependence for economic support on the male sex. In a word, the new woman sought rights regardless of her biological differences from the male citizen. The birth-control movement divorced women from the biological necessity of childbirth and expressed this drive for equality in marriage and mate-selection. Davenport supported this female urge for equality if, in the process, the biologically superior were maintained and the number of the unfit decreased.[9]

In application, the eugenics program became partly one of economics. The expert must distinguish between the undeserving and deserving poor in social welfare and charity investigations. Only by breeding for superiority would the numbers of the weak and unfit diminish, "thus the need for charity in its narrow sense," Davenport maintained, "will diminish because of being bred out by the operation of the greater charity."[10] Society saved money by sterilizing female inmates of state institutions, so that these potential wrongdoers would

8. Davenport, Review of W. C. Whetham, *Heredity and Society* (London, 1912), in *Science*, n.s. XXXVI (August 1912), 151; Davenport, *The Feebly Inhibited*, Publication #236 (Washington, 1915), p. 26. Davenport, *Body-Build and Its Inheritance* (Washington, 1923), p. 7.

9. Editorial, "The Woman Movement and Eugenics," *American Breeders Magazine*, II (Third Quarter, 1911), 225–228; Davenport "Research in Eugenics," *Eugenics, Genetics and the Family*, p. 25.

10. Davenport, "Eugenics and Charity," *Proceedings of the National Conference of Charities and Corrections* pp. 281–282.

be prevented from reproducing their own kind.[11] The cliché about an ounce of prevention being worth a pound of cure was a major premise for Charles B. Davenport.

Davenport adhered to the Galtonian distrust of the cities as being destructive of a nation's germ plasm. "Germ plasm" was a general term meaning the hereditary material passed from generation to generation. The term, popularized by Weismann, distinguished itself from nonhereditary body cells. In the same Galtonian approach, Davenport saw crime as a result of nondisciplined instinct, with each child in his development recreating the evolution of the species. Recapitulation was inevitable, accordingly, for the child "represents the ape-like stage." [12]

In summary, Davenport believed that heredity caused the various sorts and conditions of mankind. It was a law of nature the social order must obey or suffer. Otherwise, the unfit—by means of altruism and sentimental charity—would increase and, in time, control society. Davenport believed that the class struggle existed, albeit in the form of naturalistic forces creating the strong and the weak. Knowledge and application of eugenics insured victory for the biologically superior. Always the philosopher and experimenter, Davenport gave the eugenic movement, with his ideological support, a scientific and academic appearance, which popular eugenic writers never imparted. Until his death by pneumonia in 1944, Davenport remained the eugenist.

In like manner, David Starr Jordan (1851–1931), educator, ichthyologist, pacifist, and philosopher, related his eugenic creed directly to reform movements. Generally, Jordan was more interested (and articulate) on current domestic and foreign affairs than was Davenport, whose major efforts were as administrator and scientist in various eugenic organizations. Although a member of various scientific, educational, and social organizations, Jordan's major contribution to the eugenic cause was connecting eugenics with other reform groups and providing philosophical justification for such a connection.

Born into humble circumstances, Jordan by perseverance and good fortune became the first president of Stanford University in 1891.

11. Davenport, "The Importance to the State of Eugenic Investigation," *Proceedings of the First National Conference of Race Betterment*, p. 453.
12. Davenport, *Heredity in Relation to Eugenics* (New York, 1911).

Later he served as chancellor. A recognized authority on fish, he held several academic positions before assuming the presidency of the new university. At Palo Alto, Jordan's life was characteristic of the nineteenth-century self-made man. Sociologically, Jordan and Herbert Hoover, Stanford's most famous alumnus, had a great deal in common. The ideological influences on Jordan's philosophy were varied and sometimes contradictory: Ralph Waldo Emerson, Abraham Lincoln, John Stuart Mill, and Charles Darwin all shaped the creed of D. S. Jordan. In addition, Jordan subscribed to the Populist-Progressive criticism of laissez-faire capitalism.[13] Reform and humanitarian ideals contributed to Jordan's career as an educator. Like other progressives, he sought the creation of an open society, of greater social mobility for the American people.

The bedrock of Jordan's thought was heredity and Darwinism. *"The blood of a nation determines its history. . . . The history of a nation determines its blood. . . . The survival of the fittest in the struggle for existence is the primal cause of race-progress and race-changes."* [14] War was biologically evil, for *"only cowards remained and their brood came forward in the new generation."* Yet Jordan tempered his Social Darwinism with traditionally American optimism and faith in the new beginning, the new generation. Thus "the child of each generation is freeborn so far as heredity goes, and the sins of the fathers are not visited upon him." [15] This environmentalism was a contradictory element in Jordan's world view: the past was and was not a burden in the creation of tomorrow's better nation. A similar ambivalence generally ran through American progressivism.

This contradiction was apparent in the educator's view of human nature. Although human nature changed slowly, Jordan thought education permitted society's better members to outlive inferior folk. Fewer of the offspring of the superior statistically contributed more.

---

13. David Starr Jordan, *The Days of a Man, Being the Memories of a Naturalist, Teacher and Minor Prophet of Democracy,* I, 542–543; Edward M. Burns, *David Starr Jordan: Prophet of Freedom,* pp. 152–153. Hereafter cited as Burns, *Jordan.*

14. Jordan, *The Blood of the Nation, A Study of the Decay of Races through the Survival of the Unfit,* pp. 7, 25. Hereafter cited as Jordan, *The Blood of the Nation.* Burns, *Jordan,* p. 37.

15. *Ibid.,* pp. 20, 53; Burns, *Jordan,* p. 134.

Therefore, he concluded, education rapidly changed the cultural manifestations of human nature. Tacitly, Jordan accepted the democratic version of the inheritance of acquired characters, which reinforced his reformist tendencies.[16] This contradiction about mankind's future was augmented by Jordan's use in biological terms of an automatically adjusted state of nature. Jordan believed improvement in one structure implied degradation in others, thus his "law of compensation." A decline of all parts, subsequently, spelled degeneration. In the same way, action was the expenditure of energy; and if the energy was not expended, the power to generate was lost. Concluding his argument with an analogy, Jordan wrote, "the arm which is not used becomes palsied."[17] Exercise, therefore, developed the individual, and as the individual improved, so did the nation. "The laws of national greatness expanded themselves from the laws which govern the growth of the single cell."[18] The laws of nature governed the affairs of man. Nature and society were one.

With biological factors so important to national welfare, the racial composition of the United States and the world worried Jordan. And yet, Jordan's optimism tempered his racism. Recognizing that all men were brothers, it was necessary, Jordan reasoned, for a superior nation, such as the United States, to govern the Philippines for their ultimate benefit and to foster independence. As a moral duty, it was necessary for the United States to have colonies for commercial advantage. In time, even a backward race might secure the blessings of self-government.[19] While believing that colonies might be a moral necessity, Jordan as a leader of the anti-imperialism movement at the beginning of the twentieth century, felt that biological-geographical factors dictated an anticolonial policy. The temperate zone was necessary for free institutions. The tropics, Jordan believed, created racial degeneration for the Anglo-Saxons. Like many thinkers during the Progressive

16. Jordan, "Is War Eternal?" *Rice Institute Pamphlets*, III (July 1916), 223; Burns, *Jordan*, pp. 60–61.

17. Jordan, *The Strength of Being Clean, A Study of the Quest for Unearned Happiness*, p. 6; see also his *The Heredity of Richard Roe, A Discussion of the Principles of Eugenics*, p. 86.

18. *Ibid.*, pp. 147–148.

19. Jordan, *Democracy and World Relations*, p. 79; Burns, *Jordan*, pp. 215–217.

Era, Jordan adopted a laissez-faire policy in regard to the Negro, since possibly the Negro's inferiority stemmed from hereditary sources.[20]

David Starr Jordan was a pacifist for biologic-eugenic reasons. Using a theory of probabilities: the same number of potential scientists, inventors, etc. appeared in each generation), Jordan believed war created a biological law of diminishing returns. War destroys the brave, the good, which leaves the weak people who are unable or un-willing to fight and to reproduce the future generation. Inferior groups limited future development. Since *"Like the seed is the Harvest,"* war weakens individual's biological strength, the ultimate and true strength of a nation. Jordan argued that militarism being expensive, it created a high national debt, an unsound economic practice. A commission of experts should decide, thought Jordan, necessary ex-penditures for national defense.[21]

His criticism of military expenditures was a mixture of classical economic theory, inheritance of acquired characteristics, and tradi-tional American distrust of economic power. "Every organ demands its functional use, and the purpose of warships is war." Besides, the classic economic thought was present in the statement, "the greater the sea power, the weaker the nation which buys it on borrowed money." Anticipating the Nye Committee of the 1930s, Jordan felt that the "defense of our nation is not protection from each other, but rather defense from the money-lender and from the armament syn-dicate." [22] Jordan did not like war and consequently used a host of arguments, some contradictory, in combating the evils of war and militarism.

Like other eugenists, Jordan considered himself a hard-headed

20. Jordan, *The Question of the Philippines*, pp. 23–25. It should be noted that *before* the United States acquired the Philippines, Jordan found biological reasons for anticolonial policy, but when the U.S. acquired an overseas empire, he explained the acquisitions by using biological and particularly moral reasons. In regard to Jordan's preacquisition philosophy, see Davies, *Patriotism on Parade*, p. 334. Jordan, *War and Waste, A Series of Discussions of War and War Accessories*, p. 270; Jordan, however, was pro-Japanese.

21. Jordan, "The Human Harvest," *Proceedings of the American Philosophical Society*, XIV (1906), 56. Jordan, *Unseen Empire, A Study of the Plight of Nations That Do Not Pay Their Debts*, p. 152.

22. Jordan, "Concerning Sea Power," *World Peace Foundation Pamphlet Series*, II (January 1912), 3–7.

realist. Operating within biological laws, their task was biological law-enforcement. Jordan forecast that the twentieth century had no place for the weak, the incompetent, the untrained, and the dissipated, for the century would be strenuous, complex, and democratic. Democracy meant, not equality, but achievement based on opportunity, Jordan thought. The strong and sober would rule future complex enterprises. To realize the fearless future, Jordan urged, like other Galtonian eugenists, an end to indiscriminate and sentimental charity, a major factor in the survival of the unfit.[23] Life was a struggle and each man's environment and heredity determined his fate, for ultimately men can only do what "has been already cut out for us." Man's desires caused pain, but Jordan warned that unscientific charity and paternalism killed pain and thereby destroyed existence.[24] Apparently man was born to suffer. American eugenic thought owed something to Calvinism.

David Starr Jordan was not, however, a doctrinal capitalist, although his Social Darwinism might suggest such an attitude. He wanted "some stopping place midway between socialism and anarchy" in which self-government and expert service would be reconciled. Applied science was the answer, and eugenics was the applied science of heredity. The Republic existed for homemaking, not for money-making. Class divisions were foreign to American democracy, argued the president of Stanford, and the tyrant, the instrument of the mob, and the weakling, would naturally be absent in a land of biologically sound and morally correct individuals. Although he recognized the dangers of monopolistic wealth in American society, Jordan felt that American capitalists would practice scientific stewardship.[25] With a nation of biologically sound individuals, where economic oppression and political tyranny were nonexistent, the mission of the United States in the world was to spread peace "by the power of example." [26] Eugenics notwithstanding, David Starr Jordan was an optimistic

23. Jordan, *The Call of the Twentieth Century*, pp. 11, 62; Burns, *Jordan*, pp. 60–69, 199. Jordan, *The Blood of the Nation*, p. 33.

24. Jordan, *The Philosophy of Hope*, pp. 13, 21.

25. Jordan, *The Call of the Nation, A Plea for Taking Politics Out of Politics*, pp. 10, 12, 15, 17. Hereafter cited as Jordan, *The Call of the Nation*. Burns, *Jordan*, pp. 37, 47–48, 56, 145, 102–103, 130.

26. Jordan, *The Call of the Nation*, p. 89.

American progressive. His eugenic belief that all great urban centers were destructive to human life committed him to the commonly held progressive belief in social goodness of the small town and farm.[27] Although Jordan saw the industrial future, he—like so many progressives—saw in rural life a more "natural" human existence. Jordan's vision was divided between a Garden of Eden past and a promising future—much the same as eugenic and progressive thought.

Much less the propagandist for eugenics than Davenport and Jordan was Edward M. East (1879–1938), botanist at Harvard University. He is an example of the group of moderate, nonracist eugenists. With but a few exceptions, East's statements of eugenics were not as extreme as Davenport's. East's eugenic publications were meager. His major interests were academic rather than dedicated realization of eugenic ideals.[28] Like most eugenists, East saw the need for strong governmental action to correct deterioration of the United States population. Of course, severe and permanent immigration restriction was urged. In any program for population and agriculture, a laissez-faire policy should be abandoned and conservation and price-stabilization be instituted. East anticipated New Deal agricultural policy, albeit for Malthusian reasons rather than for a sociopolitical concern for the farmer's problem.[29]

As an exponent of eugenics, East felt the better families should replace themselves. It was necessary for society to understand and use "hereditary instincts" in the increased replacement of the better social groups. The one remarkable characteristic of East's eugenic thought was his emphasis on the individual—that no particular race has a monopoly on genetic virtue. His books merely told of the genetic basis of human types. Eugenics, therefore, was simply a reduction in the survival rate of the unfit.[30] Yet, on occasion, East was quite the racist in regard to the union of the races. He was against

27. Burns, *Jordan*, pp. 41–42; "All great cities are destroyers of life." Jordan, *The Blood of the Nation*, p. 41.

28. *Who Was Who in America*, I (1943), 354.

29. E. M. East, "Population in Relation to Agriculture," *Eugenics in Race and State*, pp. 228, 230.

30. East, *Mankind at the Crossroads*, pp. 342–343, 350–351. East, *Heredity and Human Affairs*, pp. 179, 296, 312.

race mixture for reasons he saw in the hereditary theories of Gregor Mendel.[31]

Edward East was not a typical spokesman for eugenics. He was too cautious, too committed, however imperfectly, to the scientific method. Although eugenics was a conservative creed, the eugenists, such as Davenport and Jordan, were ideologists and quickly moved from the known to the unknown in speculating about the future. East only said in regard to the future that man's instincts and dissimilarity of individual endowment would endure.[32] Little wonder that, compared with such men as Charles Davenport and Francis Galton, Edward East was a mild exponent of eugenics.

Unlike East, Harry H. Laughlin (1880–1943) was more the administrator and lobbyist for the American eugenics movement and prone to dramatic conclusions similar to those of Jordan and Davenport. Trained as a biologist, Laughlin was a teacher at North Missouri Normal School when Davenport chose him to be on the staff of the Eugenics Record Office at Cold Spring Harbor, Long Island. Later, Laughlin served as consulting eugenist for the Municipal Court, Chicago, in addition to various jobs such as member of the Permanent Emigration Committee of International Labor Office of the League of Nations. Also, he served as an associate editor of *Eugenical News*. His major influence on public policy was as eugenics expert for the Committee on Immigration and Naturalization, House of Representatives, 1921–1931.[33]

Laughlin based his study of immigration on the premise that women were the salvation of the social order, racially and morally, for "as long as the basic instinct and the social ideals of mankind remain as they are today, and have been since man first appeared, racial evolution and assimilation will lead toward the rare types of men which

31. E. M. East and Donald F. Jones, *Inbreeding and Outbreeding, Their Genetic and Sociological Significance*, p. 255.

32. East, "Biology and Human Problems," *Biology in Human Affairs*, p. 2.

33. *Who Was Who in America*, II (1950), 314. The discussion of Laughlin in this chapter is limited to his influence on United States immigration policy. See Robert Divine, *American Immigration Policy, 1924–1952* for a fuller account of immigration restriction. As the chapter on sterilization indicates, Laughlin was a leader in eugenic sterilization.

the women of the particular nation choose as mates." [34] By restricting
immigration of the inferior southern European, the biological superiority of Anglo-Saxon women was protected. Like Jordan and the
general eugenic attitude, Laughlin believed that the blood of the
nation was the strength (and virtue) of a nation. Besides, from the
eugenics viewpoint, immigration restriction was economical, and the
appeal of a simple solution to the problems of a melting-pot society.
Laughlin wanted Congress to be aware of the financial burden immigrants placed on the charitable and philanthropical systems of the
United States.

Commissioned by the government as a result of a report given
to the House Committee in 1920, Laughlin showed the biological relationship between immigration and social degeneracy. Presented in
1922 and printed in 1923, the report aided in the formulation of the
1924 immigration law based on the national-origin plan. His methodology was faulty and his conclusions were from the 1910 census,
even though the 1920 census returns were available.[35] These conclusions were racist and prejudicial against Southern Europeans.

Like other Galtonian eugenists, Laughlin did not modify his views
with the passing years and increased scientific knowledge in genetics
and anthropology. In 1939, as in 1900, Laughlin as a racist viewed
history as a biological record of human migration and conquest. Assimilation was, therefore, the key to a nation's welfare, and the Negro
for social genetic reasons could not be absorbed in the country's
bloodstream.[36]

Two factors worked against the socially healthy assimilation of
Negroes and Southern Europeans. The immigrant should truly desire
to become an American by giving "up the old ways of life and to adopt
the American way." The second factor, Laughlin concluded, was an
"innate one; it requires that the immigrant must be made out of such
inborn stuff that when subjected to American environment he readily
adopts the American pattern and proceeds to live in the American

34. Harry H. Laughlin, "Race Assimilation by the Pare-Sire Method," *The
Journal of Heredity*, XII (July-August 1916), 263.
35. Oscar Handlin, *Race and Nationality in American Life*, pp. 97–98, 131–
133, 137–138.
36. Laughlin, *Conquest by Immigration*, p. 6, p. 22.

Way." [37] Harry Laughlin ironically assumed an environmental in-fluence factor in the creation of Americans. Environment in the United States brought out the innate abilities of races.

Colonial America was fortunate, Laughlin the biologist-historian wrote, because the frontier Anglo-Saxons brought their own women. As home-types, these people created the United States. Adventurers and soldiers who married with other racial stock only weakened the biological and moral strength of the country.[38] Like many middle-class nineteenth-century Americans, Laughlin stressed the domestic virtues as maintaining the social order and the nation. For sociobio-logical reasons, Laughlin felt it was imperative that American women keep the nation's blood pure by not marrying the colored races (Negroes and Southern Europeans) for if "men with a small fraction of colored blood could readily find mates among the white women, the gates would be thrown open to a final radical race mixture of the whole population." The racial moral was apparent to Laughlin. "The perpetuity of the American race and consequently of American institu-tions depends upon the virtue and fecundity of American women." [39] Mate-selection apparently was a question of racial and, therefore, of national patriotism. Despite scientific knowledge to the contrary, Laughlin wrote as if blood were the transmitting agent in heredity and nationality were race. On these two misconceptions, or poor terminologies, Harry Laughlin constructed his program of immigra-tion-restriction.

The eugenic creed expressed naturalism, but a defensive naturalism for the status quo, stressing hereditary determinism in human behavior and social institutions. To be sure, Jordan was a pacifist, but his moral code—which he expressed in biological terms—and that of other eugenists came from nineteenth-century conservatism with rationaliza-tions grounded in spiritual thought.[40] Although historically naturalism aided revolutions in literature, social and natural sciences, eugenics

37. *Ibid.*, p. 96.
38. *Ibid.*, p. 28.
39. *Ibid.*, pp. 30–31.
40. Merle Curti, *The Growth of American Thought*, second edition, pp. 633–659.

was a conservative adaptation of the revolutionary message of Charles Darwin, the gentle naturalist.

The effectiveness of eugenics depended upon the individual citizen's racial consciousness. The American birth-control movement, led by Margaret Sanger, sought to instill that awareness by stressing the conservative and naturalistic values of planned parenthood.

5

MARGARET SANGER:
THE RADICAL
AND THE
RESTORATION
OF NATURE

IN THE progressive era, where the United States was the battlefield for many armies of reform, eugenics—the conservative creed—enlisted under the avant garde banner of the birth-control movement. The sources of the birth-control movement are varied. One common theme of the historic agitation for birth control has been the attempt to restore to human reproduction a balance, which for a variety of circumstances was upset, and thus allow human society to return to a natural manner of existence. Suffice it to say, urbanization and industrialization have been used as explanations for the rising birth rate.

A young English clergyman, Thomas Malthus, published in 1798 *The Essay on Population,* a dividing line in the history of demography. His analysis has shaped the controversy since the publication of his views on the causes and cures of human misery.[1] Various schools of thought responded and reacted to Malthus's contention that popula-

1. See Thomas Malthus, "A Summary View of the Principle of Population," originally published in 1830, reprinted in Thomas Malthus, Julian Huxley, Frederick Osborn, *Three Essays on Population,* pp. 13–63. The essence of Malthusiasism is that the food supply increases in an arithmetical progression while the population increases in a geometrical progression. The only method to forestall misery is therefore to control the birth rate. Malthus trusted moral restraint.

tion tends to increase more rapidly than food supply and is limited only by such positive checks as war, famine, malnutritional disease, or by abstinence from marriage. Within a short time Michael Sadler (1780–1835), another philosopher of the period, argued that privation was most favorable to human fecundity. Consequently, a rising standard of living would automatically solve the problem of overpopulation. Thomas Doubleday (1790–1870), another student of population, advanced a similar thought that human beings increased in fertility as danger increased to the species. Therefore, social well-being would solve the problem of overpopulation. Herbert Spencer (1820–1909) offered a third theory which was post-Darwinian in origin: modern industrial life reduced man's natural rate of increase.[2] These three theories along with other concepts were used in the progressive era. One important common characteristic of these ideas was their environmental orientation which allowed man to change or restore natural law or a natural situation in regard to population problems.

Since 1798, Americans have questioned the validity of Malthus's conclusions. For example, James Madison rejected Malthusian fatalism: the United States, the exception to Malthus's analysis, was only partially cultivated and still highly fertile.[3] In the progressivism of Margaret Sanger and the birth-control movement, a pessimistic concern for the future biological well-being of an industrial America replaced traditional American optimism. Naturalism and natural law in this case contributed to the progressive desire to restore society to a correct relationship with nature.

The birth-control movement in the nineteenth century ran counter to romantic love, the idea of fidelity to conjugal ties. As will be seen later, the belief that birth control led to moral irresponsibility and free love encrusted the movement with a great deal of moralism. In brief, birth control was not respectable. Only inmates of the intellectual underworld discussed it. No doubt the advocate of free love, Frances Wright, and her endorsement of birth control hurt its acceptance among the middle classes. Robert Dale Owen was another reformer whose interests included birth-control agitation. Like Sanger

2. Franklin H. Hankins, "Demographic and Biological Contributions to Sociological Principles," *Contemporary Social Theory*, pp. 285-286.
3. Edward McNall Burns, *The American Idea of Mission*, p. 77.

in the twentieth century, Owen's interest in birth control was based on eugenic (hereditary) and neo-Malthusian considerations.[4]

The link between Malthusianism and the birth-control movement was a eugenic concern. At the same time, both movements expressed a desire to improve the family atmosphere by limiting the number of children. In fact, an early birth-control organization was entitled the National Scientific Family Culture Institute. With such a title, its founder, James F. Morton, Jr., appealed to several intellectual interests in the United States. The institute's chances of success were limited. Romantic love, both legal and informal censorship of information, and a general public taboo against any public discussion of sexual matters were barriers too strong for early birth-control pioneers. England, however, was by 1877 the home of an active Malthusian League which became the New Generation League after World War I. Like her American counterpart, Margaret Sanger, Marie Charlotte Carmichael Stopes mixed romanticism, poetic racial notions, psychological insights on family life, and scientific facts to advance the birth-control cause.[5]

The success of such birth-control works as Robert Owen's *Moral Physiology* (1830) and John Humphrey Noyes's *Male Continence* was limited because of the reform activities of their authors. Among American physicians, only Charles Knowlton of Massachusetts wrote in behalf of contraception. Bay State authorities suppressed his book, *The Fruits of Philosophy*, in 1833, and Knowlton, fined, served a jail term at hard labor. In England, however, more than 40,000 copies of Knowlton's pioneer stride in contraception were sold.[6]

Informal hostility to the distribution of birth-control information

4. Sidney Ditzion, *Marriage, Morals and Sex in America*, pp. 87, 105. Although not the first to discuss birth control in the United States, Owen's *Moral Physiology* was a pioneer in the publication history of sexual ideas. See Victor Robinson, *Pioneers of Birth Control in England and America*, pp. 105–106. Hereafter cited as Robinson, *Pioneers of Birth Control*. Richard Leopold, *Robert Dale Owen, A Biography*, p. 83.

5. Robinson, *Pioneers of Birth Control*, p. 64. Hankins, "Birth Control," *Encyclopedia of the Social Sciences*, II, 561. Hereafter cited as Hankins, "Birth Control," *Encyclopedia of the Social Sciences*, Ditzion, *Marriage, Morals and Sex in America*, p. 377.

6. Oscar Cargill, *Intellectual America, Ideas on the March*, pp. 544–546. Hereafter cited as Cargill, *Intellectual America*.

achieved legal sanction in New York in 1869, with the passage of an
obscenity act which forbade the dissemination of contraceptive information and materials. Using the act as a model, Anthony Comstock
influenced Congress to enact Section 211 of the Penal Code in 1873.
The law prohibited the transmission of pornographic literature through
the mails. Moreover, the law expressly forbade the mailing of any
device or drug or printed matter designed to prevent conception.
The medical profession was not exempt from the law, since no distinction was made between the scientific and the lewd. Many state laws of
a similar nature followed in the wake of the federal legislation.[7]

In the last twenty years of the nineteenth century the subject fell
in the domain of reformers whose objectives included more than family
limitation. Moses Harman used birth control as part of a larger scheme
of marriage reform and the eugenic improvement in conception.[8]
Only similar, obscure fellow reformers gave credence to his thoughts.
Republican, agnostic, and free-thinker Robert G. Ingersoll advocated
birth control to limit the number of unwanted children in charitable
and public institutions.[9] In this instance, birth control supported the
universal desire to cut taxes. Ingersoll's reputation as a godless man
did not help the birth-control cause. The struggle, therefore, in the
twentieth century was to make the birth-control movement respectable
and, for reasons noted later, a *natural* practice.

In addition, the birth-control movement expressed the larger cause
of the new woman. American women agitated for change, in organized
labor and in charitable endeavors. Three major factors aided in the
female drive toward equality and freedom. Economically, the emanci-
pated woman was gaining a subsistence wage. The mere presence of
the birth-control controversy marked an important change in the
attitude of women toward sexual matters. The third factor, the disas-
sociation of the law and procreation, directly supported the birth-
control movement. Modern literature was instrumental in the latter
factor.[10] To be sure, the advocators of birth control emphasized
marital sexual relations. The revolution had its limits.

7. Hankins, "Birth Control," *Ency. of the S.S.*, II, 562.
8. Ditzion, *Marriage, Morals and Sex in America*, p. 196.
9. Sidney Warren, *American Freethought, 1860–1914*, pp. 133–134.
10. Cargill, *Intellectual America*, p. 544.

The fears and aspirations of the progressive era influenced the birth-control agitation. Neo-Malthusianism was inevitably part of birth control; Mrs. Sanger and others assumed marked differences in fertility of the social classes, with the lower and subnormal classes out-pro-creating the upper classes. The sentiment of a leading eugenist, Samuel J. Holmes, expressed a common belief when he wrote, "The trouble with birth control is that it is practiced least where it should be practiced most." [11] With eugenics, birth control, and immigration restrictions, Anglo-Saxon-minded social scientists attempted to stop the "alien menace" in the United States.[12] Yet, eugenics was respectable conservatism, the restoration of the family unit as a basic social institution in a society disrupted by industrialization and urbanization. Language and methods of agitation notwithstanding, the birth-control movement sought the creation of family life based on natural law by the scientific application of birth-control techniques. Five years before World War I, William J. Robinson Winfield Scott Hall, and Margaret Sanger wrote books and pamphlets about sex and family life.[13] Their objective was social control, although their language bespoke anarchy to the defenders of the status quo.

Other individuals shared Mrs. Sanger's interest in the free distribution of birth-control information. Like her, they centered their cause around Malthusianism, eugenics, and a defense of motherhood based on the appeal of scientific facts. Like many social philosophers, Walter Lippmann defended birth control on the grounds that unwanted children, conceived within or without wedlock, eventually became a burden on all of society because of parental neglect.[14]

Lippmann's attitude revealed the progressive theme of a scientific

11. Holmes, *Studies in Evolution and Eugenics*, p. 184.

12. Solomon, *Ancestors and Immigrants*, pp. 150–151. "Showing the folly of closing our gates to aliens from abroad, while having them wide open to the overwhelming progeny of the least desirable elements of our city and slum population" was the warning of Annie G. Porritt in her article, "Immigration and Birth Control, An Editorial," *The Birth Control Review*, VII (September 1923), 219. *The Birth Control Review* is hereafter cited as *BCR*.

13. Frederick Osborn, *Preface to Eugenics*, revised edition, p. 318. Ditzion, *Marriage, Morals and Sex in America*, p. 359.

14. Reprint of Walter Lippmann's editorial from the New York *World* for May 8, 1924 in *BCR*, VIII (June 1924), 181.

"mothercraft." For the reformers of the age, motherhood was not merely a biological process, but rather the scientific application and understanding of the concepts instructing the new woman in her physical and psychological responsibilities to the child.[15] In fact, one writer felt that birth control "would give protection to woman's health and ensure greater vitality to her offspring" which with a smaller family provided "sounder citizenship." [16] He concluded that the rising cost of living made smaller families an economic necessity.

In England and the United States, eugenic considerations were part of the birth-control program. The eugenists in both countries claimed that the inferior classes outbred the better classes. Democracy, the eugenists maintained, needed superior biological quality. In fact, echoing a Galtonian assumption, they thought social and political advances futile without corresponding hereditary improvements; in this regard, the environment was limited in reform. Repeating an old criticism, an American eugenist noted that modern medicine and humanitarianism aided the weakest members of society in opposition to natural selection. With their opposition to a naturalistic social philosophy such a condition disturbed eugenists because the prolific masses always posed a challenge to the upper classes and the social order.[17]

Natural selection per se was not the answer. Social Darwinists denounced interference with the various forms of natural selection which they believed characterized progressive thought and social action. Nature, they maintained, would attend to reckless breeding by "the whips of flood, disease or war." [18] In this instance, the conserv-

15. Mary L. Read, "Mothercraft," *The Journal of Heredity*, VII (August 1916), 339–542. Also see A. E. Hamilton, "Babies in the Curriculum," *The Journal of Heredity*, VII (September 1916), 387–394.

16. F. A. Blossom, "Birth Control," *BCR*, I (February 1917), 12.

17. E. W. MacBride, "British Eugenists and Birth Control," VI (December 1922), 247. Allen P. Van Duren, "Birth Control as Viewed by a Sociologist," VIII (May 1924), 133. L. J. Cole, "Animal Aristocracy and Human Democracy," *ibid.*, VII (January 1924), 22; Caroline Nelson, "Ellen Key: A Sketch," *ibid.*, II (May 1918), 13; Horatio Pollock, M.D., "The Problem of the Unfit," *ibid.*, VI (October 1922), 206. Charles H. Garvin, M.S., "The Negro Doctor's Task," *ibid.*, XVI (November 1932), 269–270. Robert J. Sprague, "Constructive Aspect of Birth Control," *The Journal of Heredity*, VIII (February 1917), 58–62.

18. "Better than Birth Control," *BCR*, I (February 1917), 14.

atives optimistically trusted the certainty of natural laws. The strength of absolute laws enforced the conservative attraction to the status quo and laissez-faire public policy.

Birth-control agitators did not trust the "optimistic" effect of natural laws (that is, natural selection). Despite being conservative, they recognized the importance of the new tools of research and social science in maintaining and controlling a social order based on eugenic principles. The traditional conservative fear of social revolution or discord lies behind this statement, "To have thousands of unwelcome children from overworked working women, and to have a one-child family or spinsters for women geniuses is equally disastrous." [19]

Restoring a balance to human reproduction and making natural selection compatible with urban life were objectives of the birth-control movement and, subsequently, of eugenics in the United States. Conservative at its core, the social philosophy of both eugenics and the birth-control movement demanded old-fashioned moral restraint of individuals and social classes. These conservatives only used the new techniques and relativism of the social sciences which created radical illusion, masking conservative objectives.

Margaret Sanger: Philosopher and Activist

Margaret Sanger (1883–1966) (neé Higgins) embodied the radical and conservative elements in birth-control philosophy. Her birth-control language created visions of a new world filled with men and women following their naturally good instincts in realizing the good life without modern civilization's corrupting influence. Birth control was a return ticket to the Garden of Eden.

Born at Corning, New York, Margaret Sanger was the sixth child in an Irish family of eleven. Her father, a radical in the tradition of Henry George and Robert Ingersoll, was a major intellectual influence on Margaret. Apparently some of Mrs. Sanger's anti-clericalism had a parental source, although her mother was a faithful Roman Catholic. A sympathetic biographer noted the generally unhappy childhood of Margaret Higgins who accepted much of her father's philosophy and

19. Anna E. Blount, "Eugenics in Relation to Birth Control," *BCR*, II (January 1918), 7.

yet had many disagreeable incidents of personality conflict over what Margaret felt was unfair treatment of her mother. Higgins once told her, "Leave the world a better place because you, my child, have dwelt in it." This sentiment is the same philosophy for the majority of American reformers raised on notions of "Puritanical" duty and stewardship. At the same time, Mrs. Sanger's guilt feelings (her lack of medical knowledge) surrounding her mother's death made her seek a career in nursing. "This was linked up," she later wrote, "with my latent desire to be of service in the world." [20] The Progressive and New Woman movements expressed the same sentiment.

After being graduated from Corning, New York, High School and Claverach College at Hudson, New York, she entered the Nurses Training School of White Plains, New York. Later she took additional training at the Post Graduate School of the Manhattan Eye and Ear Hospital. Her marriage in 1900 to William Sanger, a New York architect, resulted in three children and, in time, a divorce, the causes of which involved her growing leadership in the organized birth-control movement. William Sanger was not, however, opposed to the distribution of contraceptual information, since he served a prison sentence for distributing his wife's pamphlet, "Family Limitation." Later, in 1922, Margaret Sanger married J. Noah Slee, founder of the Three In One Oil Company.

Margaret Sanger's experiences as a nurse on the East Side in New York during the early years of the twentieth century sparked an interest in birth control. She saw a relationship between poverty and large families.[21] In 1913 she founded a short-lived periodical, *The Woman Rebel,* which merely discussed the need for birth control without giving any practical techniques for contraception. After six

20. See Margaret Sanger, *My Fight for Birth Control,* and her *An Autobiography* (New York 1938). These two books are quite similar. The *Autobiography* was page after page taken from *My Fight.* Margaret Sanger's life and thought is evidence of William Wasserstrom's contention that the New Woman of the twentieth century was the daughter of a radical nineteenth-century father. See William Wasserstrom, *Heiress of All The Ages, Sex and Sentiment in the Genteel Tradition,* 81–82. For a fuller discussion of the progressive profile see George Mowry, *The Era of Theodore Roosevelt,* 85–105.

21. For the shock that poverty had on the progressive mind, see Robert H. Bremner, *From the Depths, the Discovery of Poverty in the United States.* For Mrs. Sanger's reaction, see her *Autobiography.*

issues, Anthony Comstock forbade such literature in the mails. Charged with violating the Obscenity Act of New York, she fled the United States to escape going to trial.

She went to Europe, Mrs. Sanger later remarked, to learn of European birth-control information and practices and thereby provide a better defense at her trial. Indeed, it was fitting that Mrs. Sanger went to England for aid and comfort since American progressives looked to the old motherland for solutions to social problems. "Both U.S. and English reformers shared the same moral and aesthetic vision. They also had a sense of history and—important for its influence on the social thought of many Americans—a belief in the superiority of the intellectual in time of social crisis." [22]

Margaret Sanger drew real support from English birth-control agitators. Years later, when she established the first birth-control clinic under medical supervision, a British friend paid the yearly salary of the physician in charge. England inspired her. "I felt a regret," she wrote, "that so little of any life could be lived in England." [23] She accepted the English Neo-Malthusian League's philosophy that birth-control techniques among the well-to-do classes must spread among the workers.

After gathering information in England and Europe, Mrs. Sanger returned to the United States to stand trial in 1916. Immediately freed from the charges of obscenity resulting from the publication of *The Woman Rebel*, Margaret Sanger went on a lecture tour attracting nationwide interest and controversy. She and her associates opened the first birth-control clinic in the United States. After being closed by legal action, the clinic reopened on appeal. The publication of the *Birth Control Review* in 1917 followed this success.

Mrs. Sanger became "The Birth Control Movement" to the majority of Americans. Publishing and lecturing, leaving organizational matters to other individuals,[24] she continued her assault for the public accept-

---

22. Arthur Mann, "British Social Thought and American Reformers of the Progressive Era," *Mississippi Valley Historical Review*, XLII (March 1956), 678.

23. Sanger, *Autobiography*, pp. 370, 359, 494.

24. See the following items for the organizational history of birth control: Oscar Cargill, *Intellectual America*, p. 628–632; Frank Hankins, "Birth Control," *Encyclopedia of the Social Sciences* II, 562; Sidney Ditzion, *Marriage, Morals and Sex in America*, 386.

ance of birth control. Despite police interference in the National
Birth Control Conference in 1924, the movement gained acceptance
among various reformers and social scientists. The police raided the
birth-control office for the last time in 1929. Public indignation prevented any further action of this type.

Margaret Sanger's major contribution to the movement of birth
control was intellectual. From the very beginning, wealthy women
directed birth-control organizations. As time passed, women of leisure
and wealth found the birth-control movement an expression of sexual
equality. In her *Autobiography,* Mrs. Sanger constantly remarks about
the wealth, background, etc. (which she often linked with physical
characteristics) of her female backers.[25]

Sanger's words and actions had a neoaristocratic flavor to them.
"Birth control must seep down until it reaches the strata where the
need is greatest; until it has been democratized there can be no
rest."[26] Intellectually she wove several threads of thought into a
mosaic of reform. Influenced by the grand old man of sexology, Have-
lock Ellis (whom she admired), Margaret Sanger combined nineteenth-century romanticism with the naturalistic science and psychology of the Progressive Era. Love, particularly its sexual aspects,
was cleansed of past ignorance to raise it to a therapeutic newness and
wholesomeness. As with H. G. Wells, her personal friend, Mrs. Sanger
welcomed the scientific revolution; she combined the basic instincts of
nature and man with a scientific program of planned parenthood and
eugenics that claimed perfectibility in social organization. The result
was a scientific return to nature and a proper restoration of woman's
instincts that would control her social behavior.

Margaret Sanger believed the popular instinct psychology of the
Progressive Era. She felt a woman's natural aspiration was toward

25. Sanger, *Autobiography,* p. 196. For example, Mrs. Anna Pinchot was a
chairman in birth-control agitation; see "New York City: National Birth Control
League," *Birth Control Review,* II (April 1918), 5. "Mrs. Sanger is too much her
own heroine and not unconsciously so. The result is a humorless book, an egotistical book, a book in which the author fails ignominiously to give full credit to other
persons and claims altogether too much for her own unaided efforts." Frank H.
Hankins, Review of Margaret Sanger, *My Fight For Birth Control,* in *BCR,* XV
(November 1931), 325.

26. Sanger, *Autobiography,* p. 494.

freedom realized in motherhood, an outward expression of an inner spiritual urge. Yet, large families destroyed this spirit. Thus, woman has always sought, however imperfectly, family limitation.

Voluntary motherhood is not looked upon as a punishment, but as a fulfillment of desire, the natural and desired fruition of every normal woman's life.

That does not mean that the normal, sane woman wishes to be immolated incessantly upon the altar of maternity, in season and out. "To everything, there is a season, and a time to every purpose under the heaven," declared the sage of Ecclesiastes. So with motherhood. Properly understood this function does not consist of giving birth to endless series of babies, left at an early age to sink or swim, to survive or die. It consists not only of conception, pregnancy, parturition and nursing, but always, more and more, of the more prolonged rearing and education to full maturity of healthy children. Above all, it means the assurance of security and self-realization in life—in short, the certainty of "life, and the pursuit of happiness."

These rewards the present group of mothers claim, not only for themselves, but for their children.[27]

Margaret wrote two major philosophical defenses of birth control, *Woman and the New Race* and *The Pivot of Civilization*. She thought of the latter volume as her "head book" and the former her "heart book." "It was good," she believed, "to classify reasons and set them in order. My opinion did emerge, and it was a great release." [28] Instinct was the basis for her birth-control philosophy. "Given free play, this supreme law of her nature asserts itself in beneficent ways; interferred with, it becomes destructive." [29] Birth control, therefore, has merely the scientific application of a natural desire of women. Like other inheritors of nineteenth-century naturalism, Margaret Sanger found an organic unity between human beings and other creatures and realms of nature.[30] This harmony was vital, Mrs. Sanger wrote, for

the female's functions in these animal species are not limited to motherhood alone. Every organ and faculty is fully employed and perfected. Through the development of the individual mother, better and higher types of ani-

27. Sanger, *Motherhood in Bondage*, pp. 412–413.
28. Sanger, *Autobiography*, pp. 266, 299.
29. Sanger, *Woman and the New Race*, p. 10.
30. This desire for orderliness of the world for society's sake influenced the thought of many nineteenth-century scientists. For example, see Donald Fleming, *John William Draper and the Religion of Science*, pp. 63–64.

mals are produced and carried forward. In a word natural law makes the female the expression and the conveyor of racial efficiency.[31]

This statement combined nineteenth-century romanticism with the concept of efficiency, a characteristic idea of progressive America.[32]

Mrs. Sanger thought this motherly urge was central to a woman's being. As if to destroy misunderstanding, she emphasized,

> It is the strongest force in her nature; it cannot be destroyed; it can be merely diverted from its natural expression into violent and destructive channels. The chief obstacles to the normal expression are undesired pregnancy and the burden of unwanted children.[33]

If used properly, birth control provided natural social control. Assuming self-preservation as the first law of nature, Mrs. Sanger believed that maternity was equally important in the psychological structure of the female. She wrote, "For the instinct of maternity to protect its own fruits, the instinct of womanhood to be free to give something besides surpluses of children to the world, cannot go astray." Branching into marriage-counseling as a result of her knowledge of the female's nature, Mrs. Sanger felt that a woman should have her first child after the mother's twenty-fifth birthday.[34] While maintaining the importance of instinct, Mrs. Sanger believed that reason tempered instinct. By knowing her true nature, woman realized freedom by a rational use of her instincts. "Knowledge and freedom to choose or reject the sexual embrace, according as it is lovely or unlovely, and these alone, can solve the problem." [35]

While Mrs. Sanger stressed the rational function of instincts, other

---

31. Sanger, *Woman and the New Race*, p. 229.

32. For efficiency and progressivism see Samuel P. Hays, *Conservation and the Gospel of efficiency*. Also see Samuel Hoper, *Efficiency and Uplift, Scientific Management In the Progressive Era, 1890–1920*. Once Mrs. Sanger used Herbert Hoover's progressive philosophy of efficiency to support her contraception creed. *Autobiography*, 434: "in an age which has developed science and industry and economic efficiency to their highest points, so little thought has been given to the development of a science of parenthood, a science of maternity which could prevent this appalling and unestimated waste of womankind and maternal effort." Sanger, *Motherhood In Bondage*, 137.

33. Sanger, *Woman and the New Race*.

34. *Ibid.*, pp. 192, 74, 89.

35. *Ibid.*, p. 117.

theorists explored the irrational aspects of human nature. *Heredity* and *environment* replaced *free will* as the major determinants in human behavior. The struggle for existence replaced intellectual development as an explanation for changes in society. Finally, the optimism of Comtian positivism succumbed to social Darwinism and scientific fatalism. Instead of crediting man with reason and logic, many social philosophers of the late nineteenth and early twentieth centuries believed that heredity dictated men's actions. Comtian intellectualism gave way to naturalistic antiintellectualism. By the last decade of the nineteenth century, social scientists began investigating irrational sources for human behavior. They investigated the nonlogical, the uncivilized and the inexplicable in the human nature. Instinct psychology supported this investigation. The objective was not to free mankind from this original irrationality (even if that were possible); it was an attempt to find a more scientific basis for social control through the careful manipulation of man's nonlogical character.[36] Both schools of thought accepted the necessity of social control. Conservatives, by their historic distrust of human nature, supported this progressive and scientific objective. The eugenists and birth-control agitators in early twentieth-century America adhered to this basic conservative concern for social control. They utilized two themes from progressive social science in their reform—irrationalism and extreme practicalism. They drew inspiration from nineteenth-century social philosophy—history as a vast impersonal process understood and guided by science.

The major challenge was the control and guidance of sex, the natural instinct. Mastery of this force might be achieved through birth control. Mrs. Sanger believed, however, that birth control was the savior of society. Although in a very real sense civilization was artificial and not naturally a part of woman's nature, it was necessary to control mankind. In short, Margaret Sanger was a romantic conservative.

Regeneration for the race and the individual, accordingly, must come from within; but the educators and the leaders of public opinion could be instrumental in this regenerative process. Since cradle com-

36. H. Stuart Hughes, *Consciousness and Society, The Reorientation of European Social Thought,* 1890–1930, pp. 17, 35–39.

petition between the fit and unfit was not the solution, it was imperative that society stress the qualitative factor in human reproduction
rather than the quantitative one. Large population was a menace to
human nature and, therefore, to human happiness. Hunger and sex,
two fundamental and conflicting forces, endangered civilization. With
birth control as scientific stewardship, the enlightened progressive
elite could save civilization from the multiplying masses. Birth control
was, thereby, conscious racial duty.[37]

Instinct was the apparent explanation for nearly everything Mrs.
Sanger thought was a personal and social good. Being a pacifist,
Margaret saw women in World War I "in violation of every human
instinct fostered in them by the greater libertarians who founded this
country." [38] Women, as breeding machines, filled sweat shops, alms-
houses and asylums with their babies and provided cannon fodder for
the war masters of the world.[39] Mrs. Sanger's pacifism was grounded
partly in the eugenic considerations that war killed the better stock.

Mrs. Sanger, then, based her program on birth control, eugenics,
and pacifism. The other alternatives were to allow the weak to die or to
kill them or to continue overpopulating the world and thereby continue famines and wars to the end of human time. The world had a
choice: Margaret Sanger wanted the choice to be birth control. She
was a conservative representative of reform Darwinism, located ideologically between William Graham Sumner and Lester Ward. Margaret Sanger's struggle for family limitation was not only recognition of
natural law but the guidance of it to a fuller realization of natural
and, therefore, just social control based on latent scientific
information.[40]

With approval, Margaret Sanger quoted Francis Galton, Karl Pearson, Robert Ingersoll, and William McDougall as authorities, and their
declarations of science as the answer to civilization's problems. The
increase of the unfit was a dangerous situation for the future security

37. Sanger, *The Pivot of Civilization*, pp. 10, 22. Sanger, *My Fight For Birth
Control*, p. 264. Sanger, *Motherhood In Bondage*, p. 396.
38. Sanger, *The Pivot of Civilization*, pp. 125–126.
39. Sanger, "Woman and War," *BCR* I (June 1917), 5. See also "Birth Control: Is It Moral?" Dr. Will Durant's Reply," *Ibid.*, VI (March 1922), 42.
40. Sanger, *Woman and the New Race*, p. 161. Sanger, *Motherhood In Bondage*, p. 221.

of the world, she wrote. The solution was apparent: selective mating and birth control. Her emphasis on individual and racial regeneration from within was similar to Galton's linking eugenics with religious sentiment.[41]

Not all eugenists recognized the importance of birth control, but one did admit, "it is one of the major influences which effect the quality of the population, and is among the instrumentalities with which eugenics is concerned for the final attainment of its program." [42] Mrs. Sanger was convinced that the feebleminded existed in large numbers. They had to be regulated. In her attitude on this problem and similar ones, she accepted the Galtonian solution. The big difference naturally was her trust in birth limitation, while the father of modern eugenics promoted programs encouraging the better classes to have more children. Mrs. Sanger distrusted certain parts of Galtonian eugenics. In discounting the significance of birth control for eugenics, she believed that Galton's program created birth-rate competition among the social classes.[43]

Philosophically moving between Emersonian compensation and economic determinism,[44] Margaret Sanger accepted much of the philosophy of the leading American eugenist C. B. Davenport. "The eugenists," she maintained, "wanted to shift the birth-control emphasis from less children for the poor to more children for the rich. We went back of that and sought first to stop the multiplication of the unfit. This appeared the most important and greatest step toward race betterment." [45] Never one to neglect name-dropping, if by so doing it contributed to the birth-control cause, Mrs. Sanger invoked Nietzche's words "Build thou beyond thyself" which she felt the movement was achieving. In the future people would have a greater concern for eugenic quality of minds and bodies. Birth control was the cornerstone of future civilization.

Margaret Sanger was in closer agreement on other elements of

41. Sanger, *The Pivot of Civilization*, pp. 170, 220, 241. Sanger, "The Eugenic Value of Birth Control Propaganda," *BCR*, V (October 1921), 5.
42. S. Wayne Evans, *Organized Eugenics*, p. 39.
43. Sanger, *Woman and the New Race*, p. 44. Sanger, *The Pivot of Civilization*, pp. 103–104.
44. Sanger, *My Fight for Birth Control*, pp. 298, 344.
45. Sanger, *Autobiography*, pp. 374–375, 496.

Galtonian social philosophy. The care of the feebleminded was expensive, and they were prolific, which led in later generations to increases in pauperism and insanity. Although not an enthusiast for the country life, she was critical of urban life, particularly the existence of slums. In the slums she believed federal and private philanthropy had failed because it unscientifically encouraged the increase of slum dwellers by providing *gratis* medical and nursing facilities to slum mothers.[46] Socially efficient charity was scientific with its emphasis on family limitation. "Looked at impartially," she urged, "this compensatory generosity is in its final effect probably more dangerous, more dysgenic, more blighting than the initial practice of profiteering and the social injustice which makes some too rich and others too poor."[47] Altruism, without being tempered, without enlightened public self-interest, was a danger to the future well-being of society.

Margaret Sanger was not a racist like Madison Grant or other individuals who labored in the behalf of immigration restriction. "Containing the best of racial elements,"[48] the melting pot would refine all immigrants. Mrs. Sanger firmly believed that there was just one cause for all the world's ills. She listed such evils as labor surpluses, aid to war, prostitution, child labor, and many others as the products of an anti–birth control population policy. She felt all reform began and ended with birth control.

The rise of the city distressed both Margaret Sanger and Galtonian eugenists. Modern civilization caused the increase in mental illness. The urban population was unnerved, especially the woman. Mrs. Sanger wrote, "Physically and nervously, the woman today is not fitted to bear children as frequently as her mother and her mother's mother. The high tension of modern life and complicating of woman's everyday existence have doubtless contributed to this result."[49] Margaret Sanger agreed with the Galtonians that modern civilization was unnatural and was therefore counter to mankind's true nature—instincts.

46. Sanger, *The Pivot of Civilization*, pp. 61–62, 82, 110, 114.
47. *Ibid.*, p. 123.
48. Sanger, *Woman and the New Race*, pp. 44, 57–58.
49. *Ibid.*, p. 69. See also Sanger, *Motherhood In Bondage*, p. 221, for the "scientific" justification for this belief.

Mrs. Sanger's hostility to urban life resulted from her fear of slums, a menace to social stability and a blight on slum dwellers. Industrialization with increased number of workers created modern slums and misery. Thus she felt that "all our problems are among the working class, and if morality is to mean anything at all to us, we must regard all changes which tend toward the uplift and survival of the human race as moral." [50] The working class was prolific and, therefore, dangerous to society. Birth control for the elite was all right. "But," she warned, "it is well to emphasize that we advocates of birth control are not much distressed that the stationary birth rate is a world-wide movement of civilization." [51] The Malthusian and class orientation of the birth-control movement were, as noted, quite real.

Birth control was not the only method to check the growth of the unfit. Mrs. Sanger endorsed sterilization because it did not deny individual sexual expression but "merely renders him or her incapable of producing children." [52] Yet, for this agitator for contraception, sterilization was only an auxiliary factor to advance the cause of racial betterment. Accordingly, eugenics without birth control was self-defeating, for economic forces had created misery for a large portion of the human population. In summary, Margaret Sanger accepted the Darwinian view of nature as struggle and strife. But as a progressive, she could not accept the cosmic optimism of natural selection; Mrs. Sanger recognized the importance of social science in maintaining and controlling a social order through birth control.

50. Sanger, "Morality and Birth Control," *BCR*, II (February-March 1918), 11–14.
51. Sanger, "An Answer to Mr. Roosevelt," *BCR*, I (December 1917), 14.
52. Sanger, "The American Birth Control League," *ibid.*, VII (November 1923). Sanger, "Birth Control and Racial Betterment," *ibid.*, I (February 1919), 11–12. For a history of sterilization, see Donald K. Pickens, "The Sterilization Movement: The Search for Purity in Mind and State," *Phylon* XVIII (Spring 1967), 78–94.

6

STERILIZATION:
THE SEARCH
FOR PURITY
IN MIND
AND BODY

THE STERILIZATION movement indicated the importance of heredity to many Americans. The average citizen during the late nineteenth and early twentieth centuries had numerous notions of heredity based on "blood" and family concepts. Many scientists at the same time stressed the effect of biological inheritance. Their fear of overpopulation augmented this emphasis on studies of heredity.

The origin for the sterilization movement was interest in the effect that a greatly increased number of feebleminded would have on the economy and the social order. Present in the nineteenth century as "moral imbecility," this effect—with the passing years—became known as "moral idiocy" or "moral degeneracy." By 1908 the term was "imbecility with criminal instincts," a term in keeping with the emphasis on instinct psychology during the progressive era.[1] Seven years later "mental defective" replaced criminal imbecility. Although the terminology changed during these years, the philosophy and plan of reform did not. The need for statistics and an informed public were two early and constant desires of the foes of feeblemindedness. That the state had a responsibility to stop the irresponsible reproduction of

1. Fink, *Causes of Crime*, p. 237.

the mentally inadequate remained a constant assumption of the advocates of sterilization.[2]

Homes for the mentally retarded are quite recent, the first private home having been established in 1848. Only two years earlier the state of New York opened an asylum for idiots. By 1890, fourteen states maintained state institutions for mental defectives. This number increased to forty by 1923. From 1910 to 1923 the number of institutions nearly doubled;[3] these progressive years also marked the high tide for the sterilization movement. Considering the biological orientation of eugenics and sterilization, it was little wonder that the twin movements were active and respectable to toughminded reformers.

The nineteenth century was remarkable for medical advances. Sterilization advocates emphasized this point in claiming that sterilization was not necessarily castration, and that the operation was not an unsexing process. To be sure, the early form of sterilization was castration. As early as 1866 a Swiss psychiatrist, August Forel, sterilized a woman suffering from sexual neurosis. By 1892 he castrated several persons for eugenic reasons. Castration is, however, a serious operation because it upsets the endocrine balance. At the turn of the century, Edwin Kehrer in Heidelberg, Germany, and Albert J. Ochsner in Chicago perfected the art of "tying" the Fallopian tubes in the woman and the operation on the vas deferens in the man. These operations became the standard practices in sterilization because they are relatively minor surgery with no ill after-effects.[4]

In the United States, Dr. H. C. Sharp, physician at an Indiana mental institution, performed vasectomies on the inmates. From 1899 to 1912 Dr. Sharp completed 236 such operations. As one eugenist wrote, "There is no expense to the States, no sorrow or shame to the friends of the individual as there is bound to be in the carrying out of the segregation idea."[5] With that statement the major justifications of

2. Ernest Bicknell, "Feeble-Mindedness as Inheritance," *Proceedings of the National Conferences of Charities and Corrections,* 23rd Annual Session (Boston, 1896), p. 225.

3. Stanley P. Davies, *The Mentally Retarded in Society,* pp. 20–22. By 1958, only one state had not provided institutional care for the retarded.

4. Henry E. Sigerist, *Civilization and Disease,* pp. 104–105. Hereafter cited as Sigerist, *Civilization and Disease.*

5. *Eugenics Review,* IV (June 1912), 204–205.

sterilization were given. As will be seen, the controversy basically turned on those reasons. Many defenders of sterilization overlooked or ignored the thrapeutic aspect and stressed the punitive. In many societies castration served as punishment for antisocial behavior.

Sharp's operations had the sanction of law, for Indiana passed a sterilization law in 1907. California's law allowed 6,000 operations from 1909 to 1929. These laws were not the first to deal with feeble-minded behavior. Connecticut in 1896, Kansas in 1903, with New Jersey, Ohio, Michigan, and Indiana two years later, passed legislation which forbade the marriage of, not only the feebleminded, but also the insane, syphilitic, alcoholic, epileptic, and certain types of criminals.[6] These broad classifications of individuals indicated the statute's unscientific nature.

Arthur MacDonald, an early scientist, studied abnormality on the various social classes and the importance of the relative fertility of such people. After studying at American and European universities, MacDonald served as a specialist on abnormal classes for the United States Bureau of Education from 1892 to 1904, during which time he published books on abnormality and criminology. Typically, Mac-Donald lumped the criminal, pauper, and defective classes together as related groups to study. Historically, within American eugenics, he expressed the middle-class belief that immigrants were mentally defective to native-born and that within the native-born element children of the professional and mercantile classes were more intelligent than working-class children.[7] This anti-immigrant and upper-class conscience characterized eugenists in progressive America. MacDonald only anticipated the mood, the class attitude.

Some scientists felt that by testing the weak-minded could be discovered and brought under society's control. Although a discussion of psychological testing is not central to a discussion of sterilization, it should be noted that an interest in eugenics and Mendelian inheritance encouraged the introduction of Binet testing methods in

6. Harry E. Barnes, "Criminology," *Encyclopedia of the Social Sciences,* IV, 591.

7. Fink, *Causes of Crime,* p. 101n; Arthur MacDonald, "Mental Ability in Relation to Head Circumference, Cephalic Index, Sociological Condition, Sex, Age, and Nationality," *Publications of the American Statistical Association,* XII.

the United States.[8] As director of a New Jersey institute for the feeble-minded, Henry H. Goddard was among the first to use Binet's tests and thereby recommended a system of classification to the 1910 meeting of the American Association for the Study of the feebleminded. Adopted by the association, this classification gave a mental-age valuation to such words as idiots, imbeciles, and morons.[9] Goddard based his research on the importance of heredity. "As long as any given strain is kept pure, we will have," he wrote, "the same mental capacity and possibilities generation after generation," but inbreeding and crossbreeding produce new combinations which will not be pure.[10] The sum of Goddard's efforts suggested hereditary determinism in regard to mental ability. With such a conclusion, programs of negative eugenics and sterilization had greater appeal.

The activities of such men as Goddard attracted governmental interest in the years before the First World War. The Secretary of the New York Board of Charities, for example, saw eugenics and sterilization as parts of a larger welfare scheme. With sterilization, he urged, feebleminded boys might have greater personal freedom and be less of a financial burden to the state. He also felt that the standard environmental reforms, such as better housing, better wages and hours, might improve the lives of high-grade defectives when coupled with sex hygiene and eugenics (which included sterilization).[11] Yet, the individual idiot was only the end-product of a long family history of feeblemindedness.

Richard L. Dugdale's report on the Juke family sparked scientific interest in the relationship between charity and heredity. Dugdale's pioneer effort, published in 1875, was followed in the progressive era by a host of similar studies. The Nams, the Hill Folk, the Pineys, and others became leading families in the community of the unfit. Practically all these reports appearing from 1908 to 1918 gave support to

8. Stanley P. Davies, *The Mentally Retarded in Society*, p. 26.
Albert Troutman, '50 Idaho 673 (1931).

9. *Ibid.*, p. 4.

10. Henry H. Goddard, "Heredity of Feeble-Mindedness," *Proceedings of the American Philosophical Society*, LI (April 19, 1912), 174.

11. Robert W. Hebberk, "The Development of State Institutions for the Mentally Defective in This State for the Next Decade," *Eugenics & Social Welfare Bulletin*, #2, Part One (Albany, 1912).

the thesis that hereditary transmission in accord with the Mendelian formula determined mental defects.[12] *The Jukes in 1915*, written by Arthur H. Estrabrook, gave an elaborate compilation of statistics and charts relating the presence of mental defectives among criminals and their hereditary origins. The book argued against prisons for criminally weak intellects. Instead, it suggested permanent custodial care and sterilization. The latter solution was particularly important, since close supervision of the individual after the operation was, therefore, not necessary, for a sterilized person was incapable of transmitting his genetic inadequacy to a future generation.[13] Some exponents of sterilization thought of the mentally incompetent as half-people whose chief characteristics were "astonishing fecundity," and a general irresponsibility creating increased demands on charity.[14] The family created the leaders of society and the mudsill. As one physician phrased the sentiment, "That a criminal father should beget a child predestined to criminality is a foregone conclusion. The father exerts a hereditary influence equal to all the previous ancestors in the paternal line." [15]

In 1915, in the noonday of progressivism, thirteen states had sterilization laws. The laws, confused in purpose, did not contain a clear distinction between sterilization for eugenic-therapeutic purposes or punitive reasons, for in many states both rapists and other sexual criminals along with the mentally inadequate were subject to sterilization. This legal ambiguity hampered administration of the laws. Advocates of sterilization saw a definite relationship between mental health and city life; this connection justified the laws. Cities were havens of venereal diseases, alcoholism, foreign immigrants, conflicts of cultural patterns and mores. Little wonder, then, that the unfit increased.[16]

Some eugenists were uneasy about the short-range influence of sterilization, for genetics was still a very young science. The problems

12. Stanley P. Davies, *The Mentally Retarded in Society*, pp. 37–38.
13. Arthur H. Estrabrook, *The Jukes in 1915*, p. 85.
14. Seth K. Humphrey, "The Menace of the Half-Man," *The Journal of Heredity*, XI (May-June 1920), 228–232.
15. Wilfred Scott Hall, "The Relation of Crime to Adolescence," *Bulletin of the American Academy of Medicine*, XV (April 1914), 86–96.
16. Fink, *Causes of Crime*, p. 209. Landman, *Human Sterilization*, p. 18.

both socially and genetically were so great that any permanent remedial eugenic effect was doubtful.[17] The majority of sterilization enthusiasts did not share such pessimism. After World War I, more than twenty states passed sterilization legislation. Like earlier efforts, the racial and eugenic factors were present in the laws. Typical was the case of Indiana's sterilization laws. That state passed such a law in 1907, had it declared unconstitutional in 1921, and passed new laws in 1927 and 1931.

In 1927 the United States Supreme Court issued a famous decision in the case of *Buck* v. *Bell,* in which the Court upheld the Virginia law permitting a salpingotomy (the cutting of the Fallopian tubes) of an inmate of the Virginia State Colony for Epileptics and Feeble Minded. Carrie Buck, the inmate in question, was an eighteen-year-old feebleminded white woman who was the daughter of a feebleminded woman in the institution. Carrie Buck, too, had given birth to a mentally defective child. The Court's opinion ruled that the operation was not a violation of due process and equal protection of the laws under the Fourteenth Amendment and, therefore, the Virginia statute was reasonable.[18]

The legal decision pleased eugenists. The genetic regeneration of the nation appeared at hand. In the years that followed, a number of cases in the nation's courts dealt with the eugenic aspect of sterilization. Advocates of sterilization constantly repeated the decision of 1927 in their agitation for more new state laws.[19]

Although eugenists were primarily concerned with therapeutic sterilization, there was, nevertheless, a primitive aspect in the history of sterilization agitation. For example, substantial medical opinion in the nineteenth century argued that criminals were born, not made. The pioneer of vasectomy, A. J. Ochsner, urged the operation on criminals.[20] As early as 1888, an Ohio reformer advocated sterilization

17. Raymond Pearl, "Sterilization of Degenerates and Criminals," *Eugenics Review,* XI (April 1916), 6.

18. *Buck* v. *Bell, Superintendent,* 274 U.S. 200 (1927).

19. Sigerist, *Civilization and Disease,* pp. 105–106. *Davies, Warden* v. *Walton,* 74 Utah 80 (1929); *State* v. *Schaffer,* 270 Pac. 604 (Kansas, 1928); *State* v. *Albert Troutman,* a '50 Idaho 673 (1931).

20. A. J. Ochsner, "Surgical Treatment of Habitual Criminals," *Journal of the American Medical Association,* XXXII (April 22, 1899), 867–868.

simply as punishment and to protect society from the "vicious, criminal and defective classes." [21] The latter justification appeared in the twentieth century, albeit with a more hereditary orientation.

The Supreme Court decision in 1942 declaring an Oklahoma law unconstitutional severely damaged the punitive aspect of sterilization. The statute—the Oklahoma Habitual Criminal Sterilization Act (1935) —was contested on the grounds of the Fourteenth Amendment. Within the provision of the law, crimes of moral turpitude were punishable by vasectomy. The Court ruled that the law violated the equal-protection clause of the Fourteenth Amendment, largely because of inequitable distinctions as to what constituted a felony involving moral turpitude.[22] For the sterilization movement, this decision eliminated the punitive justification. As will be seen later, the factors of general welfare, health of the individual, and the environmental factors of income and number of children became the leading arguments for *voluntary* sterilization.

Two major developments took place within the sterilization cause. The first major process in sterilization was the growth of a eugenic concern about the American population. The second was the gradual abandonment of racist considerations for socioeconomic factors. Yet, before these developments may be understood, it is necessary to see the political philosophy of sterilization in the years before the Great Depression of 1929–1937. Charles B. Davenport wrote, "The life of the commonwealth takes precedence over the right of reproduction of the individual." [23] In a word, the state over the individual. With that statement, Davenport linked United States eugenics and sterilization with the ancient and historic conservative desire for strong government. His contribution to this conservative attitude was the use of biological argument for the social necessity to control the reproductive process of mankind. Davenport and twentieth-century Social Darwinists believed that society was an organism.

21. The author not given, but Fink, *Causes of Crime*, p. 188, cites "Asexualiation as a Penalty for Crime and the Reformation of Criminals," *Cincinnati Lauret-Clinic*, XX (March 1888), 377–380.

22. *Skinner* v. *Oklahoma es sel Williamson, Attorney General*, 316 U.S. 535 (1942).

23. Margaret Sanger, ed., *Proceedings of the World Population Conference 1927* (London, 1927), p. 242.

Of course, eugenists interested in sterilization believed that the state (that is, society) had not only to destroy the degenerate groups but also to prevent the demise of valuable germ plasm. Correct from the eugenic point of view, this policy upheld the state over the individual. Invoking history, Harry Laughlin claimed that "in the long run individual effectiveness and happiness is assured only by individual subordination and occasional personal sacrifice." Natural rights notwithstanding, the individual was but a means to the goal of greater happiness for the greater community, the nation or the race. The improved human beings made better citizens. Since race betterment was not only possible but imperative in the eugenic creed, the state must act.[24]

Both conservatives and liberals began to abandon natural rights in the twentieth century. Only since midcentury have liberals found more to natural-rights philosophy than its past values (particularly in the nineteenth century when the creed was known as Manchester Liberalism). Although Morton White has ably pointed out the implications of relativism in early twentieth-century American social science, conservatives also employed relativism to advance or retard certain public policies. Paul Popenoe, a major eugenist for sterilization, wrote in 1922, "The theory which I am here upholding is of course to be classed as relativistic and empirical." The ethical basis was the good act which would lead to the survival of the race. Despite Popenoe's assumption that instinct was elementary to human behavior and morality,[25] he used the language of modern liberalism to advance eugenics and sterilization. For similar reasons the progressive-reformer and sociologist E. A. Ross accepted the necessity for sterilization legislation.[26]

Margaret Sanger supported sterilization for the most honorable ✓ political reason in United States history—lower taxes. Arguing that the public was overtaxed for the support of an ever-increasing class of

24. Laughlin, "The Legalization of Voluntary Eugenical Sterilization," *Eugenics Review*, XIX (April 1927), 12–13. Laughlin, *Eugenical Sterilization in the United States*, p. 339.

25. Paul Popenoe, "Eugenics and Human Morality," *The Journal of Heredity*, XIII (February 1922), 77, 79.

26. *BCR*, XII (March 1928), 90.

morons, she felt that a government pension should be given to every
unfit person who voluntarily submitted to sterilization. The solution
was clear. "There is only one reply to a request for a higher birth
rate among the intelligent and that is to ask the government to *first*
take the burden of the insane and feebleminded from your back.
Sterilization for these is the solution." [27] Economic determinism
prompted the sterilization movement: the lower taxes created a better
social order. Economics and biology were but twin expressions of the
same naturalistic condition.

Quoting statistics about the increase of mental illness and rising
taxes, Myra McCormick compared eugenic sterilization to vaccination
for typhoid or smallpox. In both cases the claim was protection of
society from degeneration and insurance of progressive racial
evolution. [28]

Given such sentiments and political orientation, an organization
expressly established to advance eugenic sterilization was nearly a
certainty. The Human Betterment Foundation, organized November
7, 1928, was a nonprofit eugenic educational corporation with a limited
membership of twenty-five persons. Noted eugenists on the first board
of trustees were Samuel J. Holmes and David Starr Jordan. E. S.
Gosney, a philanthropist from Pasadena, California, was the creator
and first president of Human Betterment. Born in Kentucky in 1855,
Gosney, as an orphan, worked his way through law school at Washington University, St. Louis. After six years as a railroad lawyer, he
moved to Arizona for his health in 1888. At Flagstaff he organized
the Arizona Wool Growers while active in banking activities. In 1910
he joined the eugenics movement by supporting the work of Davenport at Cold Spring Harbor. Davenport's work with sheep attracted
Gosney's attention to planned breeding for humans. After moving to
Pasadena, Gosney founded the organization for sterilization. The Human Betterment Foundation pressed for compulsory state sterilization

27. Sanger, "The Function of Sterilization," *BCR* (October 1926), p. 299.

28. Myra McCormick, "Eugenic Sterilization," *BCR*, XVI (October 1932),
241–242. This article is an excerpt from an address before the Indiana State
Medical Association in May 1932.

laws and urged voluntary operations for those individuals who were aware of their hereditary inadequacy.[29]

Paul Popenoe, as secretary, directed organizational activities and contributed an active pen to sterilization and allied causes. Gosney, however, noted the vital distinction between birth control and sterilization. The important difference was that eugenic sterilization was applied to irresponsible people by the state; contraceptives were used by responsible people, voluntarily. Irresponsible people belonged to families "without the intelligence, emotional stability or self-control to handle contraception successfully." [30] The social order reflected this condition; the lower classes had more children than the far-sighted upper classes.

Paul Popenoe, born in 1888, became interested in eugenics in 1907–1908 when at Stanford University he took a course from David Starr Jordan. This interest shaped Popenoe's entire career. In 1913, when the American Breeders Association became the American Genetic Association, Popenoe served as editor of *The Journal of Heredity*, the new organ for the eugenic cause. He gave up the editorship in 1917 when the army drafted him. The following year he and Roswell H. Johnson of the University of Pittsburgh published the first edition of *Applied Eugenics*, a standard reference and textbook. In addition to his duties with the Human Betterment Foundation, Popenoe created the American Institute of Family Relations in 1930. This latter organization, which is still functioning, grew out of Popenoe's successful publication in 1925 of his *Modern Marriage*. Popenoe's interest in marital problems was no doubt augmented by his experience in the army of dealing with social-disease problems.[31]

Philosophically, Popenoe was in the Darwinian-naturalist tradition. Biological and hereditary considerations were dual supports for his analysis of economic and social problems in American life. War, there-

29. *Scientific and Technical Societies in the United States,* fourth edition (1942), p. 164; "The Human Betterment Foundation," *Eugenics,* II (March 1929), 2–7; *Who Was Who in America,* II, 216.

30. E. S. Gosney, "Sterilization and Contraception," BCR XV (July 1932), 202.

31. Pastore, *The Nature-Nurture Controversy,* p. 96; correspondence of the author with Paul Popenoe, February 20, 1962. Ditzion, *Marriage, Morals and Sex in America,* p. 389.

fore, was a biological problem; "instinctive in origin, being an expression of man's inherited nature, it cannot be reasoned out of existence."[32] The solution lay in the creation of more intelligent people, aware of man's true nature, joyfully having more intelligent children to offset the immoral multiplication of the unfit.[33]

For the above reason, Popenoe questioned the eugenic effect of birth control on an improved social order. Since only the intelligent used birth control, it aided the growth of undesirable elements in society. Race deterioration, therefore, increased if the immoral and stupid class went unchecked. Sociologically, birth control was inefficient. Compulsory and voluntary sterilization was the answer. Marriage counseling also might benefit in perfecting the ratio between the moral (intelligent) and immoral (mental defective) in the nation's population.[34]

Despite the insistence on sterilization laws, Popenoe's conservatism came from naturalism. Every social policy, accordingly, had to be judged on its genetic merits—the maintenance of the intelligent in society. Like many conservative-progressives, Popenoe encouraged the back-to-the-farm movement, while aiding the increase of superior aspects of urban America. In fact, Popenoe and Johnson fit the progressive profile as outlined by George Mowry, historian of the progressive movement. Little wonder, then, that Johnson and Popenoe distrusted the democratic general will and placed their emphasis on experts in the creation of public policy.[35]

They considered socialism a menace because the philosophy did not allow for or recognize the basic and natural inequality of mankind. This criticism is an ancient statement of conservative reaction. Johnson and Popenoe's cautious "naturalistic" approach allowed a serious questioning of the totally eugenic effect of child labor laws. They questioned the social-biological wisdom of minimum-wage legislation, mothers' and old age pensions. Such reforms, they argued, contributed

32. Popenoe, "Is War Necessary?" *The Journal of Heredity,* IX (October 1918), 257–262.

33. Popenoe, "Will Morality Disappear?" *The Journal of Heredity,* IX (October 1918), 269–270.

34. Popenoe, "Birth Control and Eugenics," *BCR,* I (April-May 1917), 6. Popenoe, "Marriage Counseling," *Decade of Progress in Eugenics,* pp. 210–211.

35. Paul Popenoe and Roswell H. Johnson, *Applied Eugenics,* pp. 359, 361.

to the growth of the biologically and mentally inefficient. In much the same way, trade unionism, according to this criticism, aided the weak and ineffective workers in competition with the individual enterprise of superior labor.[36]

Not all reform, however, was biologically undesirable. Compulsory education laws, particularly in regard to vocational guidance and training, succeeded in avoiding more than a minimum of inferior families. Education was important; an informed public would desire sterilization laws. In any educational program, Popenoe and Johnson wanted sex hygiene, and they favored prohibition of alcohol for eugenic as well as for pathological and economic reasons.[37] Racial welfare was central in reform. The individual was but a part of a greater destiny, the race-nation.

Popenoe's defense of the antimiscegenation laws expressed his naturalistic moralism. His plan prevented further Negro-white amalgamation by legislative restriction on interracial sexual intercourse. If the last situation were not realized, society courted danger by going against a biological law. "Miscegenation," he warned, "can only lead to unhappiness under present social conditions and must, we believe, under *any* social condition be biologically wrong."[38] The races indicated natural and elementary inferiority and superiority. Heredity created successful civilization according to Popenoe's interpretation. "Is not one forced," he wrote, "to conclude that the Negro lacks in his germ-plasm excellence of some qualities which the white races possess, and which are essential for success in competition with the civilization of the white races at the present time?"[39] Thus, the caste system existed because the Negro, according to this progressive, was inferior.

Popenoe cited statistics indicating the social origin of feeblemindedness, pointing out that it was not restricted to certain races. Accordingly, in the Los Angeles schools, Popenoe wrote that the laboring class produced 46 percent of the sterilized feebleminded and 55 percent of the retarded children, while creating only 1 percent of the

36. *Ibid.*, pp. 369, 375–376, 385, 386.
37. *Ibid.*, pp. 371, 385–388, 389.
38. *Ibid.*, p. 297.
39. *Ibid.*, pp. 284–285.

very bright youngsters.[40] Given his naturalistic assumptions, Popenoe no doubt felt that social class expressed mental ability and worth to society.

As late as 1939, Popenoe warned that sterilization was the only effective policy for combating the increase of mental disease in the American social order. The moronic classes outmultiply the more intelligent and better educated people in the community.[41] Sterilization was the effective answer. Apparently, from his point of view, the problem was that the intelligent classes did not think with their blood but allowed rationalism to hamper natural instincts about large families.

Modern civilization caused this immoral and unnatural occurrence. Like so many eugenists and other social prophets in United States history, Popenoe disliked the ethical basis of modern civilization. It was counter to Nature's plan. Survival of the fittest under laws of heredity was the only way the human race had developed, according to Social Darwinist Paul B. Popenoe. "Modern civilization, human sympathy, and charity have intervened in Nature's plan. The weak and defective are now nursed to maturity and produce their kind." [42] The result was family suicide and race degeneracy, since the efficient voluntarily limited their families. The city and modern charity aided the biological misfits to endure and increase. Like other progressives, Popenoe saw the city as the destroyer of old-time virtue in allowing increase of the inefficient. Charity, to be racially just, must be scientifically oriented to prevent the unnecessary and dangerous increase of the inadequate.

The 1930s saw a decline in sterilization agitation as economic problems and foreign affairs changed the social thought of the nation. Generally, the environmentalists, if such a term might be used, carried the day. In Europe, Nazi Germany passed sterilization laws enforced by Hereditary Health Courts. Although nominally the law covered physical and mental defects, sterilization served political and punitive

40. Paul Popenoe and E. S. Gosney, *Twenty-Eight Years of Sterilization in California*, p. 27.
41. *Ibid.*, p. 3.
42. E. S. Gosney and Paul Popenoe, *Sterilization for Human Betterment*, p. v.

purposes.[43] No doubt Hitlerism contributed to the decline of American interest in eugenics and sterilization.[44] Yet, in 1940, one American authority, Henry E. Sigerist, wanted the public to distinguish eugenic sterilization from Nazi ideology and to realize that Scandinavian laws on the subject also existed.[45] Sigerist was in the minority camp because popular, scientific, and eugenic thought abandoned compulsory sterilization.

The Committee of the American Neurological Association for the Investigation of Eugenic Sterilization urged a wholesale reorientation of the problem. Recommendations noted that the lack of good genetic knowledge prevented sterilization of normal people who *might* produce abnormal offspring. Immorality was a cultural, not a biological factor, and environment shared equally in the creation of human nature. With these assumptions, the committee recommended that laws be voluntary and regulatory rather than compulsory, with no group or class discrimination. Adequate administrative processes should be created with surgeons for legal protection. Selective sterilization, however, might be needed in cases dealing with certain diseases.[46]

The primary assumption of eugenic sterilization was that mental deficiency was basically hereditary in nature and followed laws of distribution. Recent research now questions this generality. One major reason, of course, is the great range of genetic possibilities from the gene combination of two individuals, coupled with the varied environmental influences, all of which constitute "human nature" in the individual. The fact still remains that certain types of mental conditions are hereditary and certain types of retardation do "run" in families. Clear distinctions are what are necessary—not past dogmatism.[47]

43. Sigerist, *Civilization and Disease*, p. 106.

44. Personal correspondence of the author with Paul Popenoe, February 20, 1962. In the letter, Popenoe wrote, "The major factor in the decline of eugenics was undoubtedly Hitlerism. The contributing factor was a movement in psychiatry which tended to deny the importance of heredity."

45. Sigerist, *Civilization and Disease*, pp. 106–107.

46. Abraham Myerson, *Eugenical Sterilization, A Reorientation of the Problem*, pp. 177–179.

47. Stanley P. Davies, *The Mentally Retarded in Society*, pp. 62, 85.

A brief mention should be made that the field of biochemistry is doing work in mental deficiencies. Dr. George A. Jervis's pioneer efforts suggest in some instances a meaningful relationship between the body's ability to metabolize properly proteins, vitamins, and other substances and mental deficiencies or retardation. In other words, a faulty metabolism might cause certain forms of mental disabilities. This faulty mechanism might be hereditary. In 1958, the New York Research Institute for Mental Retardation, the first of its kind in the United States, began investigations along such lines hoping to discover chemical causes of mental deficiencies and, if possible, their cures.[48]

Despite a decline in public and scientific interest in eugenic sterilization, the movement continued and began to urge voluntary sterilization for socioeconomic and psychological reasons. At Princeton in 1943 the local New Jersey Sterilization League became Birthright, a national organization. Five years later, after acquiring the records of the Human Betterment Foundation, Birthright (reorganized as the Human Betterment Association of America) advocated voluntary sterilization using social, economic, and personal health arguments.[49] At that time, R. L. Dickinson's studio in the New York Academy of Medicine became headquarters for the organization. Working in the areas of birth control and marriage counseling, Dr. Dickinson led the Association until his death in 1951. The organization then moved to 105 West Fifty-fifth Street in New York City, where it still functions.[50]

Contemporary interest in sterilization among the public is no doubt slight. Mark Haller, an authority on American eugenics, argues that sterilization was not popular among advocates of eugenics. Dr. Haller says that eugenists believed the laws to be unscientific and poorly written and basically unnecessary because many sterilized individuals

48. *Ibid.*, pp. 86–87.

49. The archival material of Gosney's organization is in warehouse storage in Pasadena, California. Author correspondence with E. B. Lewis, Secretary of Genetics Society of America, October 23, 1962. The Human Betterment Association of America, Inc., in correspondence with the author (Ruth Proskaver Smith, Executive Director, March 9, 1962) clearly stressed *voluntary* sterilization. The printed material of the Association views sterilization as a convenient method of birth control. The material in question is the possession of the author.

50. *Sterilization for Human Betterment,* a pamphlet of the Human Betterment Association of America, Inc., in the possession of the author.

remained in institutions, and the laws were not consistently enforced. He goes on to point out that neither the National Committee for Mental Hygiene nor the Committee on Provision for the Feebleminded endorsed sterilization.[51]

All of Dr. Haller's observations are true and *yet* sterilization was an important part of eugenic agitation. Just as *The Birth Control Review* devoted issues to eugenics, it likewise encouraged sterilization.[52] Also, as pointed out in this chapter, Davenport, Popenoe, and Gosney, all of whom were connected with the eugenics cause, were also active in sterilization work.

Not all eugenists were enthusiastic about sterilization, but in popular thought and in the philosophy of the various state laws, sterilization was a prerequisite to race betterment. In the social thought of an era based on naturalism, the reform of the nation by sterilization was considerable. The state laws witness the situation. Progressivism, as shaped by theorists and politicians, assumed and indeed stressed naturalistic values for American reforms.

51. Haller, "American Eugenics," p. 275.
52. For example, see BCR, XVII (April 1933), 83–111.

7

PROGRESSIVISM

Creed and Faith of Reform

PROGRESSIVISM, heir to the nineteenth century with its concern about Darwinism, naturalism, revolution, class struggle, industrialization, and the multitude of urban problems, was not a pure substance; rather, it was an alloy through which ran sizable streaks of conservatism and, on occasion, a vein of reaction. The progressive theme ran from optimism founded on utopian assumptions to deep naturalistic despair. Little wonder then that eugenics from 1900 to 1929 was a synthesis of those moods.

Facing the scope and complexity of the times, the progressives responded partly with a yearning for the world that used to exist before degeneration became a reality. The contemporary scene lacked old-fashioned economic virtue, political independence and character.[1] To E. L. Godkin, Herbert Croly, William Allen White, and Theodore Roosevelt, society's moral failure caused the nation's ills.

1. Richard Hofstadter, *The Age of Reform from Bryan to F.D.R.*, pp. 5–6, 11. Hereafter cited as Hofstadter, *The Age of Reform*.

The Gay Nineties were misnamed. The decade was alive with change in all spheres of American life: politics, literature, and the social sciences. Many contemporaries mistook the status revolution for the Marxian class struggle. Even Henry Adams disliked the alliance of the social elite with such men as U. S. Grant and the spoilsmen who surrounded him and controlled the Republican party. Anticipating the middle-class protest by Croly and White, Adams saw the people as the mystical force in history, shaping national destiny. By the beginning of the twentieth century, naturalism fused with patriotic nationalism created part of the ideological landscape of progressivism.[2]

Biology, as previously noted, assisted in the creation of "tough minded" conservatism. It also affected the founders of pragmatism which, in twentieth-century social thought, was the philosophical rationale for the new reformism, the new liberalism.[3] The objective of social reform was an environment in which "good blood" controlled the social order.[4]

Frank Parsons accepted this philosophy. A left-of-center reformer in nineteenth-century Boston, he based his ideas for reform on a eugenic ideal. Parsons viewed natural selection as wasteful, since it did not automatically provide for the survival of the fittest. In Parsons's utopia, the biologist first discovered the scientific laws of nature, then directed them to produce a predictable intelligent society of superior people.[5] He was representative of the collectivist-liberal interpretation of naturalism. Even as a reform Darwinist, Parsons's interest and support of eugenics indicated the attraction this type of naturalism had for all kinds of social philosophers.

Naturalism—the racial factor in human affairs—influenced individuals other than liberal reformers. Edwin Lawrence Godkin (1831–1902) was such a person. A conservative reformer and founder of the *Nation,* a weekly journal of opinion in 1865, he advocated a consistent

2. For the development of this general theme, see Henry S. Commager, *The American Mind,* and Ray Ginger, *Altgeld's America.* William H. Jordy, *Henry Adams: Scientific Historian,* pp. 87, 213.

3. Wiener, *Evolution and the Founders of Pragmatism,* pp. 4–5.

4. Henry Smith Williams, "The Lessons of Heredity," *The North American Review,* CLVII (September 1893), 353.

5. Arthur Mann, *Yankee Reformers in an Urban Age,* p. 134.

policy of laissez-faire economics and limited public policy. Coming from an Irish Presbyterian background, Godkin immigrated to the United States to study law. He turned instead to journalism and for half a century measured public issues and programs against the "naturalism" of Manchester Liberalism.[6] Godkin saw the major task of statesmanship as separating the activities of the political and the economic man. The state and the market were different worlds governed by different laws—human and natural.

Historians have repeatedly pointed out Godkin's trust in the absolutism of the laws of supply and demand in governing the affairs of man and society. However, they have generally neglected the naturalistic influences on his economic and social attitudes. Considering the age of Darwin and the impact of naturalism on the American mind in the nineteenth century, Godkin did not escape the effects of naturalistic ethics. To be sure, his emphasis on orthodox capitalism subordinated influence on these ethics. Perhaps one reason historians and critics have missed noting Godkin's naturalism was that at several points in his philosophy capitalism and natural selection were quite similar in that they pointed to a common solution to public issues. Both laws operated independently of human wishes, making human happiness possible only when society recognized and obeyed those laws. Both systems of thought also stressed individual success, measuring the same by material standards. Most important, the laws—biological and economic—defended the status quo from meddlesome theorists of collectivistic reforms.

Godkin believed that human nature was the desire for distinction and difference among men and groups of men. Environmental schemes for leveling mankind were certain to fail. He thought human nature was eternal.[7] Both biological and economic law in nineteenth-century

6. For biographical background on E. L. Godkin, see William M. Armstrong, *E. L. Godkin and American Foreign Policy, 1865–1900;* Alan P. Grimes, *The Political Liberalism of the New York Nation, 1865–1932;* James Hart, *The Oxford Companion to American Literature,* third edition, pp. 279–280; Richard B. Morris, ed., *Encyclopedia of American History,* p. 666; Rollo Ogden, ed., *Life and Letters of Edwin Lawrence Godkin,* two volumes.

7. E. L. Godkin, *Problems of Modern Democracy, Political and Economic Essays,* second edition, p. 59. This book is a collection of magazine articles which Godkin wrote over several years. Hereafter cited as Godkin, *Problems of Modern Democracy.*

thought assumed that individual differences resulted in the successful response of the individual to natural selection and the market. Godkin viewed man as a greedy animal. He saw a "remnant of the old aboriginal instinct" which was "implanted for the protection of the species in times when everyone looked on his neighbor's bone with a hungry eye, and the man with the strong hand was apt to have the fullest stomach." [8] So it was, Godkin felt, in the growth of modern corporations, resulting from individual intelligence.[9] Naturally, E. L. Godkin discounted those who criticized the social application of survival of the fittest. The doctrine could have only limited appeal, since the vast majority of mankind was unfit and only the intelligent minority recognized the logic of this application. The critics of natural selection only bewailed the inevitable.[10]

Godkin had a theory of progress. To insure progress government must insure the increase of the fittest. His solution was laissez-faire capitalism. Society's well-being depended upon the progress of the elite, not on the material satisfaction of the masses. General population increase was not desirable, according to the *Nation's* editor, for the Malthusian law "of population works everywhere, and with increasing severity, other things being equal, as the population increases." [11] Godkin accepted Malthus's conclusions, for in the nineteenth century Malthusian speculations provided a bridge between the territories of capitalistic economics and Darwinian biology. Godkin was not the only man to cross that bridge in the history of American thought. Believing that poverty existed because the masses "multiply close up to the provision which the earth normally makes for them," [12] Godkin placed his social philosophy on such a premise. Progress in human society or in nature, therefore, was the realization of the competitive principle. "We can hardly conceive of its being made in any other way," Godkin wrote with finality.[13]

Godkin saw poverty as a constant auxiliary to progress, and since

8. Godkin, *Reflections and Comments, 1865–1895* p. 25.
9. *Ibid.*, p. 14.
10. Godkin, *Problems of Modern Democracy*, p. 84.
11. *Ibid.*, pp. 86, 85.
12. *Ibid.*, p. 204.
13. *Ibid.*, pp. 205–206.

the former was eternal and an individual's concern, progress consisted of a person's attempts to gain material well-being. The labor movement was, therefore, in basic error. Each man must solve the labor problem for himself. Collective attempts to improve or end working-class poverty failed because the efforts ran counter to the individualistic natural laws of human nature and society. "The labor problem," Godkin sadly concluded, "is really of making the manual laborers of the world content with their lot. In my judgment this is an insoluble problem." [14] Agitation or discontent forever, but success never, for natural laws set the limits of social or economic improvements.

At the other end of the socioeconomic scale, Godkin expressed concern about the investor's future. Vital to progress, the rich contributed investment funds. Without this group society suffered.[15] To replace the investor class with governmental investment was wrong, for this to Godkin was socialism, and his version of human nature forbade such a prospect. Since human nature ruled out socialism, Godkin urged a public policy to increase wealth for the investor class. Once again, laissez-faire social philosophy answered society's needs and once again Thomas Malthus provided the solution to the emerging problems of industrial America in the nineteenth century. Godkin saw social problems solved because nature solved them.

Godkin, however, was not at peace with the social order. He anticipated the progressives of Roosevelt and Wilson's time. The decline of the legislative process indicating transfer of power from the rich to the poor troubled him.[16] For him, modern democratic government was poor men governing rich communities. Like later progressives, Godkin's concern for good city government expressed itself as a demand for more "municipal spirit" in which men of sound business principles and character, regardless of party label, led urban government.[17]

Questioning the civic value of universal suffrage, Godkin saw urban

14. *Ibid.*, pp. 179, 193.
15. *Ibid.*, pp. 237, 241.
16. *Ibid.*, p. 292.
17. Godkin, "The Problems of Municipal Government," *Annals of the American Academy of Political and Social Science,* IV (May 1894), 865, 882.

government as the root of contemporary troubles. Like a John the Baptist of progressivism, Godkin warned against immigrants (particularly the Irish) as the curse of the Republic *by being votes for corrupt political machines.* The saloon only provided an easy meeting hall for this disruptive element in the population.[18] Godkin's views gained respectability as elements of reform progressive ideology. The status revolution had begun.

Democracy was the villain, according to Godkin. Some later progressives shared this opinion but did not express it with such candor. Particularly, Godkin criticized the Jacksonian legacy to American politics, the common man as office-holder. With increased complexity in human affairs, Godkin urged that the governmental expert become part of the political landscape. Special fitness, he argued, equipped certain individuals for certain tasks. Political parties as part of human nature complicated the problem. Combined with nominating conventions and party loyalty, the creation of the political machine was easy.[19] To men like Godkin, the ultimate dilemma was human nature. On the one hand, Godkin calmly accepted situations as results of human nature. On the other hand, he issued encouragements toward improvements which transcended the very human nature he felt was eternal and never changing. No wonder Mr. Godkin moaned over the paradoxes of democratic governments.

The political boss caused the scarcity of "good" men in public life. Like progressive followers of Theodore Roosevelt, Godkin found that the boss and the machine prevented the effective use of distinguished men and experts in legislative matters. Civil service reform provided the answer.[20] In accord with middle-class reformers of the early twentieth century, Godkin sought an answer to the nation's ills by political means—voting and the encouragement of superior individuals in public service.

In further anticipation of pre–World War I reform, Godkin worried about corrupt municipal government. Assuming that urban government was similar to a business enterprise, he called for the increased use of experts. At the same time, he urged that enlightened public

18. Godkin, *Problems of Modern Democracy*, pp. 123–133.
19. Godkin, *Unforeseen Tendencies of Democracy*, pp. 37, 46, 59, 63, 67.
20. *Ibid.*, pp. 80, 82, 93.

servants must destroy the evil connection between the city and the state government.[21] This plea, of course, marks Godkin as a forerunner of the urban-rights movement, an issue generally associated with the progressive era.

Godkin's kinship with American progressivism was apparent with his desire for the direct election of United States senators, his concern over public opinion, and his urge that judicial review gave the valid check on democracy.[22] Not all reformers shared this last point, for probably Theodore Roosevelt lost a great deal of middle-class reform support in the campaign of 1912 by his advocacy of the popular recall of judges. The vast majority of Americans in the twentieth century— reformers or not—have had high regard for the Supreme Court and the judicial system. Effective reform worked within the limits of public images of governmental and social institutions.

Believing that the free market rewarded natural superiority, Godkin, like later supporters of Woodrow Wilson's progressivism, saw the tariff as the mother of civic mischief. The tariff was immoral because it ran counter to human nature. "That such a system could long prevail in any country without damage to the moral constitution of those who were benefited by it, all experience of human nature forbids us to expect," he wrote against the protectionist system.[23] In a word, tariff destroyed the moral character of a nation. The worst feature of the tariff was the creation of a proletarian class. The progressive era mirrored Godkin's concern when the major problem was the relationship of the social classes in America and particularly the "squeeze" on the middle class by the industrial autocrats and the urban poor. The progressive middle class expressed alarm over the extremes of wealth and poverty.

E. L. Godkin criticized irresponsible capitalists, a charge repeated in later progressive literature. From Godkin's point of view, the major concern of public administration was that the poor masses and irresponsible capitalists gained power in modern government, particularly on the state level. In combination, these two social groups ruled with disregard for public welfare or national service. The capitalists

21. *Ibid.*, pp. 116, 146, 149, 171.
22. *Ibid.*, pp. 222, 231.
23. Godkin, *Problems in Modern Democracy*, pp. 103, 121.

ignored the proper procedures of society in their zeal for wealth. An unholy alliance resulted with the spoilsmen in public office who sold public services to corrupted capitalists. According to Godkin, the answer was to keep strictly limited the numbers of "prizes" the government could sell.[24] At once the Manchester liberal solved the dilemmas and paradoxes of capitalism and democratic government by a return to the creed of the separation of the market and the legislature. Given his attitude toward human nature, Godkin repeated an obsolete solution to the sociological and psychological challenges of late-nineteenth-century industrialization.

Ultimately, E. L. Godkin believed that the United States would never be a democratic despotism. Tracing the growth of immigration and the rise of the urban political machine, Godkin saw a racial reason why the country must reject the leveling influences of absolute democracy. Drawing on the naturalistic temper of the nineteenth century, he thought the competitive nature of the Anglo-Saxon Americans effectively checked democracy's leveling tendencies.[25] Suffice it to say that Godkin's analysis and solution to the problems of his generation demonstrated the naturalistic predilections of post-Appomattox United States. Naturalism did not die at century's end but continued to be a major factor in early-twentieth-century formulation of the progressive mind. Racism, as a factor, cut across the battle lines of reform and reaction. Nowhere was a condition for the future greatness of the nation as apparent as in Herbert Croly's plan of reform. Herbert Croly and E. L. Godkin were intellectually akin, although each man might have denied it. Both thinkers were worshippers of the hero in history. Other points can be noted, as the superstructure of Croly's philosophy, like Godkin's, revealed naturalistic assumptions.

Herbert David Croly (1869–1930) was a New York journalist whose books include several on architecture. In addition, he edited the *Architectural Record* for six years. A founder of the *New Republic* in 1914, Croly wrote biographies of Mark Hanna and Willard Straight. The latter gave financial aid to the *New Republic*. *The Promise of*

---

24. *Ibid.*, p. 110.
25. Godkin, *Unforeseen Tendencies of Democracy*, p. 259.

American Life, published in 1909, was Croly's masterpiece, an American classic in reform literature. In 1914 Croly wrote *Progressive Democracy,* a study of the evolution of democracy since the time of Hanna. The book was not the intellectual equal of *The Promise of American Life.*[26]

Herbert Croly never truly overcame the influence of Auguste Comte. Both his parents were disciples of the French philosopher. Positivism provided the basis for their interest in reform and gave a scientific moral scheme of values. Comte assumed that scientific values had replaced orthodox religious values in the creation of the new scientific age. The nineteenth-century age in which young Croly matured was an age of science, or at least of scientific aspirations, for reform.[27]

While at Harvard, Croly absorbed elements of the philosophies of the three giants of the Harvard Department of Philosophy—Royce, Santayana, and James. Josiah Royce, the idealist, contributed his concept of "organic society," idealism, and patriotism to the thought of Croly, the future philosopher of America's promise. He used George Santayana's emphasis on heroism, saintliness, and, of course, elitism. William James gave Croly pragmatism, allowing flexibility in answering problems of reform for industrial America.[28] Yet, under all these influences remained a solid center of naturalism that utilized a particular view of human nature.

Published in 1909, *The Promise of American Life* became the bible for members of Theodore Roosevelt's band of progressives.[29] Croly's view of human nature depended upon instinct psychology and the assumption that the social order correctly mirrored competition in nature. He noted natural selection as instrumental in creating a dynamic nation. Croly saw the instincts of self-preservation and business adventure behind American economic growth which was caused by

26. James Hart, *The Oxford Companion to American Literature,* third edition, p. 170; Charles Forcey, *The Crossroads of Liberalism,* pp. 3–51.

27. Eric Goldman, *Rendezvous with Destiny,* pp. 190–191; Forcey, *The Crossroads of Liberalism,* p. 15.

28. *Ibid.,* pp. 18–20.

29. An excellent history of Croly's book, its reputation and ideas, is in Forcey, *The Crossroads of Liberalism,* pp. 3–51, *passim.* Suffice it to say, however, that Forcey fails to point out fully the naturalistic orientation of *The Promise of American Life.*

the social utilization of natural competitive methods.[30] Croly felt that
society must base any realistic public policy on the inevitability of
selection, and it was a national responsibility to "interfere on behalf
of the selection of the really fittest." [31] Millionaires were, therefore, a
natural inevitability in American democracy because any system had
social discrimination as well as biological differences. The task for
reform was one of making this group of millionaires aware of the
social obligations of wealth, for Croly argued that cautious use of
millionaires' wealth destroyed class envy contempt.[32]

Thomas Jefferson was the villain in Croly's morality play of American politics. According to him, Jefferson's philosophy of individualism
allowed selfish aggrandizement and collective irresponsibility. Alexander Hamilton's policies, however, fused with the democratic faith,
meant the realization of national efficiency and, therefore, contributed
to the national good.[33] Nongovernmental Jeffersonian interference
ruined the task of economic reform. The state must take a larger role
in the economy. Hamilton saw this necessity. The task of modern
reformers must make intervention democratic. Croly blessed Theodore
Roosevelt's policies because they gave "democratic meaning and purpose to the Hamiltonian tradition and method." [34] No wonder Roosevelt appreciated Croly's keen and scholarly insight into the philosophical issues of progressive politics.

Like many of the eugenists of his time, Croly saw reform as a process of restoration, of repairing the "earlier homogeneity of American
society." In this way, reform was a higher species of conservatism
striving to save what the nation once possessed. Democracy was not
the same as equality, according to Herbert Croly, the neo-Tory. He
warned, "The principle of equal rights encourages mutual suspicion

30. Croly, *The Promise of American Life*, pp. 107, 115.
31. *Ibid.*, p. 191.
32. *Ibid.*, pp. 196, 202–204. Croly's case was for scientific stewardship or
scientific philanthropy that would destroy an old nationalist fear—the class struggle. Progressives hated the class warfare concept, for it weakened class loyalty to
the nation and thus damaged national efficiency which was central to the progressive credo.
33. *Ibid.*, pp. 50, 152–153. For an exceptional analysis of Jefferson's reputation
in progressive ideology, see Merrill D. Peterson, *The Jefferson Image in the
American Mind*, pp. 330–347.
34. Croly, *The Promise of American Life*, p. 169.

and disloyality." [35] Once again this type of democracy threatened national patriotism, the core of Croly's promise of America's greatness.

At the same time, any irrational Jeffersonian demands for equal rights hampered an honored theme of progressivism—efficiency. Means and ends must be separate in Roosevelt's progressive scheme of values, according to Croly. The end was always a higher nationalism. Democracy was only the method, not an end in itself. For the creation of a higher type of individual and associated life, sacrifice must be necessary within Hamiltonian nationalism.[36] Croly and his associates were not fascists. Yet his philosophy, as has been observed, shared some elements of nineteenth-century thought which in the extreme position created twentieth-century fascism.

Like many progressives, Croly took for granted the racial inferiority of the Negroes. Croly noted that they "were a race possessed of moral and intellectual qualities inferior to those of the white man." [37] Obviously then, Croly, in writing *The Promise of American Life,* spent no time with the problems of civil liberties or minority rights, which are two major concerns of modern liberalism. The probable reason for the omission of these two subjects was that any philosophical defense of the two issues would weaken national unity and efficiency. Considering Croly's attitude toward the Negroes, one can easily see why his progressivism was for white men only. Thus a flower of naturalistic racism blossomed in the garden of progressivism.

In a like manner, Croly disdained trade unionism because the worker might place his allegiances to class and union above his duty to state and country. The class struggle (and many progressives recognized its existence) defeats national purpose. According to Croly, labor unions sought special privileges which naturally took unity from middle-class nationalism. In a burst of patriotism, Croly disallowed labor unions because, once again, the unionist's loyalty to his organization illustrated the breakdown of the traditional American system. Croly apparently believed that in the nation's origin there had existed

35. *Ibid.,* pp. 139, 145–147, 185.
36. *Ibid.,* pp. 264, 280. The evil of political corruption for progressivism was that corruption was a wasteful and unscientific method of government.
37. *Ibid.,* p. 81.

no classes to menace the mission of America. In the same vein of criticism, he rejected socialism for its internationalism.[38]

Yet Croly accepted social class realities, the products of human nature and natural selection. Social class was particularly important in the national government. He also maintained that the country should train young men for political leadership, echoing an earlier demand by E. L. Godkin. In like manner, Croly saw the need for the governmental expert and for specialization in the entire society. In line with this emphasis on the strong individual in government, Croly, like many progressives, saw a greater danger to the nation in legislative usurpation than in executive power.[39] Godkin was another philosopher trusting the strong man in society and the state. Theodore Roosevelt's administrative achievements no doubt encouraged the growth of such an attitude.

From Croly's point of view, the emphasis on the superior individual in government came from his analysis of changing American history. The wilderness was gone. The frontier, with all its virtues and rewards, had disappeared. Now was the time, Croly reasoned, to use a new method in taking advantage of old opportunities. Americans must sacrifice traditional methods, particularly the Jeffersonian individualistic creed. Even military power might be necessary in the realization of the promise of the United States. The promise changed with the close of the frontier and now the nation's right arm was a sword.[40] In a word, the economy had changed, and scarcity existed. Conservatism was imperative for the United States to maintain its position in the affairs of the planet. Croly saw war as a recognized and legitimate expression of national policy. It was a crisis for the old-fashioned virtues of laissez-faire capitalism. His task was, therefore, to restore these virtues in a meaningful relationship to an industrial and urban United States.

In his defense of war, Croly claimed that a war waged for "an excellent purpose contributes more to human amelioration than a

38. *Ibid.*, pp. 128–129, 206, 210.
39. *Ibid.*, pp. 103–104, 199, 69.
40. *Ibid.*, pp. 2, 5, 14, 21.

merely artificial peace." [41] His progressivism, verbiage removed, was only old-fashioned patriotism. Unlike the progressive David Starr Jordan, Croly accepted war and colonies. Herbert Croly saw colonies as social safety valves, since the adventurous of a nation immigrated to the colonies and did not stay at home and cause trouble.[42] Imperialism was not alien to the progressive mind, and Croly was no exception.[43]

Although national efficiency and unity created the fulfillment of America's promise, human natures created problems, according to Croly. Human nature was destructive, but national organization might save the situation and restore the promise. Ultimately, the strength of American society must be a realistic understanding of human nature. By World War I, patriotism and instinct psychology encrusted this human nature, typical of early twentieth-century naturalism. Croly's final solution for reform was instinct (or herd) psychology. Like many psychologists of the progressive era, Croly saw imitation as an instinct. It was the purpose of national leaders to provide good models or examples to make this instinct socially useful and thus realize the promise—democratic nationalism based on policies of Alexander Hamilton.[44]

William Allen White shared many of the assumptions and aspirations about America that characterized the thought of Herbert Croly. White (1868–1944) was a long-time editor of the Emporia, Kansas, *Gazette,* who in the presidential campaign of 1896 published the now famous editorial, "What's the Matter with Kansas?" a conservative attack on populism, bringing him to national notice. Later, White was active in the Bull Moose Party of Theodore Roosevelt. A life-long Republican, White was never a regular party man, and in his later years he supported parts of the New Deal and was a personal friend of Franklin D. Roosevelt. White's career was long and active. In addition to his newspaper work, he wrote a number of books, both

41. *Ibid.,* p. 256.
42. *Ibid.,* p. 261.
43. William E. Leuchtenburg, "Progressivism and Imperialism: The Progressive Movement and American Foreign Policy, 1898–1916," *Mississippi Valley Historical Review,* XXXIX (December 1952), 496.
44. Croly, *The Promise of American Life,* pp. 440, 454, 145.

fiction and nonfiction.[45] White's biography of Calvin Coolidge is still the standard work on that President.

The most important book that White wrote for his contemporary view of progressivism and politics is *The Old Order Changeth*, published in 1910. One historian, Richard Hofstadter, describes this book as an expression of reform optimism and "a statement of what was probably White's philosophy of politics." [46] Despite the optimism, White's philosophy was much the same as the outlook of Godkin and Croly on most points.

The common ground among the three men was their analysis of human nature. This human nature was the working of instincts. White, for example, did not deny the importance of technology, but the key to politics was man's struggle between selfish and unselfish instincts. The Kansas editor saw, not a class struggle, but a "contest in the heart of the common people." [47] Psychologically, it was a fight between altruism and egoism. At once one can note that wonderful mixture of naturalism and democratic romanticism that was so characteristic of American progressivism. For White, public policy moved between the forces of these instincts.

In his book White discusses the common themes of naturalistic progressivism—instinct psychology, agrarian myth, fear of the city (and the class struggle), and racism. In his discussion of democracy, White did not forget his version of human nature. He always related it to the particular issue. Thus, in regard to the role of legislature, White saw merit in maintaining the legislative districts, so that the cities would not overrun the country districts in the control of state affairs. Aside from the fact that White was part of rural Kansas, he saw that the country had virtues which cities did not possess.[48] Rural folk simply lived closer to nature.

His theory of agrarian superiority mated with observations on the necessity of urban political reform. White's analysis was not always

45. For biographical information, see William Allen White, *The Autobiography of William Allen White;* Walter Johnson, *William Allen White's America;* and James Hart, *The Oxford Companion to American Literature*, p. 822.

46. Hofstadter, *The Age of Reform*, p. 258.

47. William A. White, *The Old Order Changeth, A View of American Democracy*, pp. 5–7, 27, 32. Hereafter cited as White, *The Old Order Changeth*.

48. *Ibid.*, p. 42.

consistent or logical. For example, like other progressives, he urged that cities have home rule and be free of state domination. Yet he claimed that the best political condition was rural control. Despite this slip in logic, White, once again in tune with reform themes, advocated that the expert and the elite lead the urban masses to civic improvement. Thus such organizations as the American Civic Association and the American Municipal League came into existence to educate people in their obligations to city life, White reasoned. White justified elitism as long as society maintained the equality of opportunity to allow for new individuals in the governing elite. He did not explore the full implications of the elitist theory. Rather, he dwelled at length on the steady progress the nation was making toward democracy—"altruism of all the classes." [49]

White felt this altruism, basic in human nature, was expressed in the philanthropic endeavors of such men as Russell Sage and Andrew Carnegie in their new charitable institutions. In short, this activity clearly demonstrated the best instinct in the human animal. At the same time, White saw such activity as good business, for "when the economic value is demonstrated, the instinct of democracy to help the needy will have no political opposition." [50] Philanthropy was at once rational (that is, good business) and a noble impulse to dull the edge of poverty in American society.

Philosophically, White's instinct theories were part of American naturalism. Race was the answer. To be sure, White's opinion changed later, but during the progressive era he was a racist at a time when some reformers accepted such opinions as a realistic insight into national problems. Time and time again, White used race as the cause or cure for particular issues. Aryan blood contained particular virtues which helped explain the evolution of American institutions. Aryan or Teutonic blood was antityranny, for such men were naturally free men. Thus the conscience of the American people knew no class;[51] and therefore the Aryan man was free to realize his objectives. White added other considerations to the Aryanism of his philosophy, for he

49. *Ibid.*, pp. 160, 125, 100, 105.
50. *Ibid.*, pp. 161, 155.
51. *Ibid.*, pp. 167, 198–199, 186.

was too conservative to allow the unrestrained instincts of the Aryan to direct public policy.

On several occasions, the Kansas progressive noted that democracy's greatest need was self-restraint, so that the law, rather than mobs, conducted society. Thus the regulatory influence of the court and the school created folk laws.[52] Once again the wisdom of blood saved the nation. Yet, paradoxically, in White's celebration of Aryan folk virtues, he accepted the melting-pot concept.[53]

Instinct and blood were the two factors which—according to White —created the United States and shaped marriage customs, allowing only the best to marry. Isolated by two oceans from the inferior races, White viewed the American as a rationalist in mate selection. This rationalism was a naturalistic matter, for there was an "instinctive race revulsion to cross-breeding that marks the American wherever he is found."[54] Little surprise, then, with a reformer such as William A. White holding such a belief, that the progressive era was a period of large amounts of racial legislation.

White believed that the American's educational demand was an instinct and, likewise, the boy's demand for physical training and practical education was an instinctive impulse realizing democratic aspirations. Associated with these educational desires, competition gave the youth physical strength and aided in attaining manhood.[55] No doubt, considering White's orientation toward Aryanism, competition was among equals.

White's analysis did not ignore environment, even though Aryan blood helped create its own environment. In fact, he saw environment as the result of the inheritance of acquired characteristics. Heredity shaped environment which in turn guided heredity. "The democratic environment fairly burns the spirit of human brotherhood upon the growing child."[56] In that sentence, White summed up the impor-

52. *Ibid.*, pp. 200, 57, 65. In a letter dated July 6, 1927, to a fellow Kansas editor, White wrote: "I never cared for the recall and differed with Roosevelt about the recall of judicial decision." See Walter Johnson, *Selected Letters of William Allen White*, pp. 273–274.
53. White, *The Old Order Changeth*, p. 130.
54. *Ibid.*, pp. 252–253.
55. *Ibid.*, pp. 178–179, 252–253.
56. *Ibid.*

tance of heredity in the creation of democracy. Aryans were natural democrats—lovers of freedom, competition, and equality.

The passage of time and events did not destroy White's faith in the virtues of race and its deterministic effects. In 1925, he saw that individuals count for little in the march of events, for there was always the inevitability of destiny which guided the affairs of nations.[57] United States history was, accordingly, divided into three cycles, "a natural evolutionary consequence of environment and heredity." The latter factor helped explain the differences between Great Britain and the United States. At times, White saw spiritual forces at work in human history, despite his belief that many moral issues were really economic problems expressed in emotional language. Modern reform was necessary, White felt, to enable man to find the ultimate—his own soul.[58] Such spiritual considerations were also part of the progressive rhetoric and temperament.

In 1939, William A. White gave a series of public lectures for the Harvard Department of History on *The Changing West,* a good summary of his views on reform, human nature, and democracy. Like many progressives, White accepted the Turner thesis—that the frontier shaped American democracy. Abundant and free land created a free people—freer than they had ever been before the nineteenth century. Understandably, White accepted the agrarian myth. He argued in 1939 that in modern society it was necessary to restrain the egotistical forces of man's nature and thus aid his altruistic desires. A strong leader provided the solution, for most men were lazy—spiritually sluggish.[59] The changed economy called for new policies.

Although the future brought change, White still saw capitalism as a democratic means of expressing man's warring instincts, the yearnings being both altruistic and acquisitive. For, after all, it has always been that strong men were mean, the weak were lazy and envious, and the

57. White, *Some Cycles of Cathay,* pp. 9–10. According to White, Theodore Roosevelt's genius was "not in making sentiment, but in directing it into sane, conservative, workable laws." See White, *The Old Order Changeth,* p. 146.

58. White, *Some Cycles of Cathay,* pp. 31–32, 34, 64, 87–88.

59. White, *The Changing West, An Economic Theory about Our Golden Age,* pp. 6, 8, 133, 141.

PROGRESSIVISM   119

mediocre completely befuddled.⁶⁰ Reform was only possible within
the context of human nature.

A naturalistic orientation joined these three philosophers of progress
and reform. Sociologically, they represented a middle-class reaction
to industrial America. The next question is, how did eugenic ideas
affect practical politics, if they did? The answer may be supplied by
examining the thought and work of an especially influential political
figure of the time—Theodore Roosevelt.

*Theodore Roosevelt: The Conservative as
Progressive Politician*

Theodore Roosevelt (1858–1919) accepted some of the naturalistic
assumptions of eugenics. As a citizen and as a politician, he injected
his racial notions into the Square Deal and thereby increased eugenics' stature as a progressive reform. His version of naturalism
suggested a mythical frontier where man confronted raw nature. It
had no validity in a society wherein power fell into corporate units
and where the power was not dependent upon biological strength but
rather cultural might, expressed in economic institutions. J. P. Morgan,
for example, did not wrestle with his industrial foes for the control
of corporate power. Wall Street was not a state of nature.

Roosevelt's limitations as a political theorist were understandable.
As historians have discovered, the progressive movement contained
some unattractive features—racism and imperialism. There must be a
balance to any criticism, for the American progressives were good
men and their aspirations on the whole were admirable and their
achievements were considerable.

Recent historians—George E. Mowry and Richard Hofstadter—
have stressed the social-psychological implications in Rooseveltian
progressivism. The "status revolution" which greatly affected the
agrarian troubles of the 1890s had its urban counterpart among the
middle-class reformers after the turn of the century. Interestingly, this
status crisis occurred during the growth of scientific philanthropy and
the country-life movement. Native-born Protestants with an urban

60. *Ibid.*, pp. 39, 143.

upper-middle-class background provided progressive leadership. Despite the reform rhetoric of their politics, they were conservative followers of Theodore Roosevelt. As members of the old social order, they felt the threat of the vulgar new-rich from above and the pushy poor from below. Though their background was urban, progressive leaders had not suffered institutional restraint, therefore they resembled more the ethical outlook of agrarian America.[61] According to some progressives, then, the United States was filling up with strangers and false prophets.

Although Roosevelt provided leadership for middle-class progressives, he was a member of the "American aristocracy." People in Roosevelt's world took for granted wealth and security; mere money-making was never attractive. Coming from such an environment, Roosevelt, following his father's example, engaged in public service and philanthropic activities. Noblesse oblige provided a rationale for his assumption that college-trained and well-to-do young men should aid in the direction of public policy. The fortunate must in the nature of things help the unfortunate, just as the English-speaking people must provide world leadership. Roosevelt felt this obligation to poor individuals as well as to poor races. Like many eugenists, however, he distinguished between the "deserving" and "undeserving" poor. This attitude strengthened the progressive dependence on a strong man.[62]

It was not surprising to find the young Roosevelt defending the well-to-do from William J. Bryan's attacks in 1896. Roosevelt argued that society should treat a man according to what he could do, whether rich or poor. In fact, Bryan's attacks, Roosevelt concluded, were un-American.[63] American eugenists—such as Edward Thorndike—took

61. George C. Mowry, "The California Progressive and His Rationale: Study in Middle Class Politics," *Mississippi Valley Historical Review*, XXXVI (July 1949), 239–250. See also his *The Era of Theodore Roosevelt, 1900–1912*. Richard Hofstadter, *The Age of Reform*, passim. Alfred D. Chandler, Jr., "The Origin of Progressive Leadership," *The Letters of Theodore Roosevelt*, ed. Elting Morrison, VIII, 1465.

62. Howard K. Beale, *Theodore Roosevelt and the Rise of America to World Power*, pp. 5–6. Hereafter cited as Beale, *T. R. and the Rise of America to World Power*.

63. Theodore Roosevelt, "The Menace of the Demagogue," *The Works of Theodore Roosevelt*, National Edition, XIV, 287. Hereafter cited as *The Works of T. R.*

a similar point of view. Material well-being apparently indicated an outward manifestation of an innate superiority—biological or moral.

Theodore Roosevelt feared the class struggle. Time and time again, in speeches and in writings, he pressed for national unity against the greed of any class, rich or poor. Men of his class should guide enlightened public opinion and defend and advance the national interest of all. Like many earlier conservatives, Roosevelt rejected the validity of class legislation as counter to America's welfare. Individual selfishness must never dictate the nation's interest.[64] In his own way, Roosevelt's reform was respectable and conservative, always in the enlightened control of the middle class.

Roosevelt expressed this reform in naturalistic terms in a letter to Charles Davenport, the scientific leader of American eugenics. "Someday we will realize that the prime duty, the inescapable duty, of the *good* citizen of the right type is to leave his or her blood behind him in the world; and that we have no business to permit the perpetuation of citizens of the wrong type."[65] In creating the new nationalism, Roosevelt expressed concern with the biological and/or moral quality of the citizenry. Despite the press of other issues and the course of American politics and foreign policy, Theodore Roosevelt was a eugenist. Naturalism always loomed large in his thought.

Roosevelt adhered to the idea that the family was the basic, intrinsic organization for civilized society. Like conservatives of his generation, he used the family as the measure of a good society where sound minds and sound bodies existed. Family size was a vital factor in the realization of mental and physical health.

Large families were important, but Roosevelt also noted the vital differences between good and bad races as a matter of social efficiency. The very word was a constant rallying cry for conservation, for governmental administration and in fact for the entire conduct of American society. Social efficiency existed only if citizens subordinated their personal interests to community interests by breeding intel-

64. Letter from Roosevelt to Edward Ross, September 19, 1907, appearing as an introduction to Ross's *Sin and Society,* pp. ix–x.

65. Letter from Roosevelt to Charles B. Davenport, January 3, 1913, quoted in Haller, "American Eugenics," p. 170. This letter is not included in Morrison editions of Roosevelt's published letters.

ligently and by being able to fight well. For these qualities, Roosevelt used measurements based on the biological nature of man, and yet social efficiency was a matter of character—moral idealism. Consequently, Roosevelt's approach to life indicated his nineteenth-century world of naturalism and high moral purpose interwoven in man and society.

Theodore Roosevelt's concern with struggle and strife in human life suggested a Social Darwinian origin. He noted parallels between the animal and human worlds, but he used mostly homologies rather than analogies. Love of luxury was not the answer nor was overspecialization of human society. In the animal and human worlds both conditions were fatal to survival and future greatness. Despite the primacy of physical excellence, idealistic factors also contributed to America's material might. A high sense of duty and stern moral obligation were the first essentials for the success of democracy. Others among the many indispensable items were knowledge and control of self and, finally, national character.[66] Roosevelt certainly agreed that character was a moral condition.

Even in his most naturalistic moments of reflection, the Rough Rider was also a practical idealist. As Henry May has noted, Roosevelt always placed a moral value on everything. While being a realistic materialist, he never underplayed the role and function of ideals.[67] Roosevelt believed that biological facts created these ideals. The philosopher from Oyster Bay inevitably linked together national greatness and racial fitness. "A race must be strong and vigorous; it must be a race of good fighters and good breeders . . . no capacity for building up material prosperity can possibly atone for the lack of the great virile virtues." [68] Roosevelt stressed this basic theme throughout his entire public career: that character and intellect were both important, but if ever one had to supersede the other, character should always be the first choice.[69]

66. Roosevelt, "Biological Analogies in History," *Literary Essays of The Works of T. R.*, XII, 21, 33, 35, 44, 52.

67. Henry May, *The End of American Innocence*, pp. 17–18.

68. Roosevelt, "The Duties of American Citizenship," *The Works of T. R.*, XIII, 281.

69. Roosevelt, "Social Evolution," *ibid.*, pp. 240–241.

Although anarchy might reign in the animal world, Roosevelt was sure that mankind needed just law and order enforced to achieve civic progress.[70] In this attitude he was closer to Thomas Hobbes than John Locke, as is true of most American conservatives. Roosevelt accepted struggle in the world, but within the limits set by the superior groups or nations. The duty of the superior was that of providing order for the world's inferior elements. The same attitude was present in the conservative naturalist use of philanthropy and charity. Paternalism in self-defense against the rise of the ignorant, the incompetent, and the biologically inferior was evident throughout the conservative version of the American progressive creed.

In summary, Roosevelt's philosophy and political career were the results of several historic forces. Nationalism and naturalism were prime movers behind his policies in domestic and foreign politics. Quite aware of his own social position with its powers and obligations, he expressed concern about class-consciousness in American society. Like many progressives, he urged national unity and purpose; sociologically, his idea was to judge each man—white or black, rich or poor— on his individual merits. The philosophy had political appeal in a society concerned with status and equality of opportunity, but it made a poor sociological analysis of complex problems of industrial America.

Roosevelt and his band of progressives believed that nature exemplified the correct and moral way for human behavior. Thus the entire temper of his philosophy and politics constantly looked backward to a natural way, a given way of doing things. The American people for a variety of reasons twisted this order, and Roosevelt's task was one of instruction, of reshaping the given greatness and promise of America. The task was a dangerous one, however. Materialism was the prime danger. Corruption and lawless violence were major menaces to national security. The former weakened the upper classes' will to counter the economic desires of the poor expressed in the latter.[71] Economic security created comforts and crises. There was much discontent between the two economic groups—the have-not people who were causing unrest in the world and the haves who, because their

70. Roosevelt, "National Duties," *ibid.*, XII, 477.
71. Roosevelt, *The New Nationalism*, ed. William E. Leuchtenburg, p. 150.

very wealth caused immoral behavior, did not have the will to defend their condition. Rich or poor, mankind was born in the struggle for survival.

Yet, being a naturalist, Roosevelt realized that struggle and conflict were permanent aspects of the human condition. Struggle was necessary for progress, and the New York aristocrat believed that progress was good. Certain groups—for example, the English-speaking people —created a superior civilization by a steady devotion to known moral law, and only through sacrifice could this civilization endure and prosper. Roosevelt thought other races realized the same progress by observing the same moral laws or rules of conduct.[72]

Theodore Roosevelt's use of the term "race" was not a model of scientific preciseness. Many times he meant "nation" instead of "race" and mistook common cultural traits, such as language, social customs, and form of government, as indices of an innate and biological uniformity within a given population. Considering, however, that both scientists and laymen of his era were equally careless or vague, it was fitting that Roosevelt the politician perpetuated the semantic difficulty. The office-seeker must speak the voter's language.

In private and public life, Roosevelt consistently emphasized racistic implications for national security. Many times his optimism or pessimism over racial strength was directly related to world events. Thus in 1897, in a letter to Cecil Arthur Spring Rice, Roosevelt calmly wrote about racial decadence.[73] Two years later he found a dangerous development in the United States. He feared the worst racial and moral consequences from the diminishing birth rate of native-American stock, especially in the New England area.[74] The American eugenists echoed this sentiment. Appropriately, while President of the United States, he wrote a couple congratulating them for having twelve children.[75] Obviously national security, like charity, began at home.

72. Beale, *T. R. and the Rise of America to World Power*, pp. 72–73.

73. Letter from Roosevelt to Cecil Arthur Spring Rice, August 5, 1896, in *The Letters of Theodore Roosevelt*, XIII, 620–621. Hereafter cited as *The Letters of T. R.*

74. Letter from Roosevelt to Anna Roosevelt Cowles, December 17, 1899, *Ibid.*, II, 1112–1113; to Cecil Arthur Spring Rice, August 11, 1899, *ibid.*, p. 1053.

75. Letter from Roosevelt to Mr. and Mrs. R. T. Bowen, *ibid.*, III, 425.

Roosevelt and conservative naturalist-progressives sought the answer to the menace of the mass man, the epitome of the unfit, in a national birth-rate increase. The eugenists were more definite on exactly who should increase their numbers, while Roosevelt spoke in more general terms. He was a politician and the dysgenic did have the suffrage—a condition that many conservatives within and without the eugenics movement hated. Theodore Roosevelt wanted the misfits of society to stop having children. He realized the importance of negative eugenics—sterilization and segregation—but recognized the limitation of such programs. "I wish very much," the ex-President of the United States wrote in 1914, "that the wrong people could be prevented entirely from breeding; and when the evil nature of these people is sufficiently flagrant, this should be done. Criminals should be sterilized and feeble-minded persons forbidden to leave offspring behind them." Roosevelt recognized the limits of this method by stressing positive eugenic policy. "But as yet there is no way possible to devise which could prevent all undesirable people from breeding. The emphasis should be laid on getting desirable people to breed."[76]

Watching the decline in native stock, Roosevelt saw a moral rather than organic flaw in the American population. The high standard of living destroyed the native American's will to meet his patriotic duty of having a large family. Americans willfully limited their families for moral rather than physiological reasons.[77] He was eternally the moralizing naturalist.

Having a large family, according to Roosevelt, was not only in the national interest of good citizenship but it was a natural, an instinctual part of human nature. Large families were natural; society emulated nature. Nature was man's best guide in the matter of family size. The fundamental instincts were basic and at the same time the loftiest drives in human nature, Roosevelt continued, moving with verbal and intellectual ease from the biological to the moral aspects of the question. "The qualities that make men and women eager lovers, faithful, duty-performing, hard-working husbands and wives and devoted fathers and mothers stand at the foundation of all possible

---

76. Roosevelt, "Twisted Eugenics," *ibid., xll*, 201.
77. Roosevelt, "Race Decadence," *ibid.*, XII, 187.

social welfare, and also represent the loftiest heights of human happiness and usefulness." [78] In this way, Roosevelt shared with other conservatives in progressivism and eugenics the conviction that instincts furnished the psychological supports to civilization and human behavior.

Roosevelt was not hesitant about the number of children that decent people should produce. Any number under four was courting racial suicide; four were ideal. With traditional assurance, the Rough Rider pushed six children as the correct number for normal stock, since the mother's health was best, and infant mortality lowest, in families with that number.[79] The boldness of the suggestion matched only the naivete of discounting the many problems of a large family in an urban environment. In racial-biological matters, Roosevelt never drew fine distinctions and conclusions.

The birth rate, therefore, was the basis for national greatness and security in a world filled with inadequate races. Roosevelt was particularly hostile toward Margaret Sanger's birth-control crusade. It was the very poor whom birth control propaganda tried to influence, and yet, Roosevelt insisted, the well-to-do groups practiced birth control. He wanted not negative preaching of birth control to the lower classes but active encouragement of a high birth rate among the self-respecting American stock.[80] Birth control, therefore, was harmful because its greatest effect was on people who should have the most children.

Being a large-family man himself, Roosevelt preached the virtues constantly. Truly he favored motherhood. The working mother did not have his respect or admiration. The national moral was simple. Being a good mother was a woman's prime duty and economic value to the entire nation. Motherhood was of the highest worth to American society. Any other occupation was inferior.[81] Theodore Roosevelt gave patriotic sanction to the family—the basic social institution. For a

78. Roosevelt, "Birth Reform, from the Positive Not the Negative Side," *Ibid.*, XIX, 160–161.

79. Roosevelt, "Race Decadence," *ibid.*, XII, p. 111. Roosevelt, "Birth Reform, from the Positive Not the Negative Side," *ibid.*, XIX, 156, 158.

80. Roosevelt, *ibid.*, 152–166.

81. Roosevelt, "Women's Rights; And the Duties of Both Men and Women," *Ibid.*, XVI, 215.

conservative such as Roosevelt, who repeatedly related his reforms to a return to a given pattern found in nature, the condition of marriage in the United States was of national importance.

Noting marriage bonds weakening in the country, Roosevelt felt that evil days were ahead for the American nation. The declining birth rate, he argued, indicated marital decay and ultimate national crisis. The health of the State and the self-respect of men and women demanded a higher birth rate. For healthy normal folk to have childless marriages was a sin against nature and the state. The result would be national and racial death.

To help avert this disaster, President Roosevelt urged national legislation on marriage and divorce.[82] Although these matters were domains for the individual state legislatures, Roosevelt doubtlessly felt that a national problem called for congressional consideration. Progressives of the new liberal dispensation were not the only reformers desiring federal legislation to correct inadequacies in American life.

Like other eugenists, Roosevelt questioned the racial value of unlimited immigration. As President, he urged restrictive measures keeping out immigrants unsound in body, mind, and character. Roosevelt, like other advocators of immigration restriction, confused organic disabilities of immigrants with their ideological outlooks. Conservative naturalists blended the biological with the cultural in their criticism of American society. Roosevelt was no exception.[83]

Theodore Roosevelt's view of the Negro in American life was an interesting mixture of paternalism and progressive racism. He did not publicly subscribe to Negro inferiority, although he had interest in maintaining racial lines between the white and the black in American life. Once again, since the Negro had the vote and Roosevelt was a national politician, he was cautious in his public utterances. He did sustain the racism found in the America of the early twentieth century. In fact, like many white Americans of his day and later, Roosevelt forced race conscience on the Negro by writing that the ignorant and

---

82. Roosevelt, "Marriage and Divorce," *ibid.*, XV, 377–378.

83. Roosevelt, "Immigration," *ibid.*, XV, 320; "True Americanism," Ibid., XIII, 13–26.

vicious Negro was a greater enemy to his own people than to the country as a whole.[84]

Taking the traditional conservative argument that civil law cannot regulate social practices, Roosevelt was anxious to keep the Negro in his place, in a sociobiological sense. All men, he wrote, should be on an equal legal basis in regard to civil privileges; but thinking men of both races wanted race purity.[85] Apparently, freedom of mate selection was the concern of social practices, not a legal right.

As leader of the Bull Moose party, Roosevelt expressed a paternalistic interest in restoring voting privileges to *deserving* Negroes under white political leadership. "Therefore it is merely the part of wisdom to try our plan which is to try for the gradual re-enfranchisement of the worthy colored man of the South by frankly giving the leadership of our movement to the wisest and justest white men of the South." [86] Roosevelt's progressivism was for whites only. The leadership of the Bull Moose was lily white and upper middle class. The racial policy was present in much of the progressive cause. Thus not just any Negro citizen would vote—only the worthy ones. Even the militant and open racist would accept that "reform" if it was open to individual interpretation. Roosevelt's stand on the Negro question was an intrigue in duplicity; he used reform vocabulary to insure the status quo caste system. The white man was the natural leader in the nation and the world.

Just as Roosevelt shared the anti-Negro sentiment of American eugenists, he gloried with them in the innate virtues of rural living. The American eugenists were active in the glorification of rural life. Roosevelt likewise always took time to express admiration for the countryside. As developed later, this admiration was part of the conservation crusade. Farm folk were the best. Roosevelt saw American civilization in the balance between rural and urban populations. The development of country life was vital. It provided not only the food and fiber but healthy biological material for urban America to withstand the pressures of modern life. This sentiment echoed throughout the conservative progressive movement among eugenists and non-

84. Roosevelt, "The Negro Problem," *ibid.*, XVI, 346.
85. Roosevelt, *ibid.*, p. 348.
86. Roosevelt, "The Progressive and the Colored Man," *ibid.*, XVII, 303.

eugenists. Roosevelt and his band of followers viewed the farmer as the cornerstone of American civilization.[87]

On occasion, Roosevelt related his agrarianism to a fear of the city, particularly of a city of foreign born. The rise of the city and the corresponding decline in rural population filled him with concern about the future. The farm was the nation's foundation and it must be strong, he warned, or the superstructure of urbanism would crash.[88]

Likewise, Roosevelt saw the Anglo-Saxon race performing a similar task in world affairs. Man's innate conflict dictated a policy of expansion for Anglo-Saxon people. They had created a mighty society; modern man must preserve and extend it by force if necessary, since the Anglo-Saxon civilization was the world's highest possible good. Theodore Roosevelt urged expansive American foreign policy. Seeing history as the English-speaking people bringing a higher civilization to the world, he knew that the United States was only doing its bit in a cosmic plan.

Unlike many eugenists, such as David Starr Jordan, Roosevelt saw great merit to the martial struggle for national greatness. "Eugenics is an excellent thing," Roosevelt wrote, but the individual must always be willing to risk his life for a good cause. The United States must, according to him, take charge in world events, particularly in Latin America and the Far East.

Because of human nature, injustices resulted, but Roosevelt was confident that expansion was correct and just; it was, from his point of view, stronger races protecting weaker nations. Thus American rule of the Filipino people and the English rule of India were two of the greatest historical processes in the last two hundred years.[90] It was a case of progressive paternalism in a global context. The en-

---

87. Roosevelt's foreword to the Report of the Country Life Commission (February 9, 1909) 60th Congress, 2nd Session, Senate Document No. 705, p. 9. Roosevelt, "The Farmer: The Corner-Stone of Civilization," *The Works of T. R.,* XIX, 116–117.

88. Roosevelt, *"The Woman and Her House," ibid.,* XVI, 164.

89. Roosevelt, "Twisted Eugenics," *ibid.,* XII, 199–200. Beale, *T. R. and the Rise of America to World Power,* pp. 26–33.

90. Roosevelt, "The Expansion of the White Rarce," *The Works of T. R.,* XVI, 258–269.

lightened white middle-class reformer governed the United States which in turn guided world events.

As Howard K. Beale has noted, later events proved the vainness of this progressive racial policy. Technology and colonial nationalism— two factors Roosevelt and his generation underestimated—have damaged confidence in racial solution to problems of "backward" areas of the world.[91]

In conclusion, then, Roosevelt, in matters of foreign or domestic policy, expressed alarm over the racial aspects of American life. The individual, because of his racial heritage, set the limits of a successful nation in world affairs and domestic reform. In a corresponding manner, the racial origin of the child largely determined the future course of American civilization, according to Theodore Roosevelt.

The naturalists, including Roosevelt, were interested in the child, for he represented the future, and his biological quality was of utmost importance in a future greatness for the nation. A strong child would help make a strong country. As noted, Roosevelt liked children: he urged large families to insure America's place among nations. A strong body and education were equally important, for the nation must instruct the young in the ways of life and the world.

In this way, educational theory was crucial in conservative naturalism. For, if heredity was a determining factor in the individual and the state, how was education, an environmental process, able to create a population worthy of its national and racial destiny? G. Stanley Hall and E. L. Thorndike, two eugenists in educational psychology, offered a progressive answer to this next problem. Ironically, these men, leaders in the radicalism known as progressive education, were firmly Galtonian conservatives. Like Theodore Roosevelt, their apparent reform was but an attempt to keep American society in the hands of the naturally superior classes. And—like Roosevelt and eugenists—their program generally urged a more effective social control under elitist leadership rather than under genuine democratic reform. The child, under proper eugenic and educational guidance, created the new race, the new nation.

91. Beale, *T. R. and the Rise of America to World Power*, pp. 458–459, 251.

8

PSYCHOLOGY

The Child and the Race

AMERICAN EUGENISTS, like English romantic poets, believed that the child was the father of the man. Given their basic hereditary bias, the conclusion was inevitable. As pointed out earlier, eugenists also used environmental techniques in the creation of a new man who, in many ways, was a specimen of preurban society. These ideas always appeared in progressive speculations on education and child welfare. The Mendelian theory of inheritance discouraged many social scientists. It appeared that epilepsy and mental illness were organically related and inheritable from even one "tainted" parent.[1]

Sir Francis Galton sought to examine hereditary data by using statistical methods in education. He saw this as a possible solution for educational psychology and a general reconstruction of society along scientific and naturalistic principles. His influence was limitless. Educators today use the correlation techniques which he perfected. In

1. For example, see David F. Weeks, M.D., "The Heredity of Epilepsy Analyzed by the Mendelian Method," *Proceedings of the American Philosophical Society,* LI (April 19, 1912), 178–190.

addition, Sir Francis advocated physical and psychological examinations, including anthropometrics, as a cumulative record for the student's file.[2] With some modifications, schools in the United States today practice this method.

Other concepts of nineteenth-century naturalism have not succeeded so well. The recapitulation theory, for example, no longer attracts academic attention. The popularity of recapitulation came from the rapid changes in scientific thought of the nineteenth century. Thomas Huxley (1825–1895), Charles Darwin's leading disciple, taught that the development of the brain followed the evolutionary history of the race. Darwin cautiously endorsed the theory, but the Darwinists quickly used the concept for the development of the embryo. The embryo—of any animal, including man—passed through the adult stages of its evolutionary ancestors.[3]

The American scientists, taking the recapitulation theory from embryology, used it to support the philosophic and historic notion that the child's development—mental and social—passed through the main stages through which the race had passed. According to this theory, the scientist, by studying the individual child's development, could also study racial mental development. By 1912 child psychology was a special area of investigation. With emphasis on the behavior, the growth, and development of the child, psychological clinics appeared.[4]

Two of the leaders of American educational psychology, G. Stanley Hall and Edward L. Thorndike, drew on nineteenth-century naturalism which contained the recapitulation theory and the statistical method of analyzing educational problems. Both men matured intellectually during the nineteenth century and subsequently they contributed greatly to the educational reforms of progressive America,

2. Helen M. Walker, *Studies in the History of Statistical Method,* pp. 45–46; Paul J. Fitz Patrick, "Leading American Statisticians in the Nineteenth Century," *Journal of the American Statistical Association,* LII (September 1957), 301–319.

3. C. Judson Herrick, "Error in Neurophysiology," *The Story of Human Error,* p. 257. A. E. E. McKenzie, *The Major Achievements of Science,* I, 212–213.

4. Fay B. Karpf, *American Social Psychology, Its Origin, Development, and European Background,* pp. 271–272, hereafter cited as Karpf, *American Social Psychology;* Gardiner Murphy, *Historical Introduction to Modern Psychology,* revised edition, pp. 392–393.

for naturalism provided the rationale for such changes in pedagogic techniques.

Granville Stanley Hall (1846–1924) was a pioneer in child psychology and related educational problems. Born and reared in a rural New England area where the Puritan ethic dominated the intellectual landscape, Hall early considered himself a rebel and a radical in educational matters. Degrees from Williams and a Ph. D. in psychology from Harvard combined with study and travel in Europe gave Hall a wider view of psychological problems than many of the psychologist-theologians of an earlier generation. Hall taught at Antioch, Williams, Harvard, and Johns Hopkins. He also served as first president of Clark University and invited Sigmund Freud to lecture for the first time in the United States. A productive scholar, Hall founded several psychological journals.[5]

Among his academic activities, Hall established the first department of anthropology in the United States in connection with his emphasis on the physical basis of much human behavior. His anthropology utilized the recapitulation theory. At the same time, many anthropologists and eugenists accepted the scientific validity of the recapitulation theory.[6] Among psychologists, in addition to Hall, James Mark Baldwin used recapitulation in lending naturalistic support to his investigations.[7]

G. Stanley Hall was not optimistic about the future, despite the apparent reassurance of the recapitulation concept. Like many naturalists of his generation, he expressed concern about racial decline. Eugenics—conservative naturalism—was the remedy. His eugenic solution covered the standard demands for sterilization and segregation

5. *Who Was Who in America*, p. 453. Early intellectual influences on Hall were Cometian positivism, Hegelianism of William T. Harris and Stephen Pearl Andrews, an early sex crusader and pioneer in birth control. G. Stanley Hall, *Life and Confessions of a Psychologist*, pp. 179, 200, 362. Hereafter cited as Hall, *Life and Confessions*.

6. Karpf, *American Social Psychology*, p. 267; Thomas K. Penniman, *A Hundred Years of Anthropology*, second edition, revised, p. 231; Harvey E. Jordan, "Eugenics: Its Data, Scope and Promise, as Seen by the Anatomist," *Eugenics: Twelve University Lectures*, p. 120.

7. Karpf, *American Social Psychology*, pp. 274–275. Baldwin's major work was *Mental Development in the Child and the Race*.

enforced with scientific charity allowing the innately superior individuals to control society. In other worlds, Hall wanted natural selection restored to its natural and prime importance in the affairs of society. This restoration was imperative in America's attitudes toward primitive races.[8]

Hall believed that nature was right and society's task was emulation of a natural process, such as survival of the fittest and natural selection. Only the individual's efforts and eugenics provided the means of improving society. The improvement was necessarily slow, since recapitulation denied the validity of catastrophic leaps in evolution.[9] Human nature set limits on improvement of society; and, dialectically, society hampered the natural processes of the evolutionary and organic world.

Eight factors, Hall maintained, developed human character, and man's biological-psychological nature controlled them.[10] By utilizing these eight concepts, eugenics could improve the physical and moral nature of individuals in society and thus save civilization from racial decay. Hall tempered his hereditary determinism with the traditional American optimism in education as a method of social salvation and reconstruction. Like many progressive educationists, he wanted sound minds in sound bodies. However, heredity provided the ultimate factor in the allocation of natural superiority.[11] Even in his acceptance of hereditary determinism, Hall saw merit in environmental forces in the improvement of the child and, subsequently, the race. "The influence of the environment at this very formative and plastic age of rapid brain change must have been great, and I cannot but believe

8. Merle Curti, *The Social Ideas of American Educators with a New Chapter on the Last Twenty-five Years,* pp. 405–406; hereafter cited as Curti, *The Social Ideas of American Educators;* G. Stanley Hall, "The Point of View toward Primitive Races," *The Journal of Race Development,* I (July 1910), 11.

9. Curti, *Social Ideas of American Educators,* pp. 404–405.

10. The eight factors were: (1) health, (2) second breath, (3) free mobilization up and down the pleasure-pain scale, (4) sympathy, (5) love of nature, (6) sublimation, (7) activity v. passivity, and (8) loyalty or fidelity. Hall, *Life and Confessions,* pp. 451–472.

11. *Ibid.,* pp. 472, 533, 537. Curti, *Social Ideas of American Educators,* pp. 412, 424.

that my psychic organization would have been quite different had I passed this period of my life upon a prairie." [12]

Hall constantly used his own childhood as an illustration of the recapitulation theory—the essence of his educational speculations. He believed the child and the race were one. Realizing some biological limitations of the theory, Hall stressed its merits for psychological investigations. Since the child repeated racial history in his development, he saw great importance in the speed with which the child repeated the racial experiences. Hall insisted that effective school shortened the child's racial history. Maybe some stages might be eliminated with no harm to the child or to society.[13]

Because of missing links and extinct ethnic types, modern man could never know the complete racial history, concluded G. Stanley Hall. Therefore, he continued, much speculation must deal only with the hereditary ability of the child.[14] Hall's view of this problem suggested the great chain of being theory, with many links forever lost to light of scientific verification.

Hall's intellectual kinship with the great chain of being was obvious in his attitudes toward the races of the world. Since heredity outweighed school and civilization, the duty of the superior white races was to set good moral and ethical standards for the primitive races who, by their very nature, were imitative. As Hall viewed the situation, the white man's burden was one of instruction by example.[15]

Fertility was the key to race relations and the destiny of civilization. As population grew, the racial problems increased, augmented by the evolutionary changes within a given race to a potentially higher form of biological existence. For example, Hall felt that structural changes in the brain created a new type of man in the evolution of life and nature. Rejecting the lower races as links to the animal or nonhuman world, Hall noted merits in the lower races as potential

12. A quotation from Hall in Lorine Pruette, *G. Stanley Hall, A Biography of a Mind,* p. 19. Hereafter cited as Pruette, *G. Stanley Hall.*

13. Hall, *Educational Problems,* two volumes, I, viii. Hereafter cited as Hall, *Educational Problems.* See also his *Adolescence, Its Psychology and Its Relation to Physiology, Anthropology, Sociology, Sex, Crime, Religion, and Education,* two volumes, I, viii. Hereafter cited as Hall, *Adolescence.*

14. *Ibid.,* I, vii.

15. *Ibid.,* II, 650, 717, 722.

carriers and creators of greater future civilizations. In his psychological studies, Hall never fully developed this optimistic trust in the lower races as noble savages because of his major insistence on heredity.[16]

The logical end of Hall's psychology was eugenics. His conservative naturalism combined with scientism and racial mysticism pointed toward eugenics. Like other eugenists, he feared the slums of modern cities that "abound in people really lower and often far more degraded than those we call savages." [17] Cities, by their very being, encouraged man's baser instincts, while the country successfully instructed the youth in the ways of human nature. Genetic psychology—Hall's label for recapitulation—incorporated the concepts of herd instinct and the collective soul which bloomed more successfully in a rural context.[18] The countryside, therefore, created the natural and true place for the realization of Hall's psychological theories and eugenics.

Hall gave great pedagogic value to rural life for raising the intelligence of young children. In this way, he supported eugenists' chronic antiurban bias by his acceptance of the inheritance of acquired characteristics doctrine. The city was unnatural: the urban child never realized his true character since the city disrupted the natural (rural) forces. In fact, Hall hinted that such a situation was un-American, for the founders of the Constitution stressed the benefits of rural life in educational matters.[19]

Rising to great philosophical heights, Hall believed that the American race would endure if the small town and rural America endured. The countryside was the birthplace, Hall emphasized, of the great middle class which, by its industry and foresight, gave America her greatness by virtues of "patriotism, conservatism, and independence. The farm was a great laboratory, tending perhaps rather more to develop scientific than literary tastes, cultivating persistency, in which

16. *Ibid.*, II, 718, 748.

17. *Ibid.*, p. 720.

18. Hall, *Life and Confessions*, pp. 145, 369, 414, 441, 442–443. Hall believed that Jung had better insight into man's true nature than did Freud because of Jung's concept of the collective unconscious. See Pruette, *G. Stanley Hall*, pp. 4–5, who quotes Hall on this matter.

19. Hall, "The Content of Children's Minds on Entering School," *Aspects of Child Life and Education*, p. 25. Hall, "Boy's Life in a Massachusetts Country Town Forty Years Ago," *Ibid.*, pp. 300–301.

country boys excel, if at the expense of versatility." [20] The country was nature and the child was a creature of nature.

The child was a savage in many ways, with an instinctual love of hunting and fishing along with other outdoor activities. The question for modern society was, therefore, how to direct these instincts for the greater benefit of the child, the race, and society.[21] Typical responses to this question in progressive United States were the public playground and national park movements.

Other basic assumptions of Hall's thesis supported the larger conservative progressive mentality. For example, he believed that the individual had a deep desire to revive ancestral experiences of the race; at least in a vicarious manner, tales of heroic exploits and virtues fulfilled this desire.[22] The progressive theme of the great man leading America no doubt filled this racial requirement. Perhaps Theodore Roosevelt's boyish ways allowed vicarious exercise in recapitulation for the American middle-class reformers.

Hall sounded a cautious note, though. The maturing process for the child was a difficult endeavor. Heredity alone seemed inadequate at times to help the child realize complete maturity "so that every step of the upward way is strewn with wreckage of body, mind, and morals." Eugenics provided the answer while racial realities provided the basis for education. "Modern life," Hall noted, "is hard, and in many respects increasingly so, on youth." [23] At the heart of the matter, conflict existed within the very nature of the individual and particularly the young person.

The young person had radical and conservative instincts, according to Hall. These instincts formed the attitudes and behavior of the young man. At best, the condition developed a delicate balance. The wrong environment could destroy this equilibrium, and the boy would become an extremist, subscribing to simple dogma in order to explain complex social and natural realities.[24] Despite Hall's reliance on naturalistic terminology, biology based on the inheritance of acquired

20. *Ibid.*, pp. 319–320.
21. Hall, *Adolescence*, I, x.
22. *Ibid.*, I, xi.
23. *Ibid.*, p. xiv.
24. *Ibid.*, II, 87.

character and instinct psychology, his analysis or interpretation was still the Puritan Ethic. G. Stanley Hall was forever representative of the New England conscience in an age of naturalism.

War expressed the dialectics of mankind's "good" and "bad" instincts. Eugenically, war was bad and yet war was a basic instinct, because hunger, sex, and power motivated men toward organized violence.[25] Murder existed as a deep desire within the human psyche. Man was his own potential murderer. Eugenics and education turned him from his evil ways by accenting the positive instincts of cooperation and the social side of man's nature. Like Galton, therefore, Hall believed that mystic forces existed behind the naturalistic importance of eugenics.

In keeping with Sir Francis Galton and American eugenists, Hall distrusted democracy, particularly direct democracy by which representatives merely reflected the voters' wishes. In this attitude, he joined the school of thought of E. L. Godkin and conservative progressives, such as Herbert Croly, William Allen White, and Theodore Roosevelt. This intellectual kinship turned on the philosophical problem of control in human affairs. Like other historic conservatives, Hall always returned to some form of control for the individual and society. He, as did the other individuals in the eugenics movement and conservative progressivism, discarded eighteenth-century rationalism, historically the source of American democratic ideals and aspirations. Apparently, they felt that the individual and society needed some manner of control to insure the racial security and happiness in the future by the return to natural selection. The average man was inadequate, and all systems of thought (such as democracy) predicated on him were doomed to failure because they ignored racial realities. So argued G. Stanley Hall and a chorus of eugenists.[26]

Edward Lee Thorndike (1874–1949) was in that chorus. Trained at Wesleyan University and Harvard, Thorndike received the Ph.D. in psychology at Columbia in 1898. He later received a number of honorary degrees. During a long and active teaching and writing career, Thorndike taught at Western Reserve University and Colum-

25. Hall, "Psychological Notes on the War," *The Journal of Race Development*, VI (April 1916), 357–369.
26. Hall, *Life and Confessions*, p. 440. Pruette, *G. Stanley Hall*, p. 44.

bia. At the latter institution he served as a professor of genetic psychology. His membership in academic and scientific societies ranged from the Galton Society to the American Association for the Advancement of Science, serving as president in 1934. During his lifetime, Thorndike created a sizable bibliography, particularly in educational psychology.[27]

Thorndike, like G. Stanley Hall, represented conservative naturalism in American educational psychology. Heredity provided the bedrock of his philosophical system. On this foundation he developed a scientific structure coupled with an observation platform of eugenics. Naturally, science was the principal building material. In fact, Thorndike was hopeful that history, utilizing concepts of heredity, would become a natural science. Original nature—heredity—limited an individual's aspirations for equality of opportunity. According to Thorndike, mere environmental reforms could not correct the innate inequality that existed among any group of individuals. In education, therefore, heredity had the edge.[28]

Although Thorndike questioned the scientific and educational validity of the recapitulation theory, he and G. Stanley Hall held membership in the same ideological tradition. Both men were genetic psychologists with a hereditary-eugenic orientation to their investigations. Like Hall, Thorndike rejected modern social reform and philanthropy because of its misguided humanitarianism encouraging the increase of the unfit and inferior. He preferred having naturalistic science direct charity.[29] Thorndike and Hall shared with the other individuals discussed within these pages the predilections of conservative naturalism—the essence of American eugenic thought.

Thorndike saw the future of religion as the concern over the bio-

27. *Who Was Who in America*, II, 532.

28. Thorndike, Review of Frederick A. Woods, *Mental and Moral Heredity in Royalty*, (New York: Henry Holt, 1906) in *Science*, n.s. XXIII (May 4, 1906, 693–694. Thorndike, "Eugenics: With Special Reference to Intellect and Character," *Eugenics: Twelve University Lectures*, pp. 323–325. Hereafter cited as Thorndike, "Eugenics: With Special Reference to Intellect and Character." Thorndike, *The Psychology of Arithmetic*, p. 294. Hereafter cited as Thorndike, *The Psychology of Arithmetic*.

29. *Ibid.*, pp. 198–199; Thorndike, *Educational Psychology*, pp. 101, 116. Curti, *Social Ideas of American Educators*, p. 480.

logical quality and the destiny of mankind. Ethics, derived from this concern, anticipated the future by the curtailment of the racially inadequate. In this manner he combined religion and science into a system based on biological realities. The future of the race was all-important for Thorndike, since the very success of civilization depended upon it. Like organisms in nature, nations compete and, in the struggle for survival among nations, the biological quality of the American population spelled success or failure.[30] Thorndike's naturalism translated into popular thought as chauvinism. Good inheritance was good patriotism. Racial and national improvement were one.

In his writings, Thorndike never wandered far from his acceptance of hereditary determinism. Accepting wide variations in a given race, he wrote, "the great majority cluster somewhat closely around the 'average man.'" This average was Thorndike's utilization of Sir Francis Galton's concept of the central type. In the same Galtonian type of analysis, the genetic psychologist noted, "Intellectual and moral individuality seems to be determined to a very large extent in the genes." Thus, each individual created his own environment by acquiring certain features of any over-all or cultural environment.[31] Thorndike quite openly expressed his intellectual admiration of Sir Francis Galton's major work, *Hereditary Genius*.[32] Like the founder of modern eugenics, Thorndike conceived a race or ancestry as a process to "reduce the variability of the offspring and determine the point about which they do vary."[33] In any problem dealing with heredity or environment, Thorndike always gave greater support to the former.[34]

Thorndike criticized American educational leaders for ignoring heredity; and it hampered the main function of education—the

30. Thorndike, "Eugenics: With Special Reference to Intellect and Character," pp. 341–342. Thorndike, "The Decrease in Size of American Families," *Popular Science Monthly*, LXIII (May 1903), 64–70.

31. Thorndike, *Individuality*, pp. 13, 39, 48–49. Hereafter cited as Thorndike, *Individuality*.

32. Thorndike, *Mental Work and Fatigue and Individual Differences and Their Causes*, pp. 221, 227, 237. Hereafter cited as Thorndike, *Mental Work and Fatigue*. See also his *Educational Psychology*, pp. 50–51, 255, 286.

33. Thorndike, *Mental Work and Fatigue*, p. 226.

34. *Ibid.*, pp. 207, 284 and his *Educational Psychology*, p. 55.

labeling of individual differences. At the same time, the lack of hereditary emphasis in school damaged the cause of eugenics. "We educate," he wrote, "the original nature of the race only by fostering its good elements and encouraging their fertility and by debarring the worse elements from reproduction or by eliminating them outright."[35]

Like eugenists in England and the United States, Thorndike based his abstractions on naturalism. Nature gave the best guide to the conduct of society; and yet, certain features of nature repulsed the Columbia educator. Fighting was natural to mankind. "The fighting instinct is in fact the cause of a very large amount of the world's intellectual endeavor," he wrote; however, like other eugenists, he rejected the battlefield as being dysgenic for racial America.[36] His social philosophy was not laissez faire, but selective social control based on the manipulation of the survival of the fittest.

E. L. Thorndike accepted instinct psychology, but always within a context of social control and toward a eugenic goal. He was the naturalist. Advocating that the teacher work with and not against instincts whenever possible, he defended the utilitarian ethic of the greatest good for the greatest number on grounds of a higher value found in eugenics. He separated Jeremy Bentham's creed (1748– 1832) from any consideration of natural rights and based it on socio-biological premises. The solution to the problem of educational techniques, according to Thorndike, was for the teacher to use "disuse, substitution, punishment" in dealing with students.[37]

"Interests are biological facts. They act," he continued, "in accordance with biological laws. We can learn how they act only by observation and experiment."[38] And since heredity was a biological law, it was necessary to defend the elite and well-to-do in society from the abuses of the biologically inferior, since the latter elements outbred the former group of people. Thorndike reminded his readers that "Boys

---

35. *Ibid.*, pp. 2, 65.

36. *Ibid.*, pp. 96, 119.

37. Thorndike, *The Principles of Teaching Based on Psychology*, p. 21, 55, 60, 83. Hereafter cited as Thorndike, *The Principles of Teaching*.

38. Thorndike, *et al.*, *Adult Interests*, p. 69. Hereafter cited as Thorndike, *Adult Interests*.

and girls should not be denied education because they are well-dressed, popular, and destined to have their way in the world." Apparently cultural superiority of individuals was a direct result of biological advantages. For this reason the natural-rights philosophy was erroneous, according to Thorndike. If a man had the mind of a pig, then society should treat him as one, and thus allocate opportunities for improvements based on innate differences of individuals.[39] Once again, society must emulate nature.

Failure in both realms of existence in society and nature was the same—extinction.[40] Eugenics, of course, always worked within the natural inequalities of men. Against twentieth-century social amelioration, Galtonian eugenists provided a conservative reaction. Eugenists, such as Thorndike and Hall, gave support to the old order despite their forward use of language and science.

Just as Marx saw the class struggle in history, eugenists like Thorndike glorified the Darwinian struggle for existence in the course of human experience. "In the actual race of life," Thorndike wrote, "which is not to get ahead, but to get ahead of somebody, the chief determining factor is heredity." [41] In one sentence, he provided a cosmic rationale for the "pecking order" in American life and for eugenic reforms. It was the touchstone for all eugenic thought.

Education was central to human improvement with naturalistic limitations. Thorndike thought the child's immorality a product of immoral ancestry, since heredity was the major cause in human behavior. Although original nature was the root of all human activities, he did not despair. Educational manipulation of instinct—particularly the herd or social instinct—prevented the growth of the biological and moral inferior. E. L. Thorndike accepted William McDougall's concepts of the instincts of submission and mastery which had value for the reconstruction of eugenic society. He definitely rejected the rationalistic notion that man's mind was a tabula rasa.[42] As a tough-minded naturalistic educator, Thorndike discounted the values of John Locke's optimism.

39. *Ibid.*, pp. 111, 115.
40. Thorndike, *Mental Work and Fatigue*, pp. 308–309.
41. *Ibid.*, p. 312 and his *Educational Psychology*, p. 399.
42. *Ibid.*, pp. 3, 27, 33, 157, 351, 370.

Morals—the end result of education—therefore expressed instincts, not the a priori considerations of a democratic society. Moral training, accordingly, was training in the use of certain (socially good) instincts. The educational processes were not entirely matters of orthodoxy, such as reading and writing. Sounding a progressive note, Thorndike advocated training for the whole human personality. In sum, education was life—a sentiment which in early twentieth-century America gained supporters. For example, he did not want the student free of economic problems, for they provided sound objective lessons for student maturity. "To sweep the pupil's life of all economic pressures and responsibility invites undesirable habits and attitudes," he warned. Education must be practical. Therefore, productive labor and schooling were good, since the child learned the economic values of society by direct experience, not through a book of theory.[43] In this manner the moral and ethical values of American capitalism grew in the soil of Thorndike's progressive and educational naturalism. Within the new expressions of values the old ideas endured.

The dangers were many, however. "Moral conduct is difficult to develop, in comparison with knowledge and most motor acts precisely because it often involves acts that conflict with strong instinctive cravings." [44] The child must have moral discipline, despite his ancestral limitations, in order to protect collective racial welfare. Discipline and social manipulation and control offered the best hope for mankind.

The public expenditures on the biologically inadequate individuals were too great, and not enough money was for the exceptional child— the seed of future greatness. The elite students' interests advanced the greatest good for the greatest number—the objective of democratic education.[45] In his way, Thorndike anticipated an attitude to appear later in the educational controversies of post–World War II United States.

For lasting improvement of American society, Thorndike turned to eugenics. By teaching that only the biologically superior had the

43. E. L. Thorndike and Arthur I. Gates, *Elementary Principles of Education,* pp. 203, 207–208.
44. *Ibid.,* p. 145.
45. *Ibid.,* p. 228.

right to reproduce, while reducing the number of the inferior, a real (racial) advance was possible. People must realize the prime importance of this issue, he felt, for no question so deeply affected the welfare of mankind.[46] The child, the race, the nation were one.

G. Stanley Hall and E. L. Thorndike were in the same school of educational thought. The men's differences were minor. They were not exceptions in the development and history of American naturalism. In many other academic and political developments, as well as in educational psychology, the creed of eugenics flourished. No doubt, as professors at Columbia, the men gave intellectual guidance to several generations of students.

Philosophically, they were materialists. They were very close to the Marxist premise of materialism in human affairs. They, of course, were not followers of Marx, but rather of Francis Galton, the genteel Victorian naturalist and philosophical materialist. Instinct psychology or genetic psychology was a Darwinian branch of materialist thought. Since, as Thorndike believed, "a good digestion is the mother of cheerfulness and peace," [47] it was imperative to understand the cultural implications of the instinct of hunger. Heredity and instincts created the deterministic mechanism in man. Thus, William McDougall, a psychologist and eugenist, turned to instinct psychology in preparation for a world created in light of eugenic principles.

Natural Man in an Unnatural World

William McDougall (1871–1938) grounded his psychology in the naturalism of the nineteenth century, and therefore his thought represented the latest development in the history of American psychology. For in the United States psychology evolved from theological and rationalistic speculations to a naturalistic science with a corresponding decline in supernatural values. Ethically, the science lost its moralistic orientation in the transition to mind-body discipline. Historically, as a result of nineteenth-century biology and twentieth-century statistics, psychology joined the ranks of behavioristic investigations. A constant

46. *Ibid.*, p. 281.
47. Thorndike, *The Principles of Teaching*, p. 14.

assumption was the fundamental concept of the unity of mind and body, of the mental and the physical. The historic forces of political democracy and mass education shaped psychology into the various schools of thought: experimental, individual, and others. The problems society faced in adjusting to the new technological environment caused an increased public interest in psychology. Like other intellectual thinkers, modern psychologists wanted a scientific field of inquiry. In Germany and in the United States the people highly admired science in general and, therefore, rapidly accepted psychology as the science of mind-and-body relationships.[48]

During the nineteenth century, "armchair" psychology was fashionable. Coupled with philosophy or theology, psychology was ill-defined or considered not worthy of specialized research. However, the Darwinian revolution in social thought changed this situation.

The impact of biological thought on the development of psychology was considerable. Particularly, the theory of the inheritance of acquired characteristics offered a legitimate solution to the twin mysteries of instinct and learning. William McDougall thought rats biologically transmitted the ability to travel mazes.[49] It was significant that at one time he was a eugenist and a leader of the instinct school of psychology.

Borrowing biological methods and concepts, students of human behavior utilized mathematical and experimental methodology in the behalf that psychology was related to the other biological sciences. To many investigators, Darwin's theories held great promise of providing a complete explanation of human behavior. Although Darwin differed at several points with such speculations, nineteenth-century scientists overlooked the distinctions in the rush to place psychology on a biological premise. The organism's function became the hallmark of the new science. Scientists took renewed interest in the history and environment of an organism—man or animal—for, after the concept of Darwinian evolution, such an approach could not be ignored. In fact, one historian claimed that during the last twenty-five years of the

48. Jay Wharton Fay, *American Psychology before William James*, p. 5; Murphy, *Historical Introduction to Modern Psychology*, pp. 3–4, 430.
  49. Hardin, *Nature and Man's Fate*, pp. 214–215.

nineteenth century, Darwinism was the greatest single force in the creation of contemporary psychology.[50]

By 1886 the emphasis in psychology had changed from a study of the soul to a study of the mind. The consciousness of the organism became the new area for the scientist. Modern psychologists rejected the soul as a valid explanation of psychic phenomena.[51] Combined with the traditional American interest in the individual, Darwinian psychologists stressed individual differences within the evolutionary process. In an age of great social and individual mobility and change, the emphasis was on the shirtsleeve democracy of money-making and survival in the growing industrial jungle.[52] The nineteenth-century psychology provided a cosmic rationale to the evolving capitalist order.

Academic adjustments matched social change, for by the end of the century psychology had become separate from philosophy. Matching the other realms of reform in the decade of the nineties, psychological activity increased with the rapid growth of laboratories, journals, and international congresses. Psychologists investigated the child, the insane, and animals, while developing new methods. By definition the science dealt with consciousness, but in reality psychologists studied man's behavior. In keeping with the characteristics of scientific subjects, psychological laboratories rapidly appeared in the United States between 1875 and 1900. By the latter date, forty-seven psychological laboratories existed in the world, twenty-five of them in the United States.[53]

Wilhelm Wundt (1832–1921) provided leadership in the growth of these laboratories. A German psychologist, Wundt trained young Americans in experimental methodology. Two of his students, G. Stanley Hall and James McKeen Cattell (1860–1944), established the first and second laboratories, respectively, in the United States. The first

50. Murphy, *Historical Introduction to Modern Psychology*, pp. 8, 108–109. Karpf, *American Social Psychology*, p. 148. Edwin G. Boring, *A History of Experimental Psychology*, second edition, pp. 470–471. Hereafter cited as Boring, *A History of Experimental Psychology*.

51. Fay, *American Psychology before William James*, pp. 166–167.

52. Boring, *A History of Experimental Psychology*, pp. 532, 507.

53. Robert S. Woodworth, *Contemporary Schools of Psychology*, revised edition, pp. 8–9. Robert S. Harper, "The First Psychological Laboratory," *Isis*, XLI (July 1950), 161.

was at Johns Hopkins University and the second at Columbia University. Basically oriented to the experimental method for individual psychology, Wundt sought to supplement social psychology with the historical technique of folk psychology. He discarded the traditional concepts of the essence of the soul, its unity, and its location and conducted his experiments based on mathematics, physiology, and experience. Metaphysics ceased to be a problem in the science. The new experimentalists, following Wundt's lead, used biological assumptions.[54]

Wundt's work influenced many workers in American social science. Besides Hall and Cattell, A. M. Small, Franz Boas, William James, John Dewey and others profited in their investigations from the German psychologist's emphasis on the organism's physiology and the experimental method. In this way, psychological thought based on the Darwinian premises invaded the social sciences.[55]

Sir Francis Galton, the Victorian genius, developed the first association experiment which Wundt quickly adapted. In his laboratory at Leipzig, Wundt used Galton's work but with an improved technique. Being the greatest Darwinist in psychology, Galton stressed individual differences neglected by previous psychology. Using the Darwinian concepts of variations, Galton attempted to measure them statistically. Of course, he used selection and adaptation in studies of the individual and the race. He believed childhood was also important in the adult personality, and this interest, through his writing, guided other investigations. Association psychology with a Darwinian orientation existed as Galton's legacy to the developing American psychology. The same evolutionary forces governed both mind and body. For the individual, for the species, the same laws governed the creation of geniuses. Once again, the aristocratic Galton changed the intellectual history of democratic America.[56]

Great Britain, however, slowly accepted Galton's experimental psychology. Only Karl Pearson among British psychologists used Galtonian

54. Karpf, *American Social Psychology*, p. 266. John T. Mertz, *A History of European Thought in the Nineteenth Century*, II, 515–516.
55. Karpf, *American Social Psychology*, p. 64.
56. Murphy, *Historical Introduction to Modern Psychology*, pp. 117, 119–120.

psychology. Even then, Pearson's bias was toward Galton's statistical method, rather than his experimental techniques.[57]

The United States was an entirely different situation. Cattell at Columbia used Galton's testing devices. Working with E. L. Thorndike, James Cattell created a special area in psychology—educational psychology—independent of child study and pedagogy. Cattell, and later Binet, perfected methods of measuring intelligence. During the height of the progressive era, psychologists claimed that they could understand, by tests and experimental laboratories, the general structure of personality, learning, motivation, emotion, individual, heredity, and environment.[58] Therefore, one American result of Galton's attempts to understand and measure natural aristocracy (genius) was coping with the problems of mass democratic education.

By 1914, psychology in the United States had become a well-defined discipline. Drawing on German experimentalism and Darwinian biology, the various fields of psychology became clear cut. The mind remained important in the study of an organism's behavior[59]—not only the mind in use, in process, in problem-solving, but also in its biological inception.

James McKeen Cattell was a major figure in the history of psychology. Born in an academic situation (his father was president of Lafayette College) he was graduated from Lafayette with both the B.A. and an M.A. degrees. During his long life, Cattell received many academic and scientific honors, including the French Legion of Honor. After receiving the Ph.D. in psychology at Leipzig in 1886, Cattell became Francis Galton's co-worker. In the United States, he taught at Bryn Mawr, the University of Pennsylvania, and Columbia University.[60]

Among Cattell's students were Robert S. Woodworth and Clark Wisster, who in turn affected the course of several fields of research in American science. To these students and others, Cattell preached the importance of applied psychology using statistics and measurement. Thus, according to Cattell, such techniques led to the understanding

57. *Ibid.*, p. 172.
58. Boring, *A History of Experimental Psychology*, pp. 569–570.
59. *Ibid.*, p. 506.
60. *Who Was Who in America*, II, 103.

of the very nature of differential psychology. E. L. Thorndike constructed his investigations on that assumption.[61] Cattell's influence on American psychology was not limited to that exerted through his students. As mentioned earlier, he established one of the first psychological laboratories in American universities.[62]

Inspired by his close association with Galton, Cattell in 1894 conducted the first battery of psychological tests ever given to a large group of individuals. The tests measured association—free and controlled—reaction time, memory, and simple perceptual processes. The Galtonian orientation of Cattell's activities was not accidental.[63]

Like Galton and other nineteenth-century scientists, Cattell assumed the unity of science. Naturally, Cattell recognized the innate relevance of psychology to the developing fields of the naturalistic social sciences. The physical and mental were, therefore, impossible for Cattell to separate in evolutionary studies.[64] A professor of psychology, Cattell was also chairman of the Department of Anthropology at Columbia from its inception in 1896 to 1902. During those years, he was closely associated with Franz Boas, a major pioneer in American anthropology.[65] Cattell's interest in anthropology extended to the American Association for the Advancement of Science, where he presented findings on the statistical analysis of eminent men. This report, the subject of which has a flavor suggestive of Galton's investigations, gave charts comparing the racial and secular distribution of the most eminent men.[66]

Despite all the influence of Galton on Cattell's intellectual life, he did

61. A. A. Robach, *A History of American Psychology*, pp. 167–175.

62. *Ibid.*, pp. 131–132. See also the controversy over the origin of experimental psychology in the United States in *Science*, n.s. II (November 8, 1895), 626–628.

63. Murphy, *Historical Introduction to Modern Psychology*, p. 164. Boring, *A History of Experimental Psychology*, pp. 793–794.

64. Cattell, "The Advance of Psychology," *Science*, n.s. VIII (October 21, 1888), 533–541. At this time Cattell was vice-president of Section H—Anthropology—of the American Association for the Advancement of Science and the article cited was an address to that group.

65. Aleš Hrdlička, "Physical Anthropology: Its Scope and Aims; Its History and Present Status in America," *American Journal of Physical Anthropology*, I (July-September, 1918), 290.

66. *Proceedings of the American Association for the Advancement of Science*, ILVI (1897), 341.

not have his mentor's dogmatism in regard to human nature. For Cattell, human nature remained complex and imperfectly realized, and human conduct rising from human nature varied from society to society and from culture to culture. Cattell's conclusions tacitly accepted relativism in the behavioral sciences.[67] In fact, he rejected the Malthusian population theory and recognized the importance of birth control in the limitation of the modern family.[68]

Instrumental in the creation of the American Association of University Professors in 1915, Cattell actively sought academic reforms. In addition, as a pacifist, he opposed the entry of the United States into World War I. As a result, Columbia University dismissed him. Aside from these activities which put him in the progessive camp,[69] Cattell's most lasting contribution to American science was a long association with scholarly publications, not as a contributor, but as editor. He was associated at various times with *The Psychological Review, Psychological Monographs* and *The Psychological Index.* Cattell organized in 1906 the *American Men of Science* and *A Directory of American Scholars.* Earlier, in 1894, he started *Science,* a weekly publication which at his death became the property of the American Association for the Advancement of Science which for some time had been the official organ of the AAAS. Onetime editor of E. L. Youman's *Popular Science Monthly,* Cattell continued its publication as *The Scientific Monthly* after their split. In addition to being instrumental in the beginning of *Archives of Psychology and Scientific Method,* he added to his list of journals in 1915 *School and Society,* as an outlet for progressive educational theories.[70] Regardless of psychology's future, its past owed much to Cattell's enterprises.

A conference on individual psychology held at Columbia in 1914 in honor of James McKeen Cattell expressed this indebtedness well. The papers reflected his prejudices by stressing physical or racial factors in

67. Cattell, "Statistical Study of American Men of Science," *Science,* n.s. XXIV (November 23, 1906), 579.

68. Cattell, "The Causes of the Declining Birth Rate," *Proceedings of the First National Conference on Race Betterment,* January 8–12, 1914 (Battle Creek, 1914), p. 67.

69. Pastore, *The Nature-Nurture Controversy,* p. 133.

70. Robach, *A History of American Psychology,* p. 171.

individual differences and measuring them by statistical methods. In the progressive era, Cattell's pioneer efforts in the area of testing had a direct bearing on the direction of psychology—toward a fuller realization of the dimensions of evolutionary naturalism. In this way, Cattell was one of the most influential psychologists in the United States, despite his meager theoretical writings.[71]

Mental testing dominated psychology—or at least the popular understanding of the discipline—in the reform decades of the early twentieth century. The search for, and thus measuring of, intelligence encouraged the use of mental tests which, as has been noted, came from the Darwinian-Galtonian scheme of thoughts which institutions and individuals, particularly Cattell, encouraged in American psychology.

Alfred Binet in 1905 first introduced his tests to the psychological community. Henry Goddard revised the tests in 1908 and introduced them two years later to American scientists at Vinelands, New Jersey. Binet based the tests on a scale which used mental age rather than physical age. In 1916 the famous Stanford Revision of Binet's tests by Lewis M. Terman further popularized the concept of I.Q. As one might expect, Terman followed Galtonian tradition in the study of individual differences and assumed that race was the basis for these differences.[72]

This assumption was logical, given the racist atmosphere of American psychology. The Binet scale implied the growth of intelligence with age. Thus, intelligence was biologically determined. By 1911 the ratio of mental age to physical age created the concept of intelligence quotient. After Terman's revision in 1916, it was a common belief that I.Q. remained approximately constant during childhood. It soon became a dogma during the twenties that I.Q. was congenital, unchanging, and thus inherited.[73] Nineteenth-century racism appeared to be valid in twentieth-century science. Yet, from 1920 to 1945 the growth of a new behaviorism based on environmental factors changed the concept of

71. Woodworth, "Conference on Individual Psychology," *Science*, n.s. XXXIX (May 15, 1914), 731–732. Woodworth, *Contemporary Schools of Psychology*, p. 72.
72. Murphy, *Historical Introduction to Modern Psychology*, p. 354; Pastore, *The Nature-Nurture Controversy*, pp. 77, 85.
73. Boring, "The Influence of Evolutionary Thought upon American Psychological Thought," *Evolutionary Thought in America*, pp. 289–290.

I.Q. and made it more culturally determinable, rather than a statement of biological inheritance.

Popular interest in mental tests increased with the publication of the Army I.Q. test results. The Army in World War I gave the tests according to ethnic groups, and they tended to show that the average soldier was nearly a moron and that groups, such as Negroes and Southern Europeans, were mentally inferior to native-born white Americans. Once again, racism appeared vindicated. Later examination by psychologists and historians indicated that the tests were inconclusive and only indicated that environment was important in any test which contained cultural values or information. The racist-inheritance school of psychology held the advantage, or so it appeared.[74]

A number of schools of psychological thought challenged racism, even in the moments of its greatest scientific achievement. In 1912 all of the modern schools of psychology existed in the United States. Functional and structural psychology, associationism, psychoanalysis, behaviorism, and others attracted psychologists to their various causes. The theories of Pavlov, Freud, and McDougall offered explanations for human behavior—all of which had important economic and political consequences. The mind, particularly intelligence, remained a major concern of psychology. It no longer conceived mental deficiency as criminal degeneracy, but the interest in this problem remained constant.[75]

This interest in intelligence combined with the naturalistic leanings of the times found expression in the practical problems of mass education in an ethnically pluralistic society. The psychological testing movement apparently supported the popular prejudice of the American Negro's innate, biological inferiority. In 1897, as well as 1917, investigators in race psychology, by using intelligence testing, found the Negro lacking in the higher powers of intelligence, and thus industrial rather than literary education was fair and just because it met the innate qualities of the individual Negro.[76] It was therefore possible for an

74. Oscar Handlin, *Race and Nationality in American Life*, pp. 198–199.
75. Woodworth, *Contemporary Schools of Psychology*, pp. 4–5, 120. Stanley P. Davies, *The Mentally Retarded in Society*, p. 42.
76. Two typical articles of this school of thought are Anna T. Smith, "A Study in Race Psychology," *The Popular Science Monthly*, L (January 1897), 354–360 and a review article in *The Journal of Heredity*, VIII (April 1917), 153–154.

individual to advocate the themes of progressive education (education for the child's innate needs and desires) and at the same time give scientific support to the racist legacy of the nineteenth century.

Impulse or instinct appeared as the source of human motivation. The mind became the method by which the organism solved problems, but not always rationally, or in light of innate moral knowledge. Freud's theories supported this assumption of irrationality in human nature. Like Dr. Morton Prince of Boston, Freud stressed the vital forces of the unconscious, of repression and conflict in human behavior. The sex life and attitude of an individual reflected the importance of these concepts.[77] As Freud's psychology became popular, his work, his very name, became synonymous with sex. Particularly for the repressed middle class, it meant sexual freedom. By stressing the sexual nature of human behavior, Freud helped the naturalistic cause in American biological and social sciences.

A. A. Brill, who published English translations of Freud's theoretical writings, aided the widespread influence of Freudian psychology in American civilization during the decade of the twenties. Freud impressed the reviewers and the reading public, despite an occasional protest that he gave undue emphasis to the erotic and unnatural in human conduct. Freud conceived of instincts as energy which, if not dissipated, could direct itself against the organism and thus cause mental illness. As a concept of energy or tensions, American psychologists saw the Freudian analysis within a biological context.[78]

American eugenists welcomed these developments in psychology. One eugenist wrote, "Romantic love, the divinest of our passions, is not purely a blind animal mating instinct, but the refinement of this instinct through age-long traditions of reason and sentiment and duty and aspirations."[79] In accord with the theory of acquired characteristics, man controlled this instinct because of the necessity for racial welfare.

77. Curti, "Human Nature in American Thought: Retreat from Reason in the Age of Science," *Political Science Quarterly*, LXVIII (December 1953), 497, 502.

78. Ditzion, *Marriage, Morals and Sex in America*, p. 362. Woodworth, *Contemporary Schools of Psychology*, p. 205.

79. William H. Carruth, "Selection from an Address on Eugenics," *Eugenics: Twelve University Lectures*, p. 292.

This was naturalism, to be sure, but with rational and racial-biological principles.

The American Medical-Psychological Association and the National Committee for Mental Hygiene saw the relevance of eugenics to the new psychological developments and demonstrated this relationship by appointing committees on applied eugenics.[80] As has been pointed out, this action supplemented other groups who took an interest in the eugenic creed and program. The hope was, of course, to save the nation by a scientific application of eugenic concepts based on a realistic or naturalistic understanding of human nature. Scholars using instinct psychology might understand and control human nature by the fusion of science with statistical and testing techniques as perfected by James Cattell.

William McDougall thought instinct psychology solved the mystery of human nature. As a psychologist, he gave the fullest expression to the crosscurrents of eugenics, instinct, and tradition of naturalism. He was born in Lancashire, England, and trained in medicine and psychology. After academic service at St. John's College, Cambridge, and University College, London, he came to the United States in 1920. After serving as a professor of psychology at Harvard for seven years, he served in a similar capacity at Duke University from 1927 until his death in 1938.[81]

A prolific writer, McDougall's books indicated the biological tradition in American psychology. Instinct provided the basis of his psychological studies or, as McDougall often termed it, the propensity. Bedrock in his study was the belief that the essential nature of man was biological (inherited) rather than socially determined. He held to this thesis with minor variations throughout his career.[82] The trend of psychology during his later years was toward the acceptance of the dynamic influence culture and society have on human conduct. Despite

80. Haller, "American Eugenics," p. 148. Charles Davenport, Irving Fisher, Robert M. Gerkes were some of the eugenists on the executive committee of these two organizations.

81. *Who Was Who in America,* I, 809; Woodworth, *Contemporary Schools of Psychology,* p. 216.

82. Karpf, *American Social Psychology,* p. 421.

his development, McDougall remained true to the older creed of heredi-tary determinism.

McDougall's list of instincts or propensities included nearly every general biological function, finding cultural expression. The instincts ranged from hunger to the acquisitive tendency. Naturally, the mating and social side of human behavior were on the list. He also included emotions. The list itself was not controversial, except where McDougall added the self-assertive and submissive propensities. In other words, drives to seek dominance or to accept obvious inferiority partially shaped man's activities.[83] The political, economic, and social conse-quences of these theories led McDougall to push for an antidemocratic and authoritarian public policy. By accepting the concepts of domi-nance and submission, he eliminated the natural-rights philosophy, historically a significant factor in American politics.

Although McDougall's scientific career occurred when Gregor Men-del's theories were creating the new science of genetics, he still sub-scribed to the older theory of human heredity. He thus believed the family was a moral force, and the individual by his own efforts could reach a higher level of development. Little wonder that McDougall spent his last years at Duke attempting to measure the inherited effect of teaching rats to solve mazes. He still championed the inheritance of acquired characteristics. He of course supported the aristocratic version of this theory—that only certain racial groups acquire the knowledge and biologically transmit it to their offspring.[84]

Obviously, McDougall thought of instincts as immutable and uni-versal in human nature, shaping the entire personality structure. He believed emotions were the same as instincts, and thus it was possible for them to change by a process of acquired characteristics. "The emo-tional tendencies," he wrote, "become fully developed by exercise; but in each man each tendency, like each bodily organ and function, is given by heredity in a degree that leads to a certain amount of develop-

83. William McDougall, *The Energies of Men, A Study of the Fundamentals of Dynamic Psychology*, pp. 97–98; hereafter cited as McDougall, *The Energies of Men;* Woodworth, *Contemporary Schools of Psychology*, p. 220.

84. McDougall, *Religion and the Sciences of Life*, p. 184. Conway Zirkle, "The Early History of the Idea of the Inheritance of Acquired Characters and of Pa-genesis," *Transactions of the American Philosophical Society*, n.s. XXXV, Part II (January 1946), 98.

ment only with a normal amount of exercise." [85] The phrenologists in the nineteenth century accepted this idea. The more immediate origin of McDougall's identification of instincts with emotions was from the Scottish metaphysical school of psychology. Philosophers of this school of thought believed that passion, functioning as a drive toward an objective, was an instinct.[86]

Because of his belief that impulses and desires which come from instinctual disposition sustain human activity, McDougall termed his psychology "hormic." [87] He saw economy in nature with form and function as one by believing "in the causal efficacy of our mental or teleological activities and in believing that teleological causation pervades the organic realm and has been an essential factor of organic evolution." [88] Thus the organism willed his behavior, but always within the context of the organism's instincts.

In social psychology, McDougall argued that social status indicated native ability. Utilizing hormic psychology, he saw, as did other eugenists, the greatest danger to civilization if the altruistic impulse functioned freely. Human altruism allowed the strongest impulse to operate —the impulse to procreate one's own kind, the Duke psychologist complained. Given the inferior condition of the masses, the dysgenic threat always existed.[89]

Nationalism provided the solution to the menace of the inadequate. National goals contributed the basis for ethics, and governmental needs determined the individual's rights. The group conflict or class struggle damaged national unity as did individual selfishness. The state's unity

85. McDougall, *Character and the Conduct of Life, Practical Psychology for Every Man* (London 1927), pp. 12, 18. Hereafter cited as McDougall, *Character and the Conduct of Life.*

86. L. L. and Jessie Bernard, *Origins of American Sociology, The Social Science Movement in the United States,* pp. 80–81. Hereafter cited as Bernard, *Origins of American Sociology.*

87. McDougall, *Psycho-Analysis and Social Psychology,* p. 113. Hereafter cited as McDougall, *Psycho-Analysis and Social Psychology.*

88. McDougall, *Modern Materialism and Emergent Evolution,* p. 120.

89. McDougall, "The Correlation between Native Ability and Social Status," *Eugenics in Race and State, Scientific Papers of the Second International Congress of Eugenics Held at American Museum of Natural History,* New York, September 22–28, 1921, II, 375–376. McDougall, *Ethics and Some Modern World Problems,* pp. v., vii.

and welfare were superior to other social considerations.[90] McDougall rejected both Marxian class struggle and natural rights philosophy. Supernationalism solved many national problems.

He saw man as the victim of a paradox. The group or the class degraded the individual below his normal life; and yet, only in social life, in group activities, did man arise above animal existence. It was a case of natural man living in an unnatural world. Organization was the method for resolving the paradox. Through organization society's weaknesses and strengths gained higher means of expression raising the members of society, rather than leading to their individual degradation. Allowing instincts of dominance and submission to function, operate freely, greatly reduce the ills of group living, concluded McDougall.[91]

McDougall shared many intellectual assumptions with Roosevelt's supporters within progressivism. In fact, McDougall's *The Indestructible Union* was in many ways a psychological adaptation of Herbert Croly's classical contribution to progressivism, *The Promise of American Life.*

Not aware of the antidemocratic drift of this thought, he saw democracy and nationalism as the triumph of humanity and reason "over the cruder instincts of the race." Only certain races, however, had the potential for civic virtue and for stable government. Although the nation required certain biological and physical conditions in order to exist, the state was, nevertheless, a spiritual fact, according to McDougall's calculations.[92]

Like E. L. Godkin, McDougall saw the greatest danger to a democracy in the theory that representatives performed as delegates to the legislature. In addition, the "delegates" expressed class interest in society which in patriotic compromise with other class desires might produce social harmony. Along with many progressives, McDougall rejected crude political class interest as harmful to national unity. With

90. *Ibid.*, p. 213; McDougall, *The Indestructible Union, Rudiments of Political Science for the American Citizen,* pp. 198–199. Hereafter cited as McDougall, *The Indestructible Union.*

91. McDougall, "Professor Freud's Group Psychology and His Theory of Suggestion," *Problems of Personality Studies Presented to Dr. Morton Prince, Pioneer in American Psychopathology,* pp. 271, 275.

92. McDougall, *The Indestructible Union,* pp. 5, 21.

good men in politics and good working-class conditions dulling the sharpness of the class struggle, national unity sought a higher stage of realization.[93]

In foreign affairs, McDougall rejected pacifism as unrealistic in a world in which the United States had too many material possessions "while the greater number of nations and peoples are of the class that has little." [94] He based his foreign policy observations on Darwinian history and laissez faire economics, rather than Marxian thought. The struggle for existence was a reality, but man's "reason" insured national unity.

McDougall did not base his conservatism on natural-rights philosophy. Rather, incorporating elements of Malthus's population doctrine, he accepted curtailment of traditional liberties with increase of human beings. He argued for the limitation of liberty because civilized men needed two mutually exclusive objectives: liberty and ordered government. All government, he concluded, was a compromise between these two desires or dual instincts.[95] In this belief, he joined American conservatists, who based their theories on the political philosophy of John C. Calhoun the archdefender of slavery in pre–Civil War United States.

The psychologist's conservative nationalism complemented Herbert Croly's formulations. Like the progressive thinker, McDougall saw merit in Alexander Hamilton's centralized government to insure natural unity. He considered Hamilton a realist, for nationalism was the psychological expression of the social tendency and an impulse to self-assertion.[96] Apparently McDougall considered Hamilton a pioneer in the application of instinct psychology to governmental policy. Similar to Croly's version of reformistic interpretation of Hamilton's philosophy, McDougall saw the need for efficient national government. He wrote, "It can only be found by returning to the path of true progress, the path of increasingly efficient national organization founded in firm moral and political organizations." [97] In this manner, he contributed to the conservative and naturalist philosophy found in American progressivism.

93. *Ibid.*, pp. 37, 177, 216–217.
94. *Ibid.*, p. 167.
95. *Ibid.*, pp. 50, 126.
96. *Ibid.*, pp. 63–64, 69–70, 100, 102.
97. *Ibid.*, p. 227.

McDougall believed race created efficient nationalism. Declaring race to be that which differentiated groups (such as skin color), he vigorously endorsed segregation and even colonization for the American Negro (although he admitted he did not know the effect of race-blending). Race indicated individual intelligence which, in turn, reflected individual social status. As if blood were the agent of transmission of inheritance, McDougall attacked the Negro as inferior intellectually. If by chance a Negro was a social success, he was a mulatto. Consequently, race shaped the individual's destiny.[98]

McDougall's racism was part of the Nordic superiority. All cultural virtue rested with the Nordic, Northern European people, in creating civilization. Nordic folk were curious, according to McDougall's analysis, and strongly guided by family considerations, while the Mediterranean people tended toward urban living and were victims of strong herd instincts. Continuing his racist dialectic, McDougall saw the Mediterranean individual as constitutionally extrovert, while the Nordic person was genetically an introvert. Thus, the former was prone to murder while the latter had a tendency toward suicide and divorce.[99]

Given these psychological assumptions or generalizations, McDougall formulated his law of the adaptation of the culture-species. This law was his synthesis of biology based on the inheritance of acquired character combined with antiurban prejudice. Society as an organism evolved from the simple to the complex. Accordingly, only the better racial elements successfully met this environmental challenge. "Our civilization," he warned, "by reason of its increasing complexity, is making constantly increasing demands upon the qualities of its bearers; the qualities of those bearers are diminishing or deteriorating, rather than improving." [100] In view of this law, McDougall expressed surprise at the remarkable war record of urban British boys in World War I.[101]

Natural man unfortunately lived in an unnatural world of urban civilization. Natural man was good, but society was corrupt. Jean J.

---

98. *Ibid.*, pp. 9, 160, 163–164. McDougall, *Is America Safe for Democracy?* pp. vii, 56–57, 67. This book was based on lectures given at the Lowell Institute in Boston, entitled "Anthropology and History, Or the Influence of Anthropologic Constitution on the Destinies of Nations."

99. *Ibid.*, pp. 80–81.

100. *Ibid.*, pp. 104, 168; see also Haller, "American Eugenics," p. 258.

101. McDougall, *Is America Safe for Democracy?* p. 4.

Rousseau's (1712–1778) French romanticism supported McDougall's naturalism. Man's chains were race and instinct. Only his will expressed in strong and centralized nationalism saved him from his hereditary fate.

The social sciences aided national aspirations of unity. The physical sciences caused many contemporary problems; but now the social sciences, based on a true understanding of human nature, could solve the world's troubles.[102] Ultimately, William McDougall, psychologist of the instincts, was a cautious optimist.

Eugenics provided the solution as a program of practical social reform. Human nature, the creation of evolution, influenced the biological factors shaping man's future. With eugenics as the practical application of hereditary science, McDougall felt his psychological activities had the sanction of biological law. His lifetime work in the naturalism of instinct psychology constantly invoked the prestige of Darwinian biology.[103]

The future respectability of instinct psychology was short. In fact, as McDougall formulated his theories, an intellectual counterattack had started. L. L. Bernard in his *Instinct, A Study of Social Psychology,* published in 1924, debunked the entire school of instinct psychology. The main criticism was the lack of any essential unity over a list of instincts, for no two psychologists gave the same list. The confusion suggested the inadequacy of the instinct methodology. In addition, Bernard stressed environment's dynamic dimensions and the individual's creative response. Bernard maintained that as a person matures the influence of environment becomes a cumulative while any instinctual effects progressively decline.[104]

Environmentalism became an active rival to the instinct dogma. John B. Watson, as leader of the behaviorist school, discounted any major influence of the instincts in human conduct. His writings emphasized the importance of education in human behavior, and he claimed en-

102. McDougall, *World Chaos, The Responsibility of Science,* p. v.
103. Pastore, *The Nature-Nurture Controversy,* p. 50; Karpf, *American Social Psychology,* p. 196; Bernard, *Instinct, A Study in Social Psychology,* pp. 245–246 (hereafter cited as Bernard, *Instinct*).
104. Woodworth, *Contemporary Schools of Psychology,* pp. 223–224; Bernard, *Instinct,* p. 524.

vironmental factors explained human nature. Watson felt that childhood experiences and training shaped the man. Learned responses to an environmental stimulus, not instincts and inherited traits, caused human action.[105] Because Watson's behaviorism reasserted man's capacities to shape his environment, the psychology gained in popularity.

Other workers in psychology and the social sciences actively destroyed the intellectual status of the instinct theory. Charles Cooley, George Herbert Mead, John Dewey, and William I. Thomas engaged in research that approached human activity by different methods. But the end product was the decline of instinct speculations. As a general label, the "behavioristic" or environmental school replaced the "instinct" or hereditary school as the leading group in American social sciences.[106]

The growth of anti-instinct thought increased during the decade of the 1920's, with John Dewey leading the attack on old-fashioned naturalism and its hereditary bias in the growth of the individual.[107] Other factors, including the Great Depression of 1929 and the subsequent New Deal, changed the social atmosphere by their emphasis on democratic liberal reform.

Bernard saw the major reason for instinct psychology's decline in the transition from Galtonian instinct theory to Mendelian inheritance. As Bernard noted, Galton essentially subscribed to eighteenth- and nineteenth-century biology. The newer biochemical theories in 1924 suggested inadequacies in Galton's hypothesis. Mendel's studies indicated a new beginning in the study of the heredity-environment relationship in human nature.[108]

The instinct school of psychology had a crude conception of environment. It was merely the background for the inherited traits and not an active partner in the creation of human behavior. Also, the instinct school drew on the prestige of biology and naturally used biolog-

105. Helen Love, "Heredity and Environment in American Social Thought, 1900–1929; The Aftermath of Spencer," Unpublished Doctoral Dissertation, Columbia University, 1950, pp. 92–93.

106. This classification was also indicative of the social scientist's politics with the environmentalists being liberal while hereditarians were conservatives in matters of public policy. See Pastore, *The Nature-Nurture Controversy*, p. 176; Karpf, *American Social Psychology*, p. 142.

107. Pastore, *The Nature-Nurture Controversy*, pp. 49–50.

108. Bernard, *Instinct*, p. 522.

ical analogies in writing about human nature. This biology, pre-Mendelian in scope and with a bias toward the inheritance of acquired characteristics, was inadequate.[109] The growth of modern genetics was a testament to instinct psychology's decline.

Just as the various trends mentioned in this chapter encouraged William McDougall's assumption that man led an unnatural existence in urban society, American anthropologists expressed similar attitudes. Society corrupted modern man; he was not organically united with the urban complex of industrial society. The result was disease and decay.

109. George A. Lundberg, "Statistics in Modern Thought," *Contemporary Social Theory,* p. 126.

9

ANTHROPOLOGY:
THE CIVILIZED
DECAY
OF NATURAL MAN

ONE THEME of anthropological thought until quite recently was that civilization (the city) contributed to man's physical and mental decay. Many eugenists and particularly Earnest Hooton (1887–1954), Harvard anthropologist, endorsed the theme of degeneration, that urban dangers existed for racial America. The origin for this sentiment was in their acceptance of the theory of inheritance of acquired characteristics.

From as early as the eighteenth century until 1930, anthropology has accepted the importance of the inheritance of acquired characteristics. Of all the theories available to the eighteenth-century thinker accounting for racial differences, this one shaped a great deal of anthropological speculation, even after Darwin published *The Descent of Man.* Twentieth-century American naturalists and eugenists accepted as valid the eighteenth-century notion that race existed because of early deviation from the original type of the species.[1] Different races of men were expressions of imperfection from a given type.

1. John C. Greene, "Some Early Speculation on the Origin of Human Races," *American Anthropologist,* LVI (February 1954), 39.

Philosophers accepted this degenerative process, along with the noble-savage concept, during the Enlightenment. Despite the limitation of man's origin, the Enlightenment philosophers claimed reason and the scientific method propelled society toward perfection and progress. For the nineteenth-century English anthropologists, however, this Scale of Nature had become rigid, and progress for the lower forms of life, including certain groups of men, became impossible. A linear biology rejected any hope that the Negro and the Asiatic were anything but moral fossils—mentally fixed at various stages of human evolution.[2]

The intellectual factors for this change in the climate of opinion varied. The development of physical anthropology contributed a major factor which, by stressing empirical differences among men, led to the conclusion that such distinctions were innately determined by the superiority or inferiority of the groups of men studied. Johann F. Blunienback (1752–1840) first used cranial measurements as a vital method of racial classification. He classified mankind into five varieties or families, based on his observations of various skulls of the world.[3] These five varieties—Caucasian, Mongolian, Negro, Malayan, American—still influence modern anthropology and popular thought regarding mankind's racial divisions. In 1836 Frederick Tiedemann perfected a method to measure a skull's internal size by filling it with millet seed and then weighing the seed. Four years later Anders Retzius created the cephalic index (the proportion of the breadth to the length of the head) and lectured before the Swedish Academy of Science on cranial classification.[4]

These two concepts of race classification and the cephalic index, combined with traditional American optimism, created the pseudo science called phrenology. Popular in nineteenth-century United States, phrenology gave scientific support to individual improvement by stressing given capacities and environmental means by which the capacities could be improved. Phrenology stressed the traditional con-

2. Eiseley, *Darwin's Century*, p. 264.

3. Ralph Linton, "Error in Anthropology," *The Story of Human Error*, Joseph Jastrow, ed., p. 300.

4. Thomas K. Penniman, *A Hundred Years of Anthropology*, second edition, revised, p. 76. Hereafter cited as Penniman, *100 Years of Anthropology*.

cept of the moral law, the free individual and the mission of America. Arguments drawn from anatomy, pathology, and craniology provided advancement for the phrenological cause.[5]

The last of these proofs, craniology, gave a scientific basis to the myth of Negro inferiority. Samuel G. Morton (1799–1851), the father of American physical anthropology and professor of anatomy at the Pennsylvania Medical College, published *Crania Americana* in 1839. This book, including a chapter on phrenology, contributed to the growing anthropological defense of slavery based on racial inferiority.[6] Morton argued that skull size determined racial fitness.[7]

The unity-plurality controversy over man's origin provided the background for the scientific debates over slavery's validity. The pro-slavery scientists argued that groups of men known as races came from plural sources, created in different places at different times. They sought justification for this thesis in ethnology, anatomy, and physiology. The antislavery scholars based their arguments on the unity theory expressed in Christianity that all men came from a common source. Significantly, these arguments, existing before *The Origin of Species*, appeared later in the public controversy over evolution.[8]

American anthropology before 1859 lacked scope and institutional expression. The American Ethnological Society, organized in 1842, primarily concentrated on Spanish America, but its scholarly influence was feeble. The organization did not publish theories of physical anthropology in its *Transactions* or *Bulletin*. Few scholars studied physical anthropology. The American Association for the Advance-

5. John D. Davies, *Phrenology Fad and Science, A 19th Century American Crusade*, pp. 128, 165–166. Hereafter cited as John D. Davies, *Phrenology*.

6. Aleš Hrdlička, "Physical Anthropology: Its Scope and Aims, Its History and Present Status in America," *American Journal of Physical Anthropology*, I (April-June 1918), 137–138. See also William Stanton, *The Leopard's Spots, Scientific Attitude toward Race in America, 1815–59*, for a fuller discussion of Morton's activities. Hereafter cited as Stanton, *The Leopard's Spots*. For the connection between early anthropological investigations and defense of slavery, see William Jenkins, *Pro-Slavery Thought in the Old South*.

7. Modern anthropologists reject this notion because of a wide intragroup variability and similar measurements for distantly related groups. Ashley Montagu, *A Handbook of Anthropometry*, pp. 42–43.

8. Edward Lurie, "Louis Agassiz and the Races of Man," *Isis*, XLV (September 1954), 242, 230.

ment of Science did not organize a section on the topic until 1882.
Darwin created the new intellectual environment. Freed from such no-
tions as the fixity of the species and special creation, the scientists dis-
covered vast and new areas of research in the nature of man's origin.[9]
Between the publication of *The Origin of Species* and *The Descent of
Man* in 1871, many "classics" in anthropological literature appeared.[10]

After the Civil War the Army Medical Museum in Washington and
the Peabody Museum in Boston encouraged physical anthropology.
Other important developments were the establishment of the Bureau
of American Ethnology and the Washington Anthropological Society.
The publication of the journal the *American Anthropologist* in 1888
and the founding of the Department of Anthropology at Clark University a year later indicated the widening interest in anthropology. All
during the latter half of the nineteenth century, museums, expositions
and the creation of academic departments of anthropology at leading
American universities increased public and scientific interest in the
discipline.[11]

The opening of remote regions of Africa to white explorers caused
an interest in the races of mankind. Francis Galton felt he gained an
insight into the physical and mental composition of primitive tribal
life through his trips to Africa as a young man.[12] Anthropologists used
Galton's word association test in early anthropological field trips to
the Torres Straits region in the 1890s. Wundt employed Sir Francis's
techniques in the analysis of folk psychology which also contributed
to the anthropological analysis of racial differences.[13]

9. Ralph S. Bates, *Scientific Societies in the United States,* second edition,
pp. 64–65; Aleš Hrdlicka, "Physical Anthropology: Its Scope and Aims, Its History
and Present Status in America," *American Journal of Anthropology,* I (April-June
1918), 180–181; T. D. Stewart, "The Effect of Darwin's Theory of Evolution on
Physical Anthropology," *Evolution and Anthropology,* Betty J. Meggers, ed.,
pp. 20–21, 25.

10. Alfred Kroeber, "Evolution, History and Culture," *The Evolution of Man,
Culture and Society* (Volume II of Evolution after Darwin), Sol Tax, ed., 10.

11. Aleš Hrdlička, "Physical Anthropology: Its Scope and Aims, Its History and
Present Status in America," *American Journal of Physical Anthropology,* I (July-
September 1918), 268.

12. C. P. Blacker, *Eugenics: Galton and After,* pp. 41–42, 89. Hereafter cited as
Blacker, *Eugenics.*

13. H. R. Hays, *From Ape to Angel, An Informal History of Social Anthropology,* p. 212; Penniman, *100 Years of Anthropology,* p. 141.

Galton's theoretical assumptions on cultural evolution also affected American investigators seeking an explanation for varied attainment among the world's people. Like a good Victorian, Galton assumed his society was the apex and that the institutions of the primitive world fell into a descending scale determined by the differences from the Victorian standard. In addition, cultures, by unilateral evolution, passed through exactly the same stages in the upward struggle toward modern existence.[14] Unfortunately, the analysis allowed that certain groups of people had stopped their evolutionary progress for a number of reasons, and thus nature assigned them to an eternal position of inferiority in the struggle for survival.

This unilateral evolution of men and culture found acceptance in the United States. The theory helped explain why certain groups such as the American Indian failed in the modern world. One writer saw divine law in this unilateral evolution in the history of the American Indian. He claimed that a law of changes existed in a movement toward perfection by Nature's elimination of innately inferior elements. The Indian passed away in accordance with this law, for he abused the gifts of Providence, instead of using them as did the industrious white man.[15] The analysis was another version of John D. Rockefeller's tale of the American Beauty rose. From this point of view, nature and society moved toward consummation of the natural and the supernatural amidst the wreckage of people and nations. As has been noted, Karl Pearson agreed.

Nineteenth-century American anthropology was functional: it supported the racial attitudes of the day. Drawing on the inheritance of acquired characters theory, the editor of *Nation*, E. L. Godkin, forecast a dismal future for the Negro and the Chinese because they failed to meet successfully the environmental challenges of the United States. Regardless of Darwin's theory, the fixity of the races foretold the cause of the failure.[16]

14. Linton, "Error in Anthropology," p. 314.
15. J. W. Scott, "Growth and Decay of Nations," *De Bow's Review*, XXX, 30; Earnest Hooton, twentieth-century anthropologist, argued that the white man's culture destroyed the American Indian. See Hooton's *Apes, Men and Morons*, p. 290. Hereafter cited as Hooton, *Apes, Men and Morons*.
16. "The Race Question," *The Nation*, XI (July 21, 1870), 39. Mixture of the race was charged against the Republicans in the Presidential election. See Ditzion,

The famous study of family degeneration, *The Jukes*, was an example of practical anthropology taking part in the expanding field of social work. Richard L. Dugdale wrote *The Jukes* as a report for the Prison Association of New York after an inspection of county jails. While examining prison records, Dugdale discovered a family with a long history of arrest and charity cases. After visiting their "ancestral breeding spot," he gave them the title of Jukes in his book. Dugdale calculated that the Jukes had cost the state of New York more than a million dollars in charity and correction since the family first appeared in the state late in the eighteenth century.[17]

The reform community gratefully received Dugdale's work. As Franklin H. Giddings pointed out, Dugdale approached heredity as an open question and repeatedly stressed the importance of environment in any scheme of improvement for such cases as the Jukes. In fact, Dugdale stressed the role of cultural isolation in creation of pauperism.[18] Ironically, the naturalistic reformers and social scientists of the nineteenth century read the book as a defense of hereditary determinism. Defenders of the hereditary school in social thought used the book as a weapon against the advocators of environmentalism.

Richard Dugdale's policy advocated industrial education, personal hygiene and, if necessary, indefinite imprisonment for the habitual-criminal class. Environment was important in creation of hard-working and peaceful citizens. He pointed out that three fourths of the criminals examined did not have a trade. Thus, idle hands were free to cause mischief and expense for society.[19] Continuing his environmental cause and cure of the Jukes, Dugdale noted the effect of hard labor to control hereditary erotic passion. He wrote,

Hard, continuous labor checks the erotic passions, prevents waste of vitality, tends to decrease its intensity by disuse, and in the course of time may en-

---

Marriage, Morals and Sex in America, p. 257n. For a minority opinion for the brotherhood of the races, see Andre De Quatrefages, "Physical Characters of the Human Race," *Popular Science Monthly*, II (March 1873), 552.

17. Cargill, *Intellectual America*, pp. 550–556.

18. Richard L. Dugdale, *The Jukes, A Study in Crime, Pauperism, Disease, and Heredity*, fourth edition, pp. 26, 42, 49–50, 65–66. Hereafter cited as Dugdale, *The Jukes*.

19. *Ibid.*, pp. 96, 114–115.

able the potential pauper to form habits of industry that will yet become organized as part of his character, and prove that pauperism can be controlled by controlling the passion which, disease aside, tends more than all other causes put together to perpetuate its heredity.[20]

With these words, Dugdale expressed the "democratic" version of the inheritance of acquired characteristics.

Accordingly, he urged a program of moral training that controlled the emotions and passions by a conscious expression of the will. Patient training and organization created character by curtailing emotions and other primitive behavior. Therefore, environment created the law-abiding and productive citizen.[21] In this way, Dugdale saw an optimistic future.

The American naturalists, however, took Dugdale's study as an explanation of the terrible sociological consequences of bad heredity. Uncertain about the role of hereditary forces in social problems, Dugdale repeatedly stressed environmental conditions as factors in social disorganization. Although he believed sex "approached an instinct," the exercise of the will, that is, character, governed this feature of man's nature.[22]

The scholarly nineteenth-century community and the eugenists of the progressive era still misunderstood Dugdale, despite his environmental orientation. For example, John Commons, noted labor historian and progressive, criticized family studies such as the Jukes on the grounds that they neglected the factor of social selection (environment). Commons concluded that the degraded parents gave both heredity and social status to the child, and therefore family studies could not effectively isolate the effects of heredity and environment.[23]

Common's criticisms applied to the Reverend McCulloch's "The Tribe of Ishmael," another famous study in family degeneracy. Draw-

20. *Ibid.*, pp. 54–55; Dugdale, "Hereditary Pauperism as Illustrated by the 'Juke' Family," *Proceedings of the Conference of Charities, Held in Connection with the General Meeting of the American Social Science Association at Saratoga* (New York), (Boston, 1877), p. 87. Hereafter cited as Dugdale, "Hereditary Pauperism."

21. Dugdale, *The Jukes*, pp. 56–57.

22. Dugdale, "Hereditary Pauperism," pp. 82, 84–85, 87, 91, 195.

23. John R. Commons, "Natural Selection, Social Selection and Heredity," *The Arena*, XVIII (July 1897), 94.

ing for inspiration from Dugdale's work, McCullock saw social degeneration resulting from social parasitism (the same as in the animal
world), from the eighteenth-century migration of criminal stock and
from a public relief allowing the descendents of this stock to be a
financial burden. McCullock believed heredity continued this menace
of the socially inadequate. His solution anticipated the eugenist's
demand for scientific charity and greater social control and direction
of the pauper's children. McCullock wanted all outdoor relief stopped
and private and indiscriminate charity discontinued. Finally, a pauper's children would become wards of the state.[24] Progressive America
later voiced these same sentiments. The scholarly interest in family
degradation extended to a study of criminality. In the years following
the War of the Rebellion, American social scientists saw most criminal
behavior expressed in particular physical limitations. Typically, one
such scientist stressed that the born criminal was detectable by "his
craniological peculiarities, the absence of a moral sense, the reckless
cruelty of his deeds." In addition, alcoholism was an innate expression
of such "sinful traits." The greatest menace, however, was politics,
since born criminals always play an outstanding role in revolutions.
Science could save the nation from criminal destruction. By increased
knowledge of physical anthropology, the legal system, and thereby
society, might permanently segregate this element from the normal
and law-abiding citizens.[25] Naturalistic social thought solved the problem of the born criminal.

Cesare Lombroso, Italian criminologist, was the father of the born-
criminal concept. Drawing on the biological assumptions of the "aristocratic" theme in the inheritance of acquired characteristics, Lombroso was not optimistic about curing the criminal or even aiding the
Negro in the modern world. The body, in effect, controlled the mind
and thus the behavior of the individual.[26] The "environmentalists"

24. The Rev. Oscar C. McCulloch, "The Tribe of Ishmael: A Study in Social
Degradation," *Proceedings of the National Conference of Charities and Corrections* (Boston, 1888), pp. 154, 159.
    25. Joseph Jastrow, "A Theory of Criminality," *Science,* VIII (July 2, 1886),
21.
    26. Cesare Lombroso, "The Heredity of Acquired Characteristics," *Forum,*
XXIV (September 1897), 200–208.

questioned the validity of such a theory of criminality. Their main criticism was that Lombroso and his followers had not clearly established a criminal type based or determined by physical characteristics alone, and mere statistical studies were of little value in such an enterprise.[27]

The naturalistic conservatives met this criticism with a defense of eugenics. Citing Galton's studies and assuming crime to be hereditary, one nineteenth-century critic urged that the law not allow criminals to reproduce, since they would pass to their offspring their criminal inadequacies.[28] Race betterment was the solution.

Just as the criminal was a problem, conservative social critics questioned the Negro's future value in American society. Reconstruction politics naturally created a public interest in the Negro's welfare. The Negro's freedom caused a reorientation in American race relations. By 1884, most conservatives accepted "local control" of the Negro. Conservative social policy enforced the traditional American belief in the innate justice of local government. The Social Darwinism of the survival-of-the-fittest concept supported the local direction of the Negro's behavior. Nineteenth-century conservatives trusted that the laws of nature prevented Negro political supremacy.[29]

Practical anthropology was the answer to the future. Nineteenth-century naturalists thought that scientific research revealed the true and innate nature of the Negro. Then the government might base public policy on the results of this racial research. The Negro and the white could never marry, but they could live in a segregated society to provide true civil accord, believed one architect of human relation-

27. Charles L. Dana, Review of Lombroso, *The Female Offender*, in *Science*, n.s. II (August 1895), 164–165; E. R. L., "The Statistical Study of Hereditary Criminality," *Proceedings of the National Conferences of Charities and Corrections* (Boston, 1895), p. 135.

28. Dr. Nathan Oppenheim, "The Stamping out of Crime," *The Popular Science Monthly*, XLVIII (February 1896), 532–533. See also Charles Davenport, "Crime, Heredity and Environment," *The Journal of Heredity*, XIX (July 1928), 310.

29. J. R. Tucker, "Race Progress in the United States," *The North American Review*, CXXXVIII (January 1884), 177; John Reade, "The Intermingling of Races," *The Popular Science Monthly*, XXX (January 1887), 344. C. A. Gardiner, "The Race Problem in the United States," *Journal of Social Science*, XVIII (May 1884), 273–274.

ships.[30] The Negro or the African, as nineteenth-century journalism designated him, was a creation of geographic determinism. Invoking biology based on the inheritance of acquired character, Nathaniel Shaler, a scientist, asserted that race mixing was biologically unwise, for it created weaker stock since miscegenation always caused feebler individuals.[31] The Negro, unable to match the white man's performance, was threatened by race rivalry. Colonization was the proper public policy, reasoned R. W. Shufeldt, a philosopher of naturalism. Calling on history and science for evidence, he urged that since the Negro has not responded properly to the American environment, a return to Africa would solve the most disturbing American problem. He found race mixture the curse of the Republic. For the national welfare, public policy must first save the white from the sociobiological danger of interracial marriage.[32] As noted earlier, Charles Davenport shared in this feeling of hostility toward the colored person.

Yet, in the long range, man's future evolution into one race encouraged Shufeldt and others. Being in the Social Darwinian tradition, they saw the Negro, the Japanese, and other human groups they disliked losing the struggle for existence. Using the "aristocratic" version of the inheritance of acquired characters, eugenists assumed that a little manipulation of principles of eugenics in race relations would restore the consequences of Darwinian natural law. Creating by eugenics a better racial atmosphere for the white men only encouraged the inevitable in the evolution of mankind and civilization.[33]

The practical applications of anthropological inquiries ultimately contributed a more natural and, thereby, a just society. Just as applied anthropology functioned in race relations, nineteenth-century social scientists saw an educational application for the children of one race. The growth of children became significant to investigators as a method

30. N. S. Shaler, "Science and the African Problem," *The Atlantic Monthly,* LXVI (July 1890), 36–37.

31. Shaler, "The African Element in America," *The Arena,* II (November 1890), 660–673.

32. R. W. Shufeldt, "The Practicability of Transporting the Negro to Africa," *Science,* XVII (January 23, 1891), 48.

33. Shufeldt, "The Man of the Future," *Science,* XVIII (October 16, 1891), 218–219; James H. Stoller, "Human Heredity," *The Popular Science Monthly,* XXXVII (July 1890), 359–365.

of analysis for mental progress. Under the sponsorship of the Social Science Association of Boston, Dr. Henry P. Bowditch (1840–1911), a professor of physiology of the Harvard Medical School, investigated the rate of growth of children in Boston. Using the statistical techniques of Adoloph Quetelet (1796–1874), Bowditch advanced the study of anthropometry within American anthropology.[34] Sir Francis Galton's statistical studies and the work of his disciple Karl Pearson in biometrics also contributed to this development in anthropology.

Given the naturalistic assumption that mind and body were related, the scholarly interest in child development increased. In 1892 Dr. W. Townsend Porter measured more than 33,000 St. Louis school children in attempting to find the physical basis for mental precocity and dullness. Using the Galtonian model of deviation from a central type, Porter urged, "no pupil whose physical development deviates more than $\pm d$ from the weight, etc. of the mean pupil of his height in a class which his mental output would otherwise entitle him to enter" should enter it until a medical doctor recommended his entrance.[35] Franz Boas, a leading American anthropologist and political progressive, welcomed Porter's study for using the techniques of physical anthropology, but Boas warned against any racial dogmatism regarding conclusions.[36]

Franz Boas spent a lifetime fighting the racial dogmatism inserted into anthropological investigation. As early as 1894 he rejected the idea of the human mind being the sole creation of race. Civilization did not create naturally innate superior or inferior human beings. Boas championed the plasticity of human nature and dynamic in-

34. Aleš Hrdlička, "Physical Anthropology: Its Scope and Aims, Its History and Present Status in America," *American Journal of Physical Anthropology,* I (April-June 1918), 156–157; Helen Walker, *Studies in the History of Statistical Method,* p. 41.

35. William T. Porter, "On the Application to Individual School Children of the Mean Values Derived from Anthropological Measurement by the Generalizing Method," *Publications of the American Statistical Association,* III (December 1893), 587; Aleš Hrdlička, "Physical Anthropology: Its Scope and Aims, Its History and Present Status in America," *American Journal of Physical Anthropology,* I (October-December 1918), 396–397.

36. Franz Boas, "On Dr. William Townsend Porter's Investigation of the Growth of the School Children of St. Louis," *Science,* n.s. I (March 1, 1895), 225–230.

fluence that culture and social tradition had on the individual.[37] His famous *The Mind of Primitive Man* was an effective and scholarly attack upon the racist notions found in popular thought.[38] Historians have noted fully the environmental tone of his thought, although Boas did not engage in dogma which is the basis for any "school of thought." [39]

In addition to his rejection of racism, Boas questioned the validity of cultural evolutionism. Noting that evolution was a valid concept of biology, Boas saw no analogy in regard to man's cultural life.[40] His emphasis stressed the functional interpretation of anthropological material.

Franz Boas held a high opinion of Sir Francis Galton and Karl Pearson, although the admiration did not deny criticism of Galton's methodology. Boas felt that if an anthropologist could measure the individual differences in a society, he could gain greater understanding of tribal culture.[41] He recognized the value of statistics and mental testing in searching for individual differences *within* a cultural group but doubted the validity in ascribing superiority or inferiority between cultural groups.

Boas did not represent the majority of scientific opinion in American naturalism. The theories of Daniel G. Brinton indicated the naturalistic mood which accepted the unity of mental performance and physical

37. Boas, "Human Faculty as Determined by Race," *Proceedings of the American Association for the Advancement of Science,* XLIII (August 1894), 327; Robert H. Lowie, "Biographical Memoir of Franz Boas, 1858–1942," *National Academy of Sciences of the United States, Biographical Memoirs,* XXIV (1947), 316. For an excellent biography and discussion of Boas's ideas, see Abram Kardiner and Edward Preble, *They Studied Man,* pp. 134–159.

38. Boas, *The Mind of Primitive Man* is a synthesis of articles dealing with the race issue and its connection with heredity and environment.

39. Robert H. Lowie, *The History of Ethnological Theory,* pp. 136–137; Nicholas Pastore, *The Nature-Nurture Controversy,* p. 140; Louis Wirth, "The Social Sciences," American Scholarship in the Twentieth Century, Merle Curti, ed., p. 64. For an analysis regarding the nonexistent "Boas school of thought," see Kardiner, *They Studied Man,* p. 159.

40. Leslie White, "The Concept of Evolution in Cultural Anthropology," *Evolution and Anthropology,* Betty Meggers, ed., p. 106. For Boas's rejection of the concept of evolution, see *The Mind of Primitive Man,* pp. 175–196.

41. Lowie, "Biographical Memoir of Franz Boas," p. 305; Lowie, *History of Ethnological Theory,* pp. 134–135.

strength in cultural achievement. Brinton wrote, "The changes in the mental are strictly correlated to those in the physical system. It is vain for ethnologists to seek to forget this elementary physiological fact." In his version of racial determinism, Brinton accepted the concept of the fixity of the race.[42] Coeditor of the anthropology section in Science, he actively supported the American Association for the Advancement of Science. His opinions and attitudes were therefore respectable. A pioneer in the history of physical anthropology in the United States, Brinton propagated the born-criminal thesis.[43]

Brinton, like his contemporaries, held to a naturalistic solution for the Negro's menace in the American population. He took comfort in the fact that the "pure blacks" had a higher mortality rate than white people, and that hybrids between the two races were less fertile and less viable than either one of the pure groups. Thus the white race would absorb the Negro without any deterioration of the dominant race.[44]

Brinton's optimistic trust in the Negro's inevitable degeneration in the presence of the superior white culture-biology changed for many American progressives to racial pessimism. As previously stated, the naturalistic conservatives, active in "progressive" reforms in education and charitable activities, feared the masses.

Max Nordau's *Degeneration*, published in 1895, forecast the American conservative progressive's concern over the degenerative effect of urban life. Nordau emphasized alcohol, tobacco, fatigue from increased sense impressions on the individual's central nervous system, and the growth of cities as causes of racial degeneration. One reviewer of the book summed up the concern of progressives over degeneracy when he wrote this solution to the situation:

The real problem of dealing with degenerates, and of checking their increase, is no doubt mainly connected with the condition of city life and the increasing use of mechanism, and is to be solved by changes in municipal

42. Daniel G. Brinton, "Racial and Ethnic Traits," *Science*, n.s. II (July 19, 1895), 66.

43. *Science*, XIX (June 3, 1872), 72.

44. Brinton, "The Future of the Colored Race in the United States," *Science*, n.s. I (March 8, 1895), 256 and his article, "Race Degeneration in the Southern States," *Science*, n.s. IV (December 4, 1896), 831.

organization adapted to the new condition of the day, combined with in-telligent direction of the work of private associations of various kinds.[45]

This attitude gained wider acceptance in the early-twentieth-cen-tury eugenics movement. Social scientists in the last decade of the nineteenth century emphasized society's need for mate selection be-cause inferior stocks outbred civilized man. Anticipating Charles Davenport's social policy, one critic rejected better housing and food to improve the nation's health and advocated marriage for only the better breeds in society. Race, the critic stressed, was not bound toward decay, but modern conditions and sentimental charity en-couraged the growth of the unfit.[46] For lasting reform, he argued, the biological condition of parents must be improved.

The intellectual confusion of the reply to improve the biological conditions of society has obscured some of the important and con-servative features of American progressivism in the early decades of the twentieth century. The concept of "environment" caused the mis-understanding. The inheritance of acquired characteristics theory has an optimistic (democratic) or pessimistic (aristocratic) version ex-pressed in contemporary politics as liberal or conservative. Thus, a conservative argued for nutritional improvement of the diet to save Americans from morbid heredity, while Charles Cooley, a progressive liberal, urged a policy of "rational social discipline, such as is already successful in enough cases to show that it might be greatly extended.[47] It was apparent that *environment* suggested different policies to the political or philosophical conservative or liberal. In like manner, this confusion existed throughout the entire scope of progressive thought.

The confusion came from nineteenth-century anthropologists who treated the whole primitive world as a single unit. Thus, anthropolo-

45. J. S. Billings, Review of Max Nordau, *Degeneration,* in *Science,* n.s. I (April 26, 1895), 465. For an indication of Nordau's influence on Europe, see Jacques Barzum, "From the Nineteenth Century to the Twentieth," *Chapter in Western Civilization,* third edition, II, 446.

46. George St. Clair, Review of John B. Haycraft, *Darwinism and Race Prog-ress* (New York, 1895), in Science, n.s. I (April 26, 1895), 467–469.

47. Charles H. Cooley, "Nature versus Nurture in the Making of Social Classes," *Proceedings of the National Conference of Charities and Corrections* (Boston, 1896), pp. 399, 402–403; M. C. Fere, "Morbid Heredity," *The Popular Science Monthly,* XLVII (July 1895), 398.

gists drew random facts to illustrate their particular theories, while scholars in other fields of social science investigated the process of social change. The error was in analogy, for nineteenth-century anthropologists lacked a corpus of classified knowledge comparable to that of biology; yet, the anthropologists used the biological concept of evolution.[48]

On the eve of the twentieth century, anthropologists also accepted the psychic unity of mankind that all men followed the same thought processes. In the following years, with the development of *cultural* anthropology, they rejected this theory along with the recapitulation theory. Whereas anthropologists concerned themselves with morphological problems and not behavior, the cultural anthropologists became more culture-centered in their investigations. This resulted in creating a gap between man and the other primates—a gap which the evolutionary theory was supposed to close.[49] Cultural anthropologists believed that evolution was no longer the answer to man's development, as individuals such as Ruth Benedict and other students of the "primitive world" discovered the dynamic nature of culture.

In early-twentieth-century America this development in anthropology was largely a matter of the future. The scientific virtue of racism was still intact. In an academic journal, one social scientist questioned the Negro's biological right to citizenship. Rejecting the legal aspects of citizenship (such as exercising the right of suffrage), the writer denied that the Negro had the intelligence for citizenship and its corresponding responsibilities. The author urged the Negro to heed the wisdom and political guidance of those superior in intelligence—the whites.[50] This concern with the mentally inferior appeared in a meeting of the American Association for the Advancement of

---

48. Kroeber, "Evolution, History and Culture," p. 16, and J. H. Steward, "Evolutionary Principles and Social Types," p. 122. Both articles are in *Evolution after Darwin* (Volume II of *The Evolution of Man, Culture and Society*).

49. Richard Hallowell, "Behavioral Evolution and the Emergence of the Self," pp. 37–38, and Russell Hoag, "The Status of Evolutionary Thought in American History" are both in *Evolution and Anthropology*, Betty Meggers, ed.

50. George R. Stetson, "The Racial Problem," *Journal of Social Science*, XXXVI (April 1901), 115; Amos W. Butler, "A Notable Factor of Social Degeneration," *Proceedings of the American Association for the Advancement of Science*, L (1901), 353.

Science. Speaking of the anthropology section, Amos Butler warned against the increase in the feebleminded whose "fecundity and animal instincts" created people with weak minds and strong bodies. Marriage regulation and custodial care provided the two solutions to the situation.[51]

The racists with their fear of the masses did not express all of the scientific opinion in the United States. Studying the physical, mental, and social traits of individuals, Robert S. Woodworth concluded that the wholesale rejection of groups based on ethnic composition was erroneous. "The part of wisdom," he wrote, "would be to select the very best individuals available from every source, rather than trusting to the illusory appearance of great racial differences in mental and moral traits, to make the selection in terms of races or nations." [52] For a number of historical reasons this attitude gained greater acceptance after 1930 and the Great Depression.

At the height of the progressive movement in 1914, a statistician, Frederick Crum, projected a gloomy future for the United States. The native stock, having succumbed to the materialistic luxuries of urban life, ignored the obligation of a large family, and the immigrants, with their higher birth rate, had first claim on the future greatness of the United States.[53] This antiurban bias continued in academic social thought for some time.[54] The career of Earnest A. Hooton indicated a continuation of such thought.

51. *Ibid.*

52. Woodworth, "Racial Differences in Mental Traits," *Science,* n.s. XXXI (February 4, 1910), 171–186, and his article, "Societies and Academies Section of Anthropology and Psychology of the New York Academy of Sciences," *Science,* n.s. XIII (April 26, 1901), 662–663. The first article cited was an address given by Woodworth to Section H, "Anthropology and Psychology" (of which he was chairman) of the American Association for the Advancement of Science in Boston, 1909.

53. Frederick S. Crum, "The Decadence of the Native American Stock, A Statistical Study of Genealogical Records," *Publications of the American Statistical Association,* XIV (September 1914), 220–221.

54. Louis Dublin, "The Mortality of Race Stocks in Pennsylvania and New York, 1910," *Quarterly Publication of the American Statistical Association,* XVII (March 1920), 43–44; Warren S. Thompson, "Race Suicide in the United States," *American Journal of Physical Anthropology,* III (January-March 1920), 140–146; H. N. Hall, "Are the Various Races of Men Potentially Equal?" *Proceedings of the American Philosophical Society,* LXIII (April 25, 1924), 208–214.

He expressed many of the sentiments found in the anthropology of the nineteenth and early twentieth centuries. Receiving a doctor of philosophy degree in anthropology from the University of Wisconsin in 1911, Hooton spent most of his academic life at Harvard University. From 1918 to 1942 he was an associate editor of the *American Journal of Physical Anthropology* along with other naturalistic conservatives having an interest in eugenics—Charles Davenport, G. Stanley Hall, and J. H. Kellogg. During Hooton's editorship, the *Journal* carried a section on eugenics which primarily served as a bibliographical review of work done in the field of eugenics.[55]

Hooton acquired this academic reputation for his studies in the anthropology of crime. He believed that a significant correlation existed between the racial and physical features of an individual and the type of crime he committed and even in the possibility of a criminal career based on the racial heredity of the individual.[56] Eugenics was the answer to crime. He reasoned that

criminals are originally inferior. Crime is the resultant of the impact of environment upon low-grade human organisms. It follows that the elimination of crime can be effected only by the extirpation of the physically, mentally, and morally unfit, or by their complete segregation in a socially aseptic environment.[57]

Hooton's interest in eugenics extended in other areas of social thought in which other eugenists have made similar judgments. Noting human behavior as having an organic basis, he saw racial physical types in association with certain sociological types. Therefore, Hooton warned, the danger for democracy was the election of low-grade public officials, because the majority of the population is extremely unintelligent, and it is this majority that elects public officials. His social philosophy was an anthropological adaptation of nineteenth-century laissez-faire capitalism. Man had raised himself above the

55. *Who Was Who in America*, III, p. 414; *American Journal of Physical Anthropology from 1918–1943*.

56. Hooton, "Preliminary Remarks on the Anthropology of the American Criminal," *Proceedings of the American Philosophical Society*, LXXI (April 22, 1932), 352; Cargill, *Intellectual America*, p. 132.

57. Hooton, *The American Criminal*, pp. 307–309. With biological qualifications, Hooton extended his analysis to nationalities who commit certain crimes. See *Ibid.*, pp. 9–10.

brute by his reason, intelligence, and volition. Therefore, where there was no repression, the intelligent individual rose to the top in the socioeconomic scale, while the stupid remained on the bottom, Hooton argued. This situation was the most reasonable, since it was impossible to perfect human culture in order to cure all of mankind's ills. "Organic liberty" was intelligence, according to Hooton. This was the capacity for dealing rationally with new situations.[58]

Hooton did not base his advocacy of eugenics on a belief in racial superiority. Rejecting Aryanism in eugenic thought, he allowed for superior individuals within any ethnic group. As did other twentieth-century eugenists, Hooton saw human improvement as primarily biological, with religion only a necessary device for maintaining ethical standards for the stupid majority of mankind.[59]

The Harvard anthropologist's conception of "environment" was indicative of much of American speculation on eugenics. He accepted as truth the biological principle that "the greater the demand put upon an organ the larger it becomes." [60] He rejected the medical ethic of saving individual lives without any regard for the racial welfare of society. Medicine must, Hooton warned, "allocate to itself the function of discovering how the animal may be improved as a biological organism. The future of mankind does not depend upon political or economic theory, nor yet upon measures of social amelioration but upon the production of better minds in sounder bodies." Hooton rejected this latter version of environment on grounds that human life is not inherently good and worthy of preservation. In a word, a fool is always a fool, and all the programs of social reform in environment will never change him. In keeping with other philosophers of eugenics, he rejected the natural-rights theories because they have created dysgenic environment, that is, war, medical science, and social ethics, and thus threaten modern society with a multitude of unfit human beings.[62] Hooton therefore declared invalid environmental

58. Hooton, *Twilight of Man,* pp. 5, 11, 54, 210, 274, 278, 299.

59. Hooton, *Apes, Men and Morons,* pp. 7, 16, 152–153, 229–236, and *Twilight of Man,* p. 149.

60. Hooton, *Apes, Men and Morons,* p. 29.

61. *Ibid.,* p. 290.

62. Hooton, 'Young Man, You Are Normal,' p. 209; *Apes, Men and Morons,* p. 267, 269.

reforms suggested by New Deal liberalism, but he accepted as socially beneficial those biological reforms which allowed the full and free expression of natural selection. Modern society with its indiscriminate charity and humanitarianism checked the purgative effects of natural selection and allowed the criminal, the insane, and the organically inferior to live and reproduce their kind.[63]

Hooton saw the march of civilization as a funeral procession for the biological elite of mankind. When man changed to an agricultural existence to gain an expanded diet, the decline of innate good health began. Urban industry and civilization multiplied men's pathologies by increasing the exchange of new and virile infections. All types of physical abnormalities increased by this process, aided in no small way by the misdirected humanitarianism of medical science. In brief, Hooton wrote, "The biological status of man seems to decline as his culture accelerates." Modern man was a physical wreck. Yet, in the primitive past natural selection eliminated the inferior groups; thus only the superior increased their numbers.[64]

In this manner, Hooton—like other eugenists—saw a biological Garden of Eden, a golden age, before the serpent of industrialization corrupted man with schemes to check the "natural goodness" of natural selection. In their desire to create a new man, the eugenists, including Hooton, wanted a new society—a new environment—to resurrect natural man. Paradoxically, the eugenists, defenders of hereditary determinism, attempted to save natural man by environmental reforms.

63. Hooton, 'Young Man You Are Normal,' p. 208; *Apes, Men and Morons,* p. 264.

64. *Ibid.,* pp. 293, 295. Hooton believed that tooth decay was the result of this process of degeneration.

10

THE
SCIENTIFIC
RESURRECTION
OF THE
NATURAL MAN

Scientific Charity

THE RACIAL degeneration of modern urban society worried American eugenists. They saw the increased number of the feebleminded in the United States, by immigration and natural increase, as definite indications of racial inadequacy. In brief, they argued that contemporary life increased the numbers of the inadequate at the expense of the adequate. The task, therefore, was of restoration, of returning the primacy of natural selection to men's affairs. Modern society protected the naturally inferior from their true destiny of extinction; eugenists urged policies of removing the restrictions on natural selection. Scientific charity, conservation, and the country-life movement provided the three means of resurrection of the natural (preurban) man in accord with the principles of science and nature.

These three techniques of restoring the biologically superior to a place of power in society had the common feature of being predicated on an idea of natural law, of following objective principles in the behavior of the world. Advocates of scientific charity, conservation, and the country-life movement denounced the artificiality of modern life, of men not allowing Nature to be their mentor in social affairs. By subscribing to this trinity of reform programs, Americans would realize the good life—of the healthy mind in a clean body, the ultimate objective of American eugenists. In the process of this restoration, the state's functions and scope increased as the advocates of these three movements succeeded in their attempts to return to the good old days of innocence and purity.

American eugenists wanted scientific charity valued for the racial consequences of such humanitarian endeavors. In other words, for example, would improved public health programs among slum dwellers increase the number of physically and morally strong individuals? The ultimate answer, according to eugenists, was the welfare of society, of the state, and not the personal welfare of a particular individual organism. The strong must inherit the future. Charity—based on objective laws and values located in nature—insured that inheritance. As will be seen later, both the scientific and religious thought of the nineteenth century supported the eugenists of pre–World War I America in their assurances about the existence and, therefore, validity of stressing racial values in charitable enterprises. The century of Sir Francis Galton upheld the notion of scientific charity found in the progressive era of the United States.

Although individual eugenists were skeptical about the validity of an individual natural rights, they, as well as adherents of the three movements under discussion, assumed the existence of universal laws, biological or social, that defined right and proper conduct for individuals in society. The mere existence of such laws, the logic continued, made them proper standards of value. Progress was the systematic comprehension and utilization of these laws in public policy.[1]

Understandably, in nineteenth-century America, with science and religion at grips over Darwinian evolution, social thinkers designated their activities "scientific" and discredited supernatural explanations of man's origin and future purpose. In many instances, the public mistook scientism for science. The growing disciplines of anthropology and Darwinian biology encouraged the search for laws of historical de-

1. J. B. Bury, *The Idea of Progress*, pp. 305–306.

velopment. The influence of biology was most apparent in analogies
that appeared in scholarly disputations on social theory.[2]

Naturalism was the intellectual milieu in which eugenics and the related fields of scientific charity thrived. Ironically, Christian sentiment
also contributed to charity movements in the America of the nineteenth
and twentieth centuries with all its naturalistic manifestations. Christianity and scientific charity both dealt with corruption and immorality;
the latter relied more on a naturalistic explanation for the evil conditions that existed. As early as 1702, Cotton Mather organized a Society
for the Suppression of Disorder to prevent the swearing of oaths and the
patronage of disorderly houses. Like its progressive counterparts two
centuries later, Mather's group saw virtue in early education and thus
investigated children's education and supervised their play.[3] The Society for the Suppression of Disorder, like later similar groups, was its
brother's keeper with a vengeance.

The concept of stewardship, supporting the charity impulses,
changed over the centuries in American history, not in kind but in
degree. For many later advocates of charity, science replaced God as
the motivating factor behind charitable endeavors. With God or science
the stewards' task was interpretation of laws. Before the
advent of Darwinian evolution social workers used many of the
same arguments for charitable activities that appeared after 1859. In
other words, Darwin's theories did not change the philosophy of charity
much—merely added biological justification to what already existed.
According to historian Clifford S. Griffin, the pre-Darwinian stewards
of wealth recognized the usefulness of charity in dulling the edge of
class conflict and for maintaining political leadership of the well-to-do
in the developing industrial nation. Religious piety and morality, therefore, maintained civic obedience in the secular order.[4] Even after the
Darwinian revolution in American thought supporting laissez-faire poli-

2. John C. Greene, "Biology and Social Theory in the Nineteenth Century:
Auguste Comte and Herbert Spencer," *Critical Problems in the History of Science,
Proceedings of the Institute for the History of Science at the University of Wis-
consin, September 1–11, 1957,* Marshall Clagett, ed., pp. 441–442.

3. Carl Bridenbaugh, *Cities in the Wilderness, The First Century of Urban Life
in America, 1625–1742,* p. 229.

4. Clifford S. Griffin, *Their Brother's Keepers: Moral Stewardship in the United
States, 1800–1865,* p. xii of the introduction.

cies, Henry Adams, cynic and historian of despair, held elitistic ideas of leadership based on class origin as a basis for stewardship.[5] The wealthy had moral obligations to provide for the poor.

Quite early in the nation's history, social workers agitated for federal assistance in meeting this charitable obligation of one social class to another. But Franklin Pierce vetoed federal assistance to the states for mental hospitals in 1852. For more than two generations, therefore, voluntary groups and individual states contributed charitable activities without guidance from Washington, D.C.[6] The veto did not stop the desire of American reformers for a scientific method of solving social problems. Calling for legislation based on scientific investigation, the editors of the *Scientific American* hailed social science as the means of destroying community evils by promoting the welfare and harmony of society.[7] They saw society as a laboratory, a place to test theories and offer objective solutions. Ministers, too, saw the same vision.

Charles G. Finney (1792–1875), for example, used a blend of science and psychology in conducting his revivals. Drawing on "laws of the mind," he believed that science and the revealed word of God were the same; thus man saved his soul and aided in the progress of society by studying and accepting the laws of the universe. Clergymen defended science long after the first impact of evolutionary speculations.[8]

Finney's synthesis of science and religion were not unique. Theologians argued that Darwin refined and exalted Christian morality by deriving it from a social instinct (and therefore community's welfare was a "natural" good derived from man's moral nature). Darwin, they argued, put ethics on a firm biological basis; this divorced utilitarianism from charges of selfishness.[9] At the same time, the religious reformers,

5. William H. Jorly, *Henry Adams: Scientific Historian*, p. 101. For an interesting analysis of stewardship broadly concerned, see Geoffrey T. Blodgett, "The Mind of the Boston Mugwump, *M.V.H.R.*, XLVIII (March 1962), 614–634.

6. Ralph E. Pumphrey, *The Heritage of American Social Work*, pp. 51–52, 125–126.

7. Editorial, "A New Science," *The Scientific American*, n.s. III (November 17, 1860), 329.

8. William G. McLaughlin, Jr., *Modern Revivalism*, pp. 86, 120. For later adjustment between Darwinism and theology, see John C. Greene, *Darwin and the Modern World View*.

9. Himmelfarb, *Darwin and the Darwinian Revolution*, p. 339.

drawing on scientific knowledge, associated happiness with health, which could be obtained for modern man through the scientific control of disease.

Reformers increasingly embraced scientific social welfare during the latter half of the nineteenth century. They saw science as the road to a collective realization of happiness. As Daniel G. Brinton, contributing editor of *Science*, remarked in 1895, "the mission of science was noble, inspiring, consolatory; lifting the mind above the gross contracts of life; preventing aims which are not at once practical, humanitarian and spiritually elevating." This hymn to progress through science ended by pointing to science as the creator of all goodness, for scientific truth was absolute and objective.[10] From this point of view, progress was a scientific certainty.

Two manifestations existed in nineteenth-century social thought. One stressed reason, natural law, the individual; the other tendency was toward culture, the nation, the race, the folk, and the state as instruments by which society might improve.[11] Eugenists in the United States employed these two developments with a greater emphasis on the race and the folk because of its Darwinian and Galtonian orientation. This latter manifestation supported eugenists particularly in assuming charitable activities in the name of science.

The developing field of social work in the nineteenth century contributed to the emerging concept of scientific charity. In an age in which the struggle for existence appeared to be innately a part of society, social workers defined social work as helping people who were unable to "keep step with the social system, and ease strains on the system itself, especially in periods of crisis." [12]

The American Social Science Association and the National Conference of Social Work issued a joint resolution endorsing civil service reform. The civil service issue was a conservative and respectable

10. Brinton, "The Character and Aims of Scientific Investigation," *Science*, n.s. I (January 4, 1895), 3–4. See the same sentiment in G. Brown Goode, "America's Relation to the Advance of Science," *Science*, n.s. I (January 4, 1898), 4–8.

11. L. L. Bernard, *Origins of American Sociology, The Social Science Movement in the United States*, p. 1. Hereafter cited as Bernard, *Origins of American Sociology*.

12. Pumphrey, *The Heritage of American Social Work*, p. 1.

reform. The resolution suggested a basic division of labor, of government by experts. The result was a victory for elitist social thought. The Jacksonian belief that any normal man could adequately perform any task in society or government changed. Specialization in society seemed natural, since the biological orders found in nature indicated a high degree of specialization and supplemented the activities of the various species. "Nature," it seemed, suggested that the naturally superior groups in society had an obligation, within limits, to aid the victims of natural selection. Under no circumstances must the biologically unfit reproduce their kind.

The concern for self-supporting citizens was the crux of the scientific charity crusade. Nineteenth-century social workers equated pauperism with antisocial behavior. A pauper was an individual supported wholly or in part by public funds. Because of the strong biological orientation to the American social philosophy of the era, speakers before the Sixth Annual Conference of Charities claimed that pauperism was hereditary.[13] The solution was eugenic: keep the poor from reproducing their own kind. As noted earlier, the state had a right to protect itself from inferior stocks. Amos Reynolds at the meeting in 1879 believed "all persons acquitted of crime on the grounds of insanity should be kept in custody the remainder of their lives." Warming to his vision, the critic concluded, "I would go further: the state should prohibit the marriage of all persons who had at any time after arriving at the age of eighteen years, been supported in any penal or charitable institution or who are suffering from any incurable bodily infirmity or deformity." [14] Like twentieth-century eugenists, to this expert on pauperism all social problems were hereditary in origin.

Although hereditary determinism affected the thought of many reformers, Robert T. Paine, president of the Associated Charities of Boston, urged a wholesale reform of the social order as a means of preventing social problems rather than curing them. He advocated philanthropy used in a judicious manner with the latest technique of social

13. Frank J. Burns, *Trends in Social Work, 1874–1956, A History Based on the Proceedings of the National Conference of Social Work*, pp. 91–92. Hereafter cited as Bruns, *Trends in Social Work*.

14. Amos Reynolds, "The Prevention of Pauperism," *Proceedings of the Sixth Annual Conference of Charities Held at Chicago, June, 1879*, pp. 210–216.

work and suggested that this might provide a solution for all types of social disorganization.[15] Eugenists, using the "aristocratic" version of this environmentalistic philosophy, continued the fight for preventive measures that men like Paine suggested.

A Yale University scientist, William H. Brewer, speaking before the National Conference of Charities and Corrections in 1895, offered an analysis and solution to social problems that indicated a nineteenth-century theistic naturalism origin of the twentieth-century eugenics philosophy. Scientists investigated God's laws of the universe, and man's work was successful only when he worked in accordance with these laws. The nature of the universe even affected matters of charity.

It [charity] must be directed along lines marked by the fixed laws of nature, that the lower strata of mankind may be bettered as well as helped; that the instinct of charity may be not by perversion become a curse to the race, increasing its lower stratum at the expense of the better part of mankind.

Brewer already understood the laws of heredity. He found them applicable to society's mental and moral defectives. Armed with such knowledge, Americans could prevent the reproduction of such individuals. It was imperative, Brewer added, because of the high cost of charities and corrections. Invoking the use of the expert like a true prophet of progressivism, the Yale professor urged an environmentalist solution to the cause of crime. "Vicious instinct," he wrote, "must be controlled by beginning with the young, charity lessened by making men more efficient and self-reliant, and reform, not vengeance, be the leading idea in our prisons." [16]

Thus nineteenth-century philanthropists urged self-help and rehabilitation for the nation's poor as well as the scientific administration of charitable organizations.[17] Both theistic evolutionists and fundamentalists aided the creation of a better society by the scientific use of

15. Robert H. Bremner, *American Philanthropy*, pp. 103–104.

16. William H. Brewer, "The Relation of Universities to Charity and to Reformatory Work," *Proceedings of the National Conference of Charities and Correction, 22nd Annual Session Held in New Haven, Conn., May 24–30, 1895*, pp. 143, 147.

17. Merle Curti, "Tradition and Innovation in American Philanthropy," *Proceedings of the American Philosophical Society*, CV (April 1961), 147.

charity. City missions and municipal reforms, advocated by revivalists, served the same end as scientific charity, stressing social conformity for the lower classes through public opinion and law.[18] Society must offer help and guidance to the urban poor and defective for either religious or secular reasons but ultimately for the protection of the social order. This attitude showed itself in charitable activities in the United States of 1900 to 1930. The result was preventive social work. Based on nineteenth-century scientism, popular theology and the concept of progress, preventive social work exerted a major pressure on the progressive's reform methodology.[19]

While these intellectual developments occurred in the history of charity, changes within the sociology of philanthropy took place. The "successful" protected the "unsuccessful." The social work of Philip C. Garrett (1834–1905) was an example of a member of the natural elite helping his unfortunate fellow humans. Retiring from business at forty-four as a wealthy man, he spent the remainder of his life in private and public charitable endeavors, especially with the American Indians.[20] This sociological process (the wealthy man's entering charity as an occupation at middle age) increased during the twentieth century, particularly during the years before World War I.

Although Andrew Carnegie (1835-1919) was an older man when he began his philanthropic career, his behavior was similar to Garrett's and at the same time part of the growth of philanthropic foundations. Carnegie advocated his particular concept of stewardship as the inevitable result of victory in life's competitive struggle. The millionaire, representing the highest form of natural selection, had a trusteeship to spend scientifically his wealth to benefit the entire community. This millionaire philanthropist, according to Carnegie, should exercise his own judgment in choosing what was good for society.

According to the historian Robert Bremner, philanthropy based on the gospel of wealth served as an antidote for radical schemes to re-

18. McLaughlin, *Modern Revivalism*, pp. 280, 257, 326, 363–364.

19. Bremner, "Scientific Philanthropy, 1873–1893," *Social Service Review*, XXX (June 1956), 173. For a more detailed description of this ideological development, see Henry S. Commager, *American Mind*, and Sidney Fine, *Laissez-Faire and the General Welfare State, 1865–1901*.

20. Bruno, *Trends in Social Work*, p. 33.

distribute property by dulling the conflict between the poor and the rich.[21] During the progressive era, wealthy businessmen established a number of philanthropic institutions in hope that scientific research might find cures for society's various ills and relax social tensions. In the years before World War I, Russell Sage (1816-1906), Andrew Carnegie, John D. Rockefeller (1839-1937), and others established foundations, not for a narrowly defined purpose or simply to relieve the poor, but as a method of destroying human misery.[22]

Just as American leaders of industry adjusted to the spirit of philanthropic enterprises and scientific charity, religious spokesmen began agitating for the new dispensation in public welfare. Revivalism, the expression of religious sentiment, also adopted a naturalistic coloration during the progressive era. Evangelists by the hundreds utilized the progressive themes of the Americanization of the immigrant, the social-service concept, and prohibition in their efforts to win the urban masses for old-time religion. Coupling sex and religion, Milan B. Williams, a typical revivalist, expressed a desire, similar to Billy Sunday's, for immigration restriction in order to save the racial virtue of Anglo-Saxon America.[23] Knowledge and technology, therefore, based on the laws of God's universe, offered secular and social salvation for man if he returned to the ways of nature.[24] This desire for mankind to return to a previous stage of perfection was a common characteristic of fundamen-

21. Bremner, *American Philanthropy*, pp. 106–107. For a discussion of the settlement house as a meeting place of people and ideas in community co-operation, see Bruno, *Trends in Social Work*, pp. 112–119. For the role of the settlement house in a context of general urban reform, see Ginger, *Altgeld's America*.

22. Bremner, *American Philanthropy*, p. 117; F. Emerson Andrews, "Growth and Present Status of American Foundations," *Proceedings of the American Philosophical Society*, CV (April 1961), 158.

23. McLaughlin, *Modern Revivalism*, pp. 390, 393, 443. For the element of nativism in progressive thought, see William Preston, Jr., *Aliens and Dissenters, Federal Suppression of Radicals, 1903–1933*, and James H. Timberlake, *Prohibition and the Progressive Movement, 1900–1920*. For good general studies of religion and urbanism, see Henry F. May, *Protestant Churches and Industrial America*; Aaron I. Abell, *The Urban Impact on American Protestantism, 1865–1900*, and his *American Catholicism and Social Action: A Search for Social Justice, 1865–1950*.

24. Reno Dubos, *Mirage of Health, Utopias, Progress, and Biological Change*, p. 21.

talist, progressive, and eugenic thought in the early part of the twentieth century.

Eugenists in the progressive era rejected the policy of aiding the social "failures" but saw the desirability of keeping such individuals limited in number and thus curtailing the menace of the mass man. Social science for the naturalists and supernaturalists was the key to efficient urban administration; just as evolution in the animal world expressed intelligence, it was the necessary duty of the more intelligent members of society to guide public policy regarding charity.[25]

As previous chapters have demonstrated, American eugenists held the child's welfare as central to the future racial well-being of the nation. Curtailment of young inferiors and encouragement of the superior remained the eugenists' major desire. Interestingly, the eugenists sought means of protecting superior children from the evils of urban life while exposing inadequate children to the brutal reality of natural selection. Eugenists attempted to "fix" the environment for the natural elite of society.

This emphasis on children and their welfare complemented the progressive's concern for preventive social work and conservation. For in the movement for conservation of forest and natural resources, some groups agitated for the preservation of children, arguing that human life and welfare are a national resource. As in many other aspects of reform, eugenists also contributed to the conservation movement in human happiness. Both groups of reformers in progressive America felt the child was indeed father of the man.

Conservation

The conservation movement in the United States was a child of the union between optimism and despair. The hope that a democratic society could plan for the national welfare and the future showed optimism; despair was implied in the conservation movement, since the scarcity of resources seemed to make controls an economic necessity. In keeping with the traditional American search for natural law, George

25. Pumphrey, *The Heritage of American Social Work*, pp. 137–138. For a defense of applied evolution to social problems, see E. W. Morse, "What American Zoologists Have Done for Evolution," *Science*, X (August 1887), 73–76.

P. Marsh's *The Earth as Modified by Human Action* (1864) stressed the need for the restoration of the harmonies which man disturbed in the organic and inorganic world. The laws of nature were correct guides to the well-being of the human race.[26] American eugenists used this concept in their agitation for the preservation of the natural man.

The reforestation movement of the 1890s was typical of this synthesis of science and positive governmental social policy. Discover the laws of science, then implement a policy of utilization based on society's needs, provided the pattern for the conservation movement in the United States and for the conservative naturalistic reform, eugenics. Conservation of trees or of people involved the same process—the establishment of harmony between man and nature.[27]

The history of the conservation movement in regard to the natural resources—land, water, wood, and minerals—is well known. The movement for the conservation of human resources is relatively unexplored, although both aspects of conservation draw on the same ideas and attitudes for guidance and inspiration. The desire for more parks in nineteenth-century American cities indicated that public planning was necessary to save the virtues of open spaces for future generations of urban citizens. With increased population, future living room was expensive; enlightened philanthropists would blaze the path of progress.[28]

Just as physical space was vital in the future city, so children were the resources of tomorrow's urban center. Laura O. Talbott, a professional social worker, believed that institutional care for homeless children was an important element in the conservation crusade. The state, by establishing training schools based on psychological and physiological principles, could save society money. At the same time she argued that such schools would rid the land of vice.[29]

26. George P. Marsh, *The Earth as Modified by Human Action* (1864) as quoted by David C. Coyle, *Conservation, An American Story of Conflict and Accomplishment,* pp. 23–24.

27. Hans Huth, *Nature and the American, Three Centuries of Changing Attitudes,* pp. 210–211, 174. Hereafter cited as Huth, *Nature and the American.*

28. E. R. L. Gould, "Park Areas and Open Spaces in Cities," *Publications of the American Statistical Association,* I (June-September 1888), 61.

29. Laura O. Talbott, "How Shall We Utilize Vagrant Children?" *Proceedings of the American Association for the Advancement of Science,* XXIX (August

The child welfare movement began in the late nineteenth century. Medical inspection in the public schools did not begin until 1894 in St. Louis, and as late as 1905 only fifty-five cities provided this service. The United States had small representation at the Second International Congress of School Hygiene in 1907. Encouraged by the eugenists and the White House Conference on Child Health, the progressive educators investigated the physical and mental defects of the students.[30]

Since the student possessed both mind and body, philanthropic organizations and other interested groups began a campaign for more playgrounds. As a problem in urban life and education, the playground cause moved from private guidance to public direction. Meeting in 1907, the Playground Association of America in its first annual meeting started a new era in combining recreational activity with human conservation.[31]

Underlying this save-the-children movement, from an artificial urban existence, was a medley of motives ranging from nature-worship to patriotism. These motives had institutional expression. In 1904, for example, the American Park and Outdoor Art Society and the American League for Civic Improvement became the American Civic Association. In this way the American Civic Association was a product of nineteenth-century nature-worship and patriotism, for in the last century the Appalachian Mountain Club and the Sierra Club were formed independently but drew on the same basic interest in the beauty of primitive nature. Likewise, the American Scenic and Historic Preservation Society strove to protect Niagara Falls, for example, from selfish private interests and to pressure the federal government into a positive attitude on such matters. The organizations fought to preserve the natural wonders of the United States so that future generations would experience the joys of living close to nature, an "organic communion" with nature. Moving independently, these organizations expressed the idealistic and utilitarian aspects of the conservation cause.

1890), 449. She has ideas on child-rearing being based on scientific principles, see "The Child of the Future," *Proceedings of the AAAS*, XLIII (1894), 336–337.

30. Curti, *The Social Ideas of American Educators*, p. 247. In this manner, the mental testing crusade was part of a larger conservation enterprise.

31. Gerald K. Massden, "Philanthropy and the Boston Playground Movement, 1885–1901," *The Social Service Review*, XXXV (March 1961), 58.

The progressive conservation movement in general and the Conference of Governors at the White House in 1908 (in which Theodore Roosevelt called on various state governors to discuss conservation policy) in particular lifted a great burden from these private organizations by shifting the leadership of the conservation cause to the state and federal governments.[32]

This "popular front" atmosphere of the conservation movement with other progressive reform prevailed in the National Conservation Congress meeting in 1909. Speeches covered subjects ranging from civic beauty and world peace to elimination of child labor. The conservation of manhood and the Anglo-Saxon race were also popular topics at the meeting.[33] Like other members of the progressive camp, conservationists had their naturalistic orientation. Eugenists expressed part of this philosophical belief.

Progressivism was an urban reform movement, and likewise the concern for child welfare centered around the city. Many progressives wondered whether city life per se had any relationship with mortality, both moral and physical. City life increased consumption. The urban lack of "organic vigor" fostered and encouraged the disease, according to James E. Baker, statistician.[34] The creation of the National Association of Tuberculosis in 1904 attacked this problem by urging programs of pasteurized milk and isolation for open carriers of the disease. For the individual and society, the organization stressed plans for hygenic living. By 1909 the first meeting of the American Conference for the Prevention of Infant Mortality began educational activities. To insure improved public health standards, the American Conference pressed for increased state supervision through the use of a state's police power.[35] Eugenists were not the only reformers pressing for greater state responsibility in the life and health of individual citizens.

32. Huth, *Nature and the American*, pp. 184–186, 1–2.
33. *Proceedings, National Conservation Congress*, 1910, IV as cited in Samuel P. Hays, *Conservation and the Gospel of Efficiency, The Progressive Conservation Movement, 1890–1920*, p. 176. Hereafter cited as Hays, *Conservation and the Gospel of Efficiency*.
34. J. E. Baker, "City Life and Male Mortality," *Publications of the American Statistical Association*, XI (June 1908), 149.
35. C. E. A. Winslow, "Public Health," *Encyclopaedia of the Social Sciences*, XII, p. 649.

Suggesting a particularly harsh method of conservation, Charles B. Davenport, the leader of the American eugenics movement, saw a pattern in the misery of urban social problems. Foreign immigration was the major cause of urban increase, with rural-to-urban migration a minor second cause.[36] Science and Darwinian biology allowed man greater control over the genetic composition of human populations, according to Davenport. He argued for greater selectivity to insure the survival of the better stocks. Death, he continued, was the best policy for inferior social classes such as prostitutes and the feebleminded.[37] Davenport at once combined scientific philanthropy, conservation, and bloody optimism to save superior stocks by the scientific manipulation of environment through public policy.

The high fecundity of foreign-born women augmented the menace of mass man.[38] Since the immigrants were innately and biologically inferior, according to the eugenist's theory, the necessity for restrictive measures compelled eugenists to save America from a diseased urban population.

Proponents of immigration restriction as a means of improving the health of the nation shared the progressive's desire to improve the social and cultural milieu of homeless children. As noted earlier, this desire had nineteenth-century roots in the soil of American naturalism. In 1914, Roger Baldwin, a future founder of the American Civil Liberties Union, was secretary to the Board of Children's Guardians of St. Louis. In that capacity, Baldwin outlined a children's code which included

36. In this opinion, other eugenists shared in Davenport's belief. Robert C. Ward, "Eugenic Immigration, The American Race of the Future and the Responsibility of the Southern States for Its Formation, The 'Survival of the Fittest,' " *American Breeders Association*, IV (2nd Quarter, 1913), 96–102; John M. Gillette and George R. Davies, "Measure of Rural Migration and other Factors of Urban Increase in the United States," *Publication of the American Statistical Association*, XVI (September 1915), 649.

37. Davenport, "The Eugenics Programme and Progress in Its Achievement," *Eugenics: Twelve University Lectures*, p. 12.

38. Joseph A. Hill, "Comparative Fecundity of Women of Native and Foreign Parentage in the United States," *Publications of the American Statistical Association*, XIII (December 1913), 604; F. Stuart Chapin, "Immigration as a Source of Urban Increase," *Publications of the American Statistical Association*, XIV (September 1914), 226.

marriage laws, care of defectives, and eugenics by curtailing the number of misfits through birth control.[39] All of these measures presupposed the increased governmental activity in child-welfare programs.

The social workers of the Rome State Custodial System at Rome, New York, combined conservation, child care and love of nature. At Rome, twenty-five inmates became Boy Scouts and began a forestry project. The value to the state, the eugenist reported, tripled the original investment in trees.[40] In this way, the idea of young men engaged in forestry work provided a eugenic forerunner to the Civil Conservation Corps of Franklin Roosevelt's New Deal.

This "return to nature" was quite evident throughout the progressive ideology. Some individuals, perplexed by the complexity of urban life, sought the good life in the primitive wilderness. Within two years, nature-lovers established The Pathfinders of America and The Associated Mountaining Clubs of America. This latter group particularly studied nature and agitated for the development of forest reserves along with state and national parks. The American Game Protective and Propagation Association, formed in 1911, climaxed nearly thirty years of devoted service to wildlife.[41] The urge to save the old-time American's rustic recreation was behind these organizations.

Just as wildlife preservation linked conservation with the restoration of nature, David Starr Jordan, as a vice-president of the Boy Scouts in the United States, fused the eugenist's concern for the biological future of mankind with nature-worship.[42] In a limited manner, the Boy Scouts sought to create the eugenic new man by stressing the old-time virtues of moral character, self-reliance and a clean mind in a clean body, united with a glorification of outdoor living. The Boy Scout movement exhibited one manifestation of the naturalistic and "eugenic" foundations of progressive thought.

39. Bruno, *Trends in American Social Work*, pp. 215–216.

40. A. E. Hamilton, "Let's Positive Our Negative Eugenics," *The Journal of Heredity*, VII (July 1916), 309–310. Judge Ben Lindsey had a similar idea of eugenics and child welfare. See Ditzion, *Marriage, Morals and Sex in America*, p. 382n.

41. Bates, *Scientific Societies in the United States*, pp. 103, 111.

42. Williams, *The Progress of Eugenics*, p. 89.

Country-Life Movement

David Starr Jordan, the eugenist, combined his activities in the Boy Scout movement with the National Irrigation Association and similar conservation groups. These organizations saved resources by efficient and scientific methods and old-fashioned character based on a love for the soil.[43]

The American eugenists concurred with this romantic view of rural life. Believing that urban life caused sterilization, particularly among the native-born Americans,[44] eugenists reaffirmed the natural goodness of country life. The Farmer's National Congress declared in 1916 that eugenics was "the paramount question of the century." The Congress urged that society apply the rules of breeding to man just as such rules applied to livestock.[45] O. F. Cook of the Bureau of Plant Industry of the United States Department of Agriculture pushed such a policy. He saw rural life as the eugenic hope of the future.[46] It had to be, since one eugenist claimed that more than half of the men in the Municipal Lodging Houses were morons. Thus Charles B. Barnes, director of the Bureau of Employment of the State of New York, concluded, "On economic as well as humanitarian grounds, therefore, a revision of methods of distributing charity, which would eliminate the feeble-minded, appear to be justified." [47] Eugenics was apparently the answer.

William M. Hays, member of the Department of Agriculture and secretary of the American Breeders Association, looked toward the country to provide superior human beings for society; the city was always more corrupt than the countryside. The country-life movement was therefore in the national interest in helping create a more efficient people.[48] This efficiency theme served as the rallying cry for the entire conservation crusade and for the whole progressive camp.

43. Samuel P. Hays, *Conservation and the Gospel of Efficiency*, p. 144.
44. "Urban Sterilization," *The Journal of Heredity*, VIII (June 1917), 268–269.
45. *The Journal of Heredity*, VIII (January 1916), 47.
46. O. F. Cook, "Eugenics and Agriculture, City Life Sterilizing Best Lines of Descent on a Large Scale—Population Must Be Held on the Farm if the Race is to Improve—Proper Appreciation of Rural Life the Greatest Influence for Eugenics," *The Journal of Heredity*, VII (June 1916), 249–254.
47. News Note, *The Journal of Heredity*, VII (July 1916), 296.
48. William M. Hays, "The Farm, The Home of the Race," *American Breeders*

Historically, the eugenists' enthusiasm for rural living was a latter-day version of the urban-rural conflict, enduring feature of United States history. The city was immoral; George W. Fiske, a eugenist, like an Old Testament prophet, denounced the city, saying life there "for the comfortably situated, is too luxurious to be good for the body, the mind or the morals." The foundation of civilized society, the farm, created the best hope for the family and the natural providence of mankind, claimed this crusader for the countryside.[49]

Paradoxically, in a nation rapidly becoming urban, the traditional aversion to city life gained in popularity. The yeoman farmer could save the nation from urban sins. Although Populism as an organized political party had disappeared, many Populist attitudes remained in the progressive era. Early in the twentieth century various civic-minded individuals sought to stop the decline of rural population by developing programs and policies for making the country more attractive. The Country Life Commission, sponsored by Theodore Roosevelt in 1908, sought an official solution to agrarian problems and in the process gave much publicity to the movement.[50]

Invoking the ethic of utilitarianism—the greatest good to the greatest number—the Commission equated its growth with conservation and democracy.[51] Holding more than thirty public hearings, Liberty Hyde Bailey (1858-1954), as chairman, sent out questionnaires to more than six thousand people. Kenyon Butterfield, President of the Massachusetts Agricultural College, Henry C. Wallace, Walter Hines Page, and Gifford Pinchot served on the Commission.[52]

Not supported by public funds, the Commission financed its own report for which Theodore Roosevelt wrote the foreword. Believing

Magazine, A Journal of Genetics and Eugenics, I (November 1912), 15–16, 18. Same philosophy was expressed by O. F. Cook, "City and Country II," *The Journal of Heredity,* XII (April 12), 167–173, and in his "Biology in Human Progress," *The Journal of Heredity,* XIV (September 1923), 253–257.

49. George W. Fiske, *The Challenge of the Country, A Study of Country Life Opportunity,* pp. 46, 33. Hereafter cited as Fiske, *The Challenge of the Country.*

50. Samuel P. Hays, *The Response to Industrialism, 1885–1914,* p. 111.

51. Coyle, *Conservation,* p. 64.

52. Andrew D. Rodgers, III, *Liberty Hyde Bailey, A Story of American Plant Science,* pp. 358–359. For an example of Gifford Pinchot's philosophical mixture of naturalism and love of nature, see his *The Country Church, The Decline of Its Influence and the Remedy,* p. 3.

that "the men and women on the farm stand for what is fundamentally best and needed in our America," Roosevelt endorsed the Commission's efforts. Rising to great naturalistic (and eugenic) heights, Roosevelt found the historic task of country people in supplying "the city with fresh blood, clean bodies, and clear brains that can endure the terrific strain of modern life; we need the development of men in the open country, who will be in the future, as in the past, the stay and the strength of the nation in time of war, and its guiding and controlling spirit in time of peace." [53] Ideologically, Sir Francis Galton wrote that passage.

The report of the Commission received Congressional attention. It was a repetition of moderate Populist demands against middlemen plus several plans for conservation in farm life and economy.[54] The report's practical results were meager, but philosophically the report expressed the thought of Liberty Hyde Bailey, chairman of the Country Life Commission.

Liberty Hyde Bailey was a botanist who had grown up on the Michigan agricultural frontier. He played a major role in the scholarly growth of Cornell University. Like the majority of scientists of his generation, Bailey advocated the environmental explanation of heredity in biology and botany.[55] He was active in the American Breeders Association when the eugenists changed the direction of the organization. Not a eugenist, Bailey nevertheless shared many of their assumptions.

In many ways, Bailey represented a mild and conservative version of a populism imbedded with a great deal of progressivism. He saw the country-life movement and conservation as the same moral process, above petty party politics. Seeking federal protection for farmers against evil middlemen, Bailey viewed the farming class as the natural balance force in society. Recognizing the antagonism between city and country folk, he found the rural people to be a buffer in the class struggle be-

53. *Report of the Country Life Commission* (Feb. 9, 1909), 60th Congress, 2nd Session, Senate Document #705, p. 4. This foreword by Roosevelt is a classic example of his naturalism with many eugenic assumptions and conclusions.

54. *Ibid.*, p. 13.

55. Liberty Hyde Bailey, *The Survival of the Unlike, A Collection of Evolution Essays Suggested by the Study of Domestic Plants,* fifth edition, and his "The Factors of Organic Evolution from a Botanical Standpoint," *Annual Report of the Smithsonian Institute,* p. 475.

tween the great corporations and the laboring classes.[56] The farmer by his closeness to the soil was the innately conservative force in society.

Bailey's social philosophy was typical of American naturalism, augmented by eugenic conclusions. Mankind struggled against itself and nature. Without challenges, men grew weak and inadequate to life's demands; the city multiplied this process, argued Bailey. The naturally inadequate person, Bailey thought, goes to the city "where he can find someone to help him fight his battles. The farmer will learn to adapt his scheme to nature, and how to conquer the things that are conquerable; and this should make it worth his while to be a farmer."[57] By providing a moderate-sized family, the farmer's wife was a major partner in the restoration of rural life.[58]

Bailey wanted the ideal farm economy to be capitalistic in form because any co-operative system implied majority rule, not the best alternative in agricultural problems. As a spokesman for the Populist tradition, he had only bitter words for the absentee landowner.[59] Yet, anticipating the growth of commercial farming, Bailey distrusted labor unions because they were not necessary in farming. With a certain naïveté he wrote, "The employer will always feel his sense of obligation and responsibility to the man he employs and to the man's family. Persons do not starve to death in the open country."[60] Apparently starvation existed only in cities.

The farmer must keep his native simplicity even as the complexity of agricultural efficiency increased. The need of society was for more good farmers, not millionaires. Make a comfortable living, raise a family, be an asset to the community and leave the farm in a productive condition were the major ingredients for the good farmer—and ultimately for the good society, according to Liberty Hyde Bailey.[61]

In conclusion, like the eugenists, this professor and other progressives sought the scientific resurrection of the natural man by the triple

56. Bailey, *The Country-Life Movement in the United States*, pp. 16, 19–20, 158, 164, 178–179, 182.
57. *Ibid.*, pp. 57–58, 60.
58. *Ibid.*, p. 87.
59. *Ibid.*, pp. 98–99.
60. *Ibid.*, pp. 140–141.
61. *Ibid.*, pp. 204–205, 220.

methods of charity, conservation, and the country-life movement. Because of the application of scientific principles, the new man—the new Adam—existed. If nature's primitive importance were restored in men's lives, and natural selection directed against the innately inferior, society would prosper.

The terrors of twentieth-century history, however—economic depression and European totalitarianism—destroyed the utopian and conservative naturalism of the nineteenth century. Truly, the intellectual revolution of naturalism had consumed its own child—Galtonian eugenics.

11

THE DECLINE
OF GALTONIAN
EUGENICS
IN THE
UNITED STATES

Two MAJOR developments in the twentieth century shaped the destiny of Galtonin eugenics in the United States. The first of these was the growth of genetics which explained the biggest mystery in Darwinian evolution—heredity. At one time earlier in this century, many of the pioneers in genetic investigations questioned the validity of the Darwinian principle of natural selection in the study of heredity. Later scholarship, however, proved the importance of natural selection in the mechanism of inheritance. The second major process effecting the eclipse of eugenics was the series of events following the Great Depression of 1929. The crash of the stock market and the subsequent crippling of the economy greatly altered the climate of opinion that had been receptive to eugenic speculations. In addition, the appearance of Nazism—a noxious weed in the garden of nineteenth-century naturalism—discredited the scientific and ethical validity of the racist hypothesis in human behavior.

Criticism of eugenics had naturally existed since the days of Sir Francis Galton. It ranged from mild disapproval or disbelief to emotional outrage at the prospect of men breeding like race horses. One of the oldest criticisms was over the matter of teleology. Despite the ability of some theologians to accept Darwinian naturalism,[1] other scholars had dubious misgivings about any teleological arrangement. Over the years, critics of eugenics repeatedly asked, what was the ultimate purpose or goal in eugenic mating? What was to be the end result? What models were available to use in anticipating future genetic needs of mankind? And last, what constituted the "fit" in a given social order or culture?[2] Galtonian eugenists used certain sociological values in answering these questions. These values discussed in this book found little support in an America filled with mass unemployment.

During the zenith of the eugenics movement in progressive America, many people were skeptical about any immediate eugenics improvement of American population. The main concern was with the clarification of the laws of heredity and thereby the construction of a scientific system for marital advice. Since positive eugenics did not have complete basis in scientific fact, the emphasis, many writers felt, should be on limiting the number of unfit by legislative means.[3]

By the middle of the 1920s, the tempo of antieugenic sentiment increased.[4] One possible reason was that eugenics, like other progressive reforms, suffered in the postwar reaction to any type of change. The greater reason, however, was in the changing complexion of naturalism. Hereditary emphasis was giving way to a form of environmental naturalism. Social scientists were exploring the vast implications of culture on the human personality. Eugenics, one critic remarked, did not allow for the significance of differential opportunity among the American public.[5] Culture was dynamic and the behavior of individuals varied within any cultural context.

L. L. Bernard, sociologist and critic of instinct psychology, viewed

1. For an example of the modern synthesis of Darwinian evolution and theology, see Greene, *Darwin and the Modern World View.*
2. Rene Dubos, *Mirage of Health, Utopias, Progress, and Biological Change,* p. 227; Crane Brinton, *A History of Western Morals,* pp. 460–461.
3. Edwin G. Conklin, "Heredity and Responsibility," *Science,* n.s. XXXVII (January 10, 1913), 46–54; James A. Field, "The Progress of Eugenics," *The Quarterly Journal of Economics,* XVI (November 1911).
4. Higham, *Strangers in the Land,* p. 327.
5. A. B. Wolfe, "Is There a Biological Law of Human Population Growth?" *The Quarterly Journal of Economics,* XLI (August 1927), 593–594.

eugenics as self-limiting because of its strongly hereditary orientation. For eugenics to be successful, he thought that the science had to use an environmental method of social control. Americans, he concluded, were not ready for direction of that type in mate selection, even if they could solve all the technical and scientific problems of eugenics.[6]

Paradoxically, as some social and biological scientists were becoming cool toward eugenic reform because of the complexity of the heredity-environment relationship in human affairs, the writers of the influential *American Charities and Social Work* were invoking Galton's work as the answer to human degeneration. As late as 1930, they felt "occult characteristics tending to inefficiency or absolute pauperism are undoubtedly transmitted, although their exact nature, either in the parent or child, cannot be ascertained and described." Unaware or ignoring the advances in genetics and anthropology, they sought justification in the adage that like breeds like. "The proof is that the child follows by some secret but almost irrepressible propulsion the history of the parent." [7] The events of the day caused that attitude to be increasingly a minority opinion in the social reform and scientific communities.

A leading British sociologist, Morris Ginsberg, expressed majority opinion in arguing that modern civilization's problems were solvable by effective organization and education and not in the slow and tedious methods of selective breeding. In a word, he saw social change as a matter of social factors, not racial.[8]

Herbert J. Muller, pioneer in genetics and discoverer of the mutagenic effect of X-rays, rejected the scientific premises of Galtonian eugenics. Using the same line of reasoning as Ginsberg, Muller added that the only validity for eugenics was its concern over human imbecility. Otherwise, Muller stressed, "eugenics under our social system cannot work." The prospect of eugenics creating bigger and better businessmen was not rewarding because that very group, following the profit motive, had led America into a major crisis. In sum, Galtonian eugenics was merely the projection and class bias of the upper

6. Bernard, *Instinct*, pp. 23–24.

7. Amos G. Warner, *et al.*, *American Charities and Social Work*, pp. 68–72.

8. Morris Ginsberg, *Essay in Sociology and Social Philosophy* (Volume I of *The Diversity of Morals*), pp. 393–394. The article in question was written in 1932.

classes. Speaking before the Third International Eugenics Congress in 1932, Muller, in his fiery address, finished Galtonian eugenics in the United States as a respectable scientific enterprise.[9]

The economic crash and subsequent depression from 1929 to 1940 was the death knell of Galtonian eugenics in the United States. At the same time, the depression challenged the conservative progressivism-naturalism giving philosophical and political support to the eugenic cause. As William A. Williams has remarked, the depression was a crisis to the progressive reformers as well as to the business community.[10] Assuming that the progressives had solved the major ills of society, the depression puzzled them. They had engaged in a moral crusade in which they generally assumed economic problems were individual problems, or at worst, problems individuals could solve with a minimum of change in the economic order. The depression mocked this assumption; the respectable middle class from which progressivism originated suffered greatly in the aftermath of the 1929 Wall Street crash. Unemployment was no longer a question of individual weakness or lack of ability to compete successfully in the market place. The depression affected the entire social order—the "lazy" working class and the "thrifty" middle class. The depression struck both the Anglo-Saxon and the alien.

Franklin D. Roosevelt's famous dictum about the nature of fear and the depression was indicative of the progressive's ambiguities toward the economic crisis and what type of reform men should use to correct it. The New Deal, among other things, was therefore an experimental effort to correct American capitalism. Because of the depression, reform in the 1930s differed from the moral naturalism of the progressive years. The entire social order sought aid, in one form or another, during the New Deal. If for no other reason than political expediency, racial explanation of sociological difficulties was no longer acceptable. The biologically "fit" and "unfit" shared in the misfortunes of unemployment.

Institutionally, the eugenics movement gave evidence of this change

9. Herbert J. Muller, "The Dominance of Eugenics," *BCR*, XVI (October 1932), 236–238; Hardin, *Nature and Man's Fate*, pp. 200–201.

10. William A. Williams, "Schlesinger: Right Crisis—Wrong Order," *The Nation*, CLXXXIV (March 23, 1957), 257–260.

in the course of American reform. For example, the Minnesota Eugenics Society, founded in 1922, had a membership of seventy-seven
people in 1927 and was nonexistent three years later. The reason was a
lack of funds. As the historian of the society remarked, "No social
reform will succeed without the eventual backing of those who hold
social power." The holders of that power in 1930 were concerned with
environmental problems—not with the hereditary moralism of Galtonian eugenics. Revived in 1945 as the Minnesota Human Genetics
League, the organization rejected the Galtonian assumptions of the
earlier group.[11] In so doing they gave further notice of the change in
American social thought. Genetics does not have the missionary zeal
of the older eugenics movement.

Just as the depression and the growth of environmental social
thought weakened the philosophical support of Galtonian eugenics,
a group of experimental biologists led by Lancelot Hogben, a British
geneticist, argued that when such large differences existed in society,
dogmatic assertations about the social consequences of a given hereditary trait could not be made.[12] The argument's appeal increased
during the depression years.

As noted earlier, American eugenists such as Charles Davenport
claimed too much for heredity and the eugenic solution. For instance,
in the case of epilepsy, Davenport compiled a list of characteristics
of the disease—all of equal hereditary value—and included other
diseases. The list became so inclusive as to be meaningless except that
many ills, physical and mental, might as well have a nurture origin as
a hereditary one.[13] Charles Davenport and the eugenic school in their
dogmatic hereditary determinism obscured many vital distinctions in
the complex study of the heredity-environment equation.

Harry Elmer Barnes summarized the eugenic criticism by noting
its racial orientation, the long time that any eugenic program would
take and the poor sociological judgment that wealth indicated biological fittness.[14] It was not surprising therefore that the eugenics

11. Sheldon C. Reed, "The Local Eugenics Society," *The American Journal of
Human Genetics*, IX (March 1957), 1–9.
12. Blacker, *Eugenics: Galton and After*, p. 145.
13. Myerson, "Error in Psychiatry," *The Story of Human Error*, p. 432.
14. Harry Elmer Barnes, "Error in Sociology," *Ibid.*, pp. 376–379.

conference of 1936 expressed a mood of caution and moderation in the future eugenic reconstruction of mankind.[15]

The criticism continued, from critical analysis of analogies used by eugenists to eugenists' confusion over the nature of a mental trait.[16] Although genetic studies in biological thought and the use of environmentalism in social theory developed to a degree independently, the two approaches were used together in critical commentary on Galtonian thought. Social scientists particularly stressed the effects of education on human behavior and expressed skepticism about the biological superiority of the upper classes. All too often, Franklin H. Hankins felt, eugenic studies have exhibited a bias in favor of the upper classes.[17]

The development of genetics—as discussed in Chapter III—destroyed the "scientific certainty of Sir Francis Galton's assumption that social position indicated hereditary worth. From 1901 to the present, genetics has rapidly expanded in technique and knowledge. Especially since 1930 and the investigations of Ronald A. Fisher, J. B. S. Haldane, two British geneticists, and Sewall Wright, an American genetic pioneer, genetics has displayed the mathematical consequences of diploid Mendelian heredity which eugenic reformers in the Galtonian tradition never imagined.[18]

As genetic knowledge increased, scientists saw the vastness of human heredity, particularly in qualitative terms. It became apparent that to decide whether a gene was "good" or "bad" was impossible. Genetics proved by its complexity that the old eugenic assumptions of fertility being related to social class, of the inborn desirability of some social and national groups, and that extremely desirable and undesirable traits breed true were very much open for debate and caused scientific hesitation over any dogmatic conclusion. The latter assumption was a particular favorite of Charles Davenport who used it in his

15. Frederick Osborn, "Development of a Eugenic Philosophy," *American Sociological Review*, II (June 1937), 391–394.

16. Landman, *Human Sterilization, The History of the Sexual Sterilization Movement*, pp. 183–197.

17. Franklin H. Hankins, "Demographic and Biological Contributions to Sociological Principles," *Contemporary Social Theory*, Harry Elmer Barnes and Howard Becker, eds., p. 324.

18. Hardin, *Nature and Man's Fate*, p. 231.

scientific investigation on the social consequences of heredity. Finally, the eugenic assumption of a limited number of genes present in a given population was erroneous. The gene pool of the world population was so large that any locally induced artificial or natural selection would have no measurable effect on the total number of genes. The exception would be if one gene were found in only one geographical area and isolated from a larger genetic community. National or local eugenics therefore was apparently impossible. Galtonian eugenists were not aware of gene frequencies in the world population and relative fitness of populations for different environments.[19] Ironically, nationalism—which originally inspired much eugenic speculation— presented the delegation of power to an international body to control and direct the eugenic development of a particular national population.

In fact, genetic data now indicate that the interaction of many genes causes and controls any given character. In the early days of genetics, where the influence of eugenics was the highest, the assumption was one gene for one hereditary character. This concept is now obsolete. As Conway Zirkle writes, "We cannot tell what gene contributes to what character until it has mutated, because we can identify genes only when they cause measurable changes and consequently we cannot know how many unmutated genes are involved in producing any end result. This is true for all characteristics." [20] American eugenists in the early twentieth century did not have this scientific information.

Eugenists were also the victims of a naturalistic fallacy. To be sure, mankind is part of the animal world and is kin to all living matter, but the eugenists were wont to transfer laboratory findings on lower animals to the human scene without any adjustment for the factors of culture or history of human beings. Under certain controlled conditions and given a large number of generations, scientists could produce selected human traits for some characters, but not all. It is an open question, even if the situation were practical, was it de-

19. L. S. Penrose, "Genetics of the Human Race," *Genetics in the 20th Century*, L. C. Dunn, ed., p. 394.
20. Zirkle, *Evolution, Marxian Biology and the Social Scene*, p. 200.

sirable?[21] Because of their social and philosophical orientation, American eugenists of Davenport's generation did not question the application of laboratory conclusions to the complexity of human existence.

Galtonian eugenics held as true certain anthropological theories. All culture followed the same evolutionary pattern and many of the cultural traits were directly related to the racial composition of the population. Thus for eugenics "human nature" controlled cultural expressions of behavior. Using the biological concept of change by imperceptible gradations, eugenists saw cultural change as an extremely slow process organically related to the hereditary nature of members of society.[22] The growth of cultural anthropology in twentieth-century United States destroyed this *simpliste* error.[23] By 1940 the American school of anthropological thought held certain basic tenets—all of which ran counter to the anthropological ideas of Galtonian eugenics; namely, the uniformity of cultural development was not consistent with historic reality. Another idea was that cultural traits traveled and that the greatest factor in cultural growth was the impact of one culture on another society.[24] Culture, to a large degree, was independent of the racial nature of its members. Kroeber's essay of 1917 on "The Superorganic" was a major source for such a theory.

Quite obviously, Galtonian eugenists saw race as a self-limiting concept: races existed in a given order in nature and heredity limited their traits. Modern genetics, noting the dynamic effect of mutation on genes, sees race—as a biological category—in terms of change. Racial traits change and therefore the nature of the race changes. Once again developments in scientific knowledge limited the applicability of Galtonian eugenics. The development of twentieth-century science—social and natural—has been in discounting the validity of the race theory of culture. Cultural adaptation by various racial stock has occurred re-

21. Ashley Montagu, *Man's Most Dangerous Myth, The Fallacy of Race,* third edition revised and enlarged, pp. 164–165.

22. Alexander Goldenweiser, "Leading Contribution of Anthropology," *Contemporary Social Theory,* p. 443.

23. Lowie, *The History of Ethnological Theory,* p. 251; see also Kardiner, *They Studied Man,* for a discussion of the impact of culture on human behavior.

24. Goldenweiser, "Leading Contribution of Anthropology," *Contemporary Social Theory,* p. 470.

peatedly in history. Like other elements of nineteenth-century naturalism, eugenics discounted man's behavioral plasticity.[25]

In part, the failure of eugenics to account for man's plasticity
resulted from the general intellectual atmosphere of the late nineteenth and early twentieth centuries. Scientists do not live in isolation
but move within a particular time and place. Because of nineteenth-
century naturalism, Galtonian eugenics was a "natural" result; likewise,
the change in the ideological milieu of this century doubtless caused
the scientific community to be aware of the larger social implications
of its work.

The rise of modern totalitarianism with its "scientific" oppression of
large segments of the world's population radically changed the universe of Sir Francis Galton. For reasons based on the growth of hereditary knowledge and the trend of contemporary history, many geneticists developed an antagonism toward eugenic schemes.[26]

The pattern of twentieth-century thought has been in the direction
of environmentalism. The inheritance of acquired characteristics no
longer is acceptable, but social scientists generally see cultural advancement offsetting any hereditary defect in a segment of the planet's
population. Technology and improved social organization may well
create new methods for utilizing the defect.[27] This possibility is the
womb of science fiction and scholarly utopias.

Eugenics per se did not end with the demise of the Galtonian form
in the 1930s. In fact, eugenics—incorporating latest social and scientific theories—has entered a new phase. The discipline in the last three
decades has sought knowledge of an environmental nature. Seeking
qualitative or statistical improvement in the distribution of births,
modern eugenics (since 1930) wants improvement in individual per-
sonalities as well as progress in mass uplifting of intelligence. Since the
psychological investigations of personality have not shown any con-

25. Stanley M. Garn, "Race and Evolution," *American Anthropologist,* LIX
(April 1957), 223. Theodosius Dobzhansky, *The Biological Basis of Human Freedom,* pp. 476–477.

26. Muller, "Progress and Prospects in Human Genetics," *The American Journal of Human Genetics,* I (September 1949), 16–17; Blacker, *Eugenics: Galton
and After,* p. 238.

27. Muller, "The Development of the Gene Theory," *Genetics in the 20th
Century,* p. 100.

clusive findings, modern eugenists recognize the limitation of this program. In addition, modern eugenics notes the importance of public opinion in any program and the existence of cultural relativism which would prevent any absolute eugenic standards for all societies.[28]

Contemporary eugenics no longer has the antienvironmental bias of its Galtonian forerunner. Concerned with the charge of class prejudice, eugenists of today do not provide pseudobiological rationales for existing distinctions in power and wealth. A balanced view of man's behavior—the complexity of social-genetic relationship in "human nature"—has resulted.[29]

With the development of population genetics, eugenics has taken on a quantitative orientation. By judicial application and mutual consent, a geneticist might, through genetic counseling, discourage a union which would result in an undesirable hereditary trait in the offspring. As Julian Huxley remarked, by raising the average of desirable traits (greater physical vigor, greater resistance to specific diseases) a great burden of hereditary suffering would disappear from mankind's existence.[30] Eugenics accordingly does not have to follow Sir Francis Galton's dictums. It is not in current eugenic programs.

Another distinction between Galtonian eugenics and the post–1930 variety has been a marked sense of modesty of ambition on the part of the latter. Frederick Osborn, a contemporary eugenist, wrote:

> For eugenics must always be approached with humility. Science, which is rapidly giving men the means to every end, cannot define the ends. The ultimate purpose of man's life on earth lies beyond the frontiers of knowledge. We can only assume that it is good to raise the average of man's native capacities. But once this assumption is made, we have opened up new possibilities for human life.[31]

28. Frederick Osborn, *Preface to Eugenics,* revised edition, pp. ix, 141, 145, 240. Hereafter cited as Osborn, *Preface to Eugenics.*

29. Morris Ginsberg, *Essays in Sociology and Social Philosophy* (Volume I of *The Diversity of Morals*), pp. xxii–xiv. See also Willystine Goodsell, "The New Eugenics and Education," *The Social Frontier,* IV (January 1938), 113–117.

30. Julian Huxley, "Genetics, Evolution and Human Destiny," *Genetics in the 20th Century,* p. 618. For a recent discussion of the current validity of eugenics by the scientific community, see Hudson Hoagland and Ralph W. Buiuie, eds., *Evolution and Man's Progress,* and Zirkle, *Evolution, Marxian Biology and the Social Scene,* pp. 142–143.

31. Osborn, *Preface to Eugenics,* p. 325.

Although the element of optimism is indicative of Galtonian eugenics, Karl Pearson or Charles Davenport or any other pioneer eugenist could never have written the passage. For one reason, the lack of
any teleological consideration set this current expression of eugenic
philosophy apart from Sir Francis Galton's creative naturalism. Humility was not a strong characteristic of American and British
eugenists, in the early days of the eugenic cause. They knew where
mankind was "going" if their nostrums were not employed; latter-day
eugenists are not so dogmatic.

An example of this cautious attitude is present in the modern
eugenist's view of the heredity-environment dialectic. No longer stressing hereditary determinism, today's eugenic position is that the organism has a hereditary tendency that under a certain environmental
situation might find expression. Heredity does not, according to this
eugenic theory, determine the nature or beginning of mental illness,
for example. "In most mental diseases, heredity can be thought of as
contributing certain susceptibilities or weaknesses which, in an un-
favorable environment, may develop into recognizable disease." [32]
Resulting from changes in the scientific and social sciences in the last
thirty years, modern eugenics now blends with the general democratic
orientation of today's science.

Men still speculate about their social-genetic future. Maybe the
technique of artificial insemination will, after changes in American
mores and sexual customs, provide a means for the genetic improvement of mankind. With progress in birth control men can control their
numbers if they so desire. Possibly the next process for man's evolving
nature is toward conscious genetic quality.[33]

The difficulties of such a future prospect are great. Change is the
essence of biological existence. No living things or their environments
are ever in a constant equilibrium. By their culture (culturally created
radiation) men add new problems of adaptations by striving always
for parabiological values, and fitness has always been more than a
biological end. The story of men shows that they constantly modify
and on occasion sacrifice their biological nature in the pursuit of new

32. *Ibid.*, p. 40.
33. Dubos, *Mirage of Health*, p. 41.

goals, new illusions.[34] Galtonian eugenics in the United States was one of those illusions.

Because of technology and the nature of heredity, mankind is unstable both culturally and biologically; yet it is the price of evolution. An entirely stable species or culture does not evolve. A certain degree or type of instability must exist for evolution to occur, but change also can bring deterioration. Progress—cultural and biological—carries the possibility of decay. The world is open; the differences between individuals are greater than either the environmental or hereditary variable, working alone, can produce.[35] Modern man has the curse of choice; he can and does create his own hell or heaven.

The heritage of the nineteenth century with its conservative and liberal interpretations of naturalism and evolution was an emphasis on biology. Maybe, as Lionel Trilling suggests, the orientation is ultimately a liberating one; it implies that culture, as a behavioristic process, is not all-powerful. Beyond the influence of cultural determinism an elemental force exists which prevents culture from being absolute.[36] The danger of this analysis is a glorious resurrection of primitive man, of natural man which was the starting point of Galtonian eugenics. In this manner, American thought comes full circuit from naturalism to romanticism to naturalism raised to a higher level of sophistication, but naturalism nevertheless. "Adam" the natural man can never be found outside the cultural values and norms of the literary and scientific hunters.

In summary, Galtonian eugenics—like so many other nineteenth-century reforms—expressed the fear of the age: overpopulation. The growth of cities and of democracy caused conservatives to worry about the future of society and caused a romantic yearning for the past. The past with its feudal social order and agrarian economy offered security to the conservative mind. In naturalistic terms, overpopulation expressed this fear of the present.

Sir Francis Galton's philosophy utilized two themes of the Victorian era—teleology and naturalism. In an age of growing religious uncertainty and skepticism, Galtonian naturalism created a teleological

34. *Ibid.*, p. 52.
35. Zirkle, *Evolution, Marxian Biology and the Social Scene*, pp. 35, 55, 448.
36. Lionell Trilling, *Freud and the Crisis of Our Culture*, p. 48.

trend in Darwinian evolution. Galton sought a religious motivation for the hereditary reconstruction of the human race. Eugenics for him was a natural religion. Mankind's hereditary future was the new covenant with physical and social sciences. Like other nineteenth-century conservatives, Galton wanted to place mankind's inborn irrationality under a more scientific social control. To achieve this objective he urged a conservative preservation of mankind's better elements.

As we have seen, Galton's creed met the psychic needs of progressive America with its status crisis. Galtonian eugenics brought the Victorian tragic vision (of the conservative-naturalist fear of the mob expressed as Malthusian concern over the degenerate masses) to American reform politics. The conservative, using eugenics, became the reformer and in the process he replaced the natural rights of eighteenth-century optimism with the natural law of Darwinian evolution—natural selection—in a return to a golden age. This Garden of Eden or golden age existed before democracy, and misguided, sentimental philanthropy protected the organically inadequate from their true destiny—extinction. Culture disrupted the "cleansing" effect of natural selection, preventing the realization of the ecological balance in nature. Eugenics accordingly was the road map to the promised land of Darwinian survival of the fittest.

Galtonian eugenics was mainly a social philosophy, based on Darwinian evolution, to maintain certain sociological beliefs which were always the supreme end. For example, in the United States, when it appeared that Mendel's theory rejected natural selection, eugenists such as Charles Davenport still held fast to Galton's social philosophy, the hereditary superiority of the aristocracy.

As this chapter notes, Galtonian eugenics experienced a double setback; the growth of genetics destroyed the scientific premises of Galton's message while the Great Depression of 1929 invalidated Galtonian sociology. Sir Francis Galton, like his conservative American counterparts, believed that the economic order was a natural and impartial judge of the innate biological worth of an individual. His social class expressed this biological merit. The decade of the depression questioned the permanence of the capitalist environment; many conservative-progressives, like the eugenists, did not understand the New Deal changes in American society. The elitist and ethical judgments of conservative progressivism—eugenics—were not part of the changing forms of American democracy. Galtonian eugenics was a victim of unemployment.

In the history of American reform movements, eugenics was, like so many others, an attempt to reform in order to save the past and the present, not for any future ideal and condition. Like prohibitionists, the eugenists were a small group, active in propaganda, who realized some legislative success but without any radical change in current behavior. The two groups were in the progressive era and chose single programs to solve the ills of mankind. For prohibitionists, the mode of expression was "religious," while eugenists stressed the "scientific" nature of their enterprise; politically, the end was a conservative response to the industrial legacy of the nineteenth century. Both movements were class-conscious; they feared the lower classes— one for moral reasons and the other for racial.[37]

And yet the significance of Sir Francis Galton's eugenic aspiration in the United States is greater than the story of one man and his movement in a particular country. Galtonian eugenics was another chapter in the eternal quest of man to understand and control himself. The Galtonian solution was, once again, in the naturalistic tradition— man as an organic part of this planet. Although sociological assumptions limited his philosophy, Sir Francis Galton's particular version of evolution was noteworthy; he tried, like so many thinkers before and after him, to know the real character, the true nature of mankind. The problem remains unsolved.[38]

37. Lane, "Heredity and Environment in American Social Thought, 1900– 1929," p. 315. For interesting intellectual crosscurrents, see Bartlett C. Jones, "Prohibition and Eugenics, 1920–1933," *Journal of the History of Medicine and Allied Sciences*, XVIII (April 1963), 158–172.

38. The scholarly speculation goes on. Using the latest biological discoveries, C. H. Waddington is dubious of eugenics. See his "Genes to Order?" *Medical Opinion and Review*, LV (March 1968), 120–129.

BIBLIOGRAPHICAL
ESSAY

The bibliography is arranged by chapters with items being cited in their pertinent location in the book. Some of the material is applicable to the other chapters and to the entire work. When possible, a periodical for a particular time span is cited rather than a listing of the articles drawn from the journal. In any event, the footnotes serve as a guide to the individual article within a particular periodical. Only works having a direct bearing on this treatment of American eugenics have been noted.

Chapter I

Alban G. Widgery's *Interpretations of History, Confucius to Toynbee* (London: George Allen & Unwin, Ltd., 1961) is a good starting point for an over-all view of theories explaining the mysteries of history. In the same way, Arthur O. Lovejoy's discussion of nature in *The Great Chain of Being, A Study of the History of an Idea* (Cambridge: Harvard University Press, 1957) explained the ramifications of an idea for a philosophy of history. Taking a wider view, Crane Brinton's *A History of Western Morals* (New York: Harcourt, Brace and Co., 1959) shows the ethical basis of man's judgment of both history and nature.

In *The Noble Savage, A Study in Romantic Naturalism* (New York:

Columbia University Press, 1928), Hoxie N. Fairchild examines one aspect of the idea that man's relation with nature was one of essential goodness and simple harmony. Lois Whitney relates this natural arrangement to future human improvement in her book, *Primitivism and the Idea of Progress in English Popular Literature of the Eighteenth Century* (Baltimore: The Johns Hopkins Press, 1934). The standard account of the history of progress is in J. B. Bury, *The Idea of Progress*, recently published in a new edition by Dover Publications, Inc. of New York in 1955. The theological implications of progress are employed by Ernest Lee Tuveson in *Millennium and Utopia, A Study in the Background of the Idea of Progress* (Berkeley: University of California Press, 1949) showing the religious origins of human improvement. In summary, the history of the idea of progress had both theological and naturalistic roots. H. Stuart Hughes in his outstanding account of European social thought from 1890 to 1930, *Consciousness and Society* (New York: Alfred A. Knopf, 1958), notes how social scientists of the age stressed man's innate irrationality which weakened the appeal of human progress based on eighteenth-century rationalism. In similar manner, biological thought since Darwin does not contain any idea of progress according to Garrett Hardin, *Nature and Man's Fate* (New York: Mentor Books, 1961).

Merle Curti in two articles traces this change from rationally determined human progress to the uncertainty of man's irrational nature in "Human Nature in American Thought: The Age of Reason and Morality, 1750 to 1860," *Political Science Quarterly*, LXVIII (September 1953), 354–375, and "Human Nature in American Thought: Retreat from Reason in the Age of Science," *ibid.*, LXVIII (December 1953), 492–510. John C. Greene notes varied influences of the new studies in biological sciences on social theory in "Biology and Social Theory in the Nineteenth Century: Auguste Comte and Herbert Spencer," *Critical Problems in the History of Science*, Marshall Clagett, ed. (Madison: The University of Wisconsin Press, 1959), pp. 419–446. Sol Tax has edited three volumes dealing with *The Evolution of Man, Culture and Society* (Chicago: The University of Chicago Press, 1960) in which social and cultural implications of evolution since Darwin are discussed by a number of authorities.

By now the standard in the field, Richard Hofstadter's *Social Darwinism in American Thought*, revised edition (Boston: Beacon Press, 1955), gives the major outline of how nineteenth-century Americans used scientific theory of evolution in explaining human behavior. Contemporary articles by Charles A. Gardiner, "The Race Problem in the United States," *Journal of Social Science*, XVIII (May 1884), 266–275, and Otis T. Mason, "The Uncivilized Mind in the Presence of Higher Phases of Civilization," *Proceedings of the American Association for the Advancement of Science*, XXX (August 1881), 345–361, demonstrate the reaction of American intellectuals to evolutionary thought in human affairs. This latter journal is a prime source of evolutionary thought in American science. Also typical of the Darwinian influence on racial attitudes in the United States after 1859 are the articles by John W. Scott, "Growth and Decay of Nations," *DeBow's Review*, XXX (January 1861), 11–30, and Richmond Mayo-Smith (a pioneer American statistician), "Statistical Data for the Study of the Assimilation of Races and Nationalities in the United States," *Publications of the American Statistical Association*, III (December 1893), 429–449.

An earlier analysis of the Darwinian influence of American thought is George S. Fullerton, "The Influence of Darwin on the Mental and Moral Sciences," *Proceedings of the American Philosophical Society* (1909), pp. 25–37. Joseph Blau's article, "The Influence of Darwin on American Philosophy," *Bucknell Review*, VIII (May 1959), 141–151, is disappointing and inadequate. In editing *Foreign Influences in American Life, Essays and Critical Bibliographies* (Princeton: Princeton University Press, 1944), David Bowers shows the complementary influence Hegel gave to the reception of Darwinian speculation in the United States. One such impact was in philosophy, as Philip P. Wiener, *Evolution and the Founders of Pragmatism* (Cambridge: Harvard University Press, 1949), notes the naturalistic origins of a genuinely "American" creed of pragmatism. A good summary of evolutionary influences in the fine arts may be found in William Irvine, "The Influence of Darwin on Literature," *Proceedings of the American Philosophical Society*, CIII (October 1959), 616–628. A revision statement that Social Darwinism did not influence the American capitalist during the latter half of the nineteenth century is Irwin G. Wyllie's thesis in his "Social Darwinism and the Businessman," *Proceedings of the American Philosophical Society*, CIV (October 1959), 629–635.

Stow Persons in a masterful survey shows the changing philosophical orientation of reform in *American Minds, A History of Ideas* (New York: Henry Holt & Co., 1958). Accordingly, David M. Potter's *People of Plenty, Economic Abundance and the American Character* (Chicago: The University of Chicago Press, 1954) outlines the materialist-naturalist basis for native optimism by drawing on the theories of behaviorist social scientists. Using basically the same technique, Richard Hofstadter in *The Age of Reform* (New York: Vintage Books, 1960) sees the psychological problems of status and institutional security as major issues during the post Civil War years of American naturalism. On the other hand, Eric F. Goldman sees a certain and definite connection between Lester Ward's philosophical naturalism and similar creeds and later reforms of the twentieth century, such as the New Deal. This thesis is developed in great detail in Goldman's *Rendezvous with Destiny, A History of Modern American Reform* (New York: Alfred A. Knopf, 1952). Unlike Potter, Hofstadter, and Goldman, Samuel P. Hays sees a many-sided reaction to the problems of American society in his *The Response to Industrialism, 1885–1914* (Chicago: The University of Chicago Press, 1957). Oscar Cargill's *Intellectual America, Ideas on the March* (New York: Macmillan, 1959) differs from the Hays volume in that Cargill is primarily concerned with the literary manifestations of naturalism in a rapidly industrialized United States.

Progressives, that generation of reformers from 1890–1920, have been in the traditional interpretation characterized as true liberals using the latest theories of the social sciences in their programs. Such a thesis, for example, Morton White develops in detail in *Social Thought in America, The Revolt against Formalism* in an edition with a new preface and epilogue published by Beacon Press of Boston in 1957. David W. Noble, in a revision counterattack, contends that a large segment of the progressive's faith in reform had conservative origins in an idealized version of America's past. Noble's *The Paradox of Progressive Thought* (Minneapolis: University of Minnesota Press, 1958) contains the complete account. Charles Forcey sharply disagrees with Noble's interpretation in *The Crossroads of Liberalism: Croly, Weyl, Lippmann and the Progressive Era, 1900–1925* (New York: Oxford University Press, 1961). Forcey views these three progressives as true pioneers of twentieth-century liberal reforms.

Barbara M. Solomon's *Ancestors and Immigrants, A Changing New England Tradition* (Cambridge: Harvard University Press, 1956) is closer to Noble's interpretation in her emphasis on the problems of status and social mobility. Two recent publications are in a revision mood. William Preston, Jr., *Aliens and Dissenters, Federal Suppression of Radicals, 1903–1933* (Cambridge: Harvard University Press, 1963), and James H. Timberlake, *Prohibition and the Progressive Movement* (Cambridge: Harvard University Press, 1963) both note the inadequacy of the progressive's defense or concern with individual personal and civil liberties. In a similar manner, C. Vann Woodward's two works, *Reunion and Reaction*, second edition (Garden City: Doubleday, Anchor Books, 1956) and *The Strange Career of Jim Crow*, new and revised edition (New York: Galaxy Books of the Oxford University Press, 1957), demonstrate the systematic lack of concern on the part of liberals and conservatives in the plight of the American Negro from the end of Reconstruction to 1920. The situation since the New Deal has improved, as Woodward mentions in the latter volume. For an account of popular and scientific anti-Negro sentiment, I. A. Newby's *Jim Crow's Defense: Anti-Negro Thought by America, 1900–1930* (Baton Rouge: Louisiana State University Press, 1965), is quite good.

Chapter II

A convenient introduction to Sir Francis Galton and his influence on science is Karl Pearson's three volumes covering *The Life, Letters and Labors of Francis Galton* (Cambridge, England: Cambridge University

Press, 1914–1930). These volumes are the closest thing to an "official biography" and show the many-sided aspects of Galton's scientific interests. Sir Francis tells his own story in *Memories of My Life*, second edition (London, 1908). C. P. Blacker's study of *Eugenics: Galton and After* (London: Gerald Duchworther & Co., Ltd., 1952) contains a bibliography of Galton's writings. Blacker, a eugenist himself, discusses the course of eugenics only in England. Helen M. Walker gives a good indication of how important Sir Francis was, for example, in the development of statistics, in *Studies in the History of Statistical Method* (Baltimore: The Williams & Wilkins Co., 1929). In *Modern Men and Mummers* (London: George Allen & Unwin, Ltd., 1921), Hesketh Pearson gives an interesting sketch of Galton in comparison with other well-known individuals of his generation.

Francis Galton was a prolific writer. Often he wrote on unusual topics, such as "Arithmetic by Smell," *The Psychological Review*, I (January 1894), 61–62. The major books dealing with his concepts of inheritance and human nature are *Hereditary Genius, An Inquiry into Its Consequences* (New York: D. Appleton & Co., 1870) and *Inquiries into Human Faculty and Its Development* (New York: Macmillan, 1883). His various articles on eugenics, written during his lifetime, were collected and published in 1909 by Macmillan in London under the title of *Essays in Eugenics*. Each article carries the original date of publication and thus provides an easy means of tracing Galton's formation of the eugenic dogma. The scientific community of nineteenth-century America respected Sir Francis Galton. For example, an anonymous feature article, "Sketch of Francis Galton," *The Popular Science Monthly*, XXIX (May 1886), 117–121, was one article in a series on outstanding scientists of the day. William K. Brooks, "The Study of Inheritance, A Review of the Writings of Francis Galton, First Paper," *The Popular Science Monthly*, XLVIII (February 1896), 480–492, which was continued in the following March issue, favorably evaluates Galton's contribution to hereditary studies. In a similar judgment, in unsigned reviews, *The Nation*, XLIX (September 5, 1889), 196–198 and *ibid.*, XXXVI (June 14, 1883), 512–513, praised Galton's major works in heredity. A note of opposition was sounded, however, by an unknown book reviewer, "Hereditary Genius," *The Catholic World*, XI (September 1870), 721–732, who rejects Galton's materialist explanation of heredity.

In the latter part of Galton's life, Karl Pearson was his companion and fellow researcher. Frank H. Hankins, "Individual Differences, The Galton-Pearson Approach," *Social Forces*, IV (December 1925), 272–281, indicates the closeness of their research and methodology. Although the holder of the first chair of eugenics, Karl Pearson during his lifetime lived in Galton's shadow. The two articles that follow relate how important Karl Pearson is in the history of statistics and biometrics: Samuel A. Stouffer, "Karl Pearson—An Appreciation of the Hundredth Anniversary of His

Birth," *Journal of the American Statistical Association*, LIII (March 1958), 23–27, and Helen M. Walker, "The Contributions of Karl Pearson," *ibid.*, 11–22. E. S. Pearson, *Karl Pearson, An Appreciation of Some Aspects of His Life and Work* (Cambridge, England: Cambridge University Press, 1938) is a fuller and highly laudatory biography of Galton's major English disciple. Karl Pearson, *National Life from the Standpoint of Science,* second edition (London: Cambridge University Press, 1900) reveals his ethics, based on Social Darwinian premise and a great trust in science to save human society from self-destruction through a systematic disregard of biological natural law.

Francis Galton and Karl Pearson were in the naturalist tradition begun in the nineteenth century by Darwin. The April 1959 issue of *The Proceedings of the American Philosophical Society* (Volume CIII) is entirely devoted to a discussion of the many effects of Darwin's *The Origin of Species.* Thomas P. Neill, *1859 in Review* (Westminster, Maryland: The Newman Press, 1959), indicated what a crucial year it was in several spheres of human activities.

John C. Greene, *The Death of Adam, Evolution and Its Impact on Western Thought* (New York: A Mentor Book, 1961) provides an excellent survey of one Darwinian evolutionary thought. Greene discusses post-Darwinian evolutionary thought in *Darwin and the Modern World View* (New York: A Mentor Book, 1963). In "Darwin and Religion," *Proceedings of the American Philosophical Society,* CIII (October 1959), 716–725, Greene shows how Darwin carefully tried to avoid the theological implications of his theories.

Loren Eiseley in *Darwin's Century, Evolution and the Men Who Discovered It* (Garden City: Anchor Books, 1961) masterfully handles the many threads of scientific thought and biographical detail in weaving an account of nineteenth-century science. Gertrude Himmelfarb maintains— *Darwin and the Darwinian Revolution* (Garden City: Anchor Books, 1959) —that in many instances the Darwinian controversy was essentially conservative in its effects on biological research and methodology while often having revolutionary consequences in other fields of human knowledge. Stanley Hyman, *The Tangled Bank, Darwin, Marx, and Freud as Imaginative Writers* (New York: Atheneum, 1962), investigates Darwin's use of figures of speech in showing the extent of his naturalism. Although not concerned with scientific thought, Walter E. Houghton has an excellent insight into midcentury English attitudes in *The Victorian Frame of Mind, 1830–1870* (New Haven: Yale University Press, 1957). The second volume of John T. Mertz, *A History of European Thought in the Nineteenth Century* (London: William Blackwood and Sons, 1903) is still a major source for the intellectual events of the last century. A recent book, George L. Mosse's *The Culture of Western Europe, The Nineteenth and Twentieth*

Centuries, An Introduction (Chicago: Rand McNally and Co., 1961), successfully traces the many elements of naturalism in the last two hundred years.

For an introduction into the heredity-environment debate which raged from the time of Galton to 1932, Nicholas Pastore, *The Nature-Nurture Controversy* (New York: Columbia University Press, 1949) presents a reasonably full picture of the debate as it affected the social sciences. Darwin's article, "Inheritance," *The Popular Science Monthly*, XIX (September 1881), 663–665, for example, did not clarify the issue. Henry F. Osborn defends the thesis of the inheritance of acquired characters in a number of articles; for instance, "The Palaeontological Evidence for the Transmission of Acquired Characters," *The American Naturalist*, XXIII (July 1889), 561–566, and another article by same title in *The Proceedings for the American Association for the Advancement of Science*, XXXVIII (August 1889), 273–276. He wrote "The Present Problem of Heredity," *Atlantic Monthly*, LXVII (March 1891), 353–364, for a popular consumption. Osborn recognized inadequacies of older theories of inheritance in his article, "The Difficulties in the Heredity Theory," *The American Naturalist*, XXVI (July 1892), 537–567. Dr. Manly Miles, "Heredity of Acquired Characters," *Proceedings of the American Association for the Advancement of Science*, XLI (August 1892), 202–211, indicates how strongly the American scientific community subscribed to the thesis before 1900. Th. Eimer, *On Orthogenesis and the Importance of Natural Selection in Species-Formation* (Chicago: The Open Court Publishing Co., 1898), is typical of the speculation on the mechanism of heredity in the nineteenth century. The material cited in Chapter III develops fully the heredity-environment argument in the United States.

In summary, given Francis Galton's activities and the growth in scientific and lay interest in naturalistic analysis of society, G. Flamingo, "The Conflict of Races, Classes, and Societies," *The Monist*, VII (April 1897), 380–414, and Frank A. Fetter, "Social Progress and Race Degeneration," *Forum*, XXVIII (October 1899), 228–238, are typical of the early writings on eugenics as a solution to the nation's ills.

Chapter III

Edwin G. Conklin's "The World's Debt to Darwin," *Proceedings of the American Philosophical Society*, XLVIII (February 23, 1909), xxxviiilvii, provides an early academic American evaluation of Darwin by a highly reputable scientist. Edward J. Pfeifer takes a more historical and wider view of Darwin's importance in American thought in "The Reception of Darwinism in the United States, 1859–1880" (unpublished Doctoral Dissertation, Brown University, 1957). This title is available on microfilm from University Microfilms of Ann Arbor, Michigan. An old study, Bert J. Loewenberg, "The

Impact of the Doctrine of Evolution on American Thought, 1859–1900"
(unpublished Doctoral Dissertation, Harvard University, 1934) provides
the major framework of later historical studies dealing with Darwin's ideas
in America. Loewenberg's thesis in its essential parts may be taken from
the following articles which he wrote: "The Controversy Over Evolution in
New England, 1859–1873," *New England Quarterly*, VIII (June 1935),
232–257; "The Reaction of American Scientists to Darwinism," *American
Historical Review*, XXXVIII (July 1933), 687–701; "Darwinism Comes to
America, 1859–1900," *Mississippi Valley Historical Review*, XXVIII (December 1941), 339–368. Sidney Ratners traces the effects of Darwin's
theories on science as philosophical explanations of life's mysteries in "Evolution and the Rise of the Scientific Spirit in America," *Philosophy of
Science*, III (January 1936), 104–122. Sidney Warren, *American Free-
thought, 1860–1914* (New York: Columbia University Press, 1943), gives
full explanation of evolution's influence on the "village atheist."

Sidney Ditzion's contribution, *Marriage, Morals and Sex in America, A
History of Ideas* (New York: Bookman Associates, 1953), is a scholarly and
major work in a field lacking monographic studies and marred by shoddy
and sensational publications.

Yankee Reformers in the Urban Age (Cambridge: Harvard University
Press, 1954) by Arthur Mann carefully notes racist notions of the Boston
reformers in the last century. Wallace E. Davies fails to develop fully the
racist ideology in his otherwise admirable study, *Patriotism on Parade, The
Story of Veterans and Hereditary Organizations in America, 1783–1900*
(Cambridge: Harvard University Press, 1955). Unfortunately, Edward
McNall Burns does not discuss the racist implications behind *The American
Idea of Mission, Concepts of National Purpose and Destiny* (New Brunswick, New Jersey: Rutgers University Press, 1957) but rather concentrates
on literary and political expressions.

Two unpublished doctoral dissertations deal with the impact of evolutionary concepts on social theory: Helen Lane, "Heredity and Environment
in American Social Thought, 1900–1929" (Columbia University, 1950),
and Mark H. Haller, "American Eugenics: Heredity and Social Thought,
1870–1930" (University of Wisconsin, 1959). Lane mentions eugenics in
connection with her main concern of tracing Herbert Spencer's influence on
American social thought. Her treatment of eugenics is brief and merely
supplementary to her main theme. Haller, however, sees eugenics as a
movement with its major emphasis on the breeding and control of feeble-
mindedness and on immigration restriction. He traces the chronology of the
science from its beginnings in England with Sir Francis Galton to the United
States. Haller's treatment is broad in scope but does not deal with the significance of American eugenists as progressive reformers. He does not attempt to relate American eugenists to any tradition of conservativism nor

does he point out its connection to naturalism in the United States. Haller, in his work, makes no effort to explore the importance of pre-Darwinian ideas such as the economy of nature, the great chain of being concept, teleology, and the inheritance of acquired characteristics. Haller's discussion of American eugenists does not fully explain the sociological factors behind the crusade that sought a racially pure United States. His dissertation was published as *Eugenics: Hereditarian Attitudes In American Thought* (New Brunswick, New Jersey: Rutgers University Press, 1963).

My main concern in this study is to explain how American eugenists with certain progressives held a common view of mankind's instinctual behavior, and, therefore, both this element in the progressive movement and the eugenists were basically conservatives. They rejected the eighteenth-century rationalism which historically contributed to the growth of American democracy. Eugenists in the progressive crusade stressed the natural order of Social Darwinism, not John Locke and Thomas Jefferson's natural rights theories of human equality. My work, therefore, is an effort to write the history of an important social movement in terms of its ideological roots, to trace its theoretical development and to identify its relationships to other major social and political movements of the period.

One area in which racial consideration loomed large was in immigration policy. John Higham handles this aspect in *Strangers in the Land, Patterns of American Nativism, 1860–1925* (New Brunswick, New Jersey: Rutgers University Press, 1955. Oscar Handlin deals admirably with ethnic factors in public policy in his *Race and Nationality in American Life* (Boston: Little, Brown and Co., 1957). *The Movement to Americanize the Immigrant* (New York: Columbia University Press, 1948) by Edward C. Hartmann tells how public opinion and various pressure groups sought the same ethical standards for all Americans. Finally, Robert A. Devine traces immigration restrictions of the last twenty-five years in *American Immigration Policy, 1924–1952* (New Haven: Yale University Press, 1957).

William Stanton, *The Leopard's Spots, Scientific Attitude Toward Race in America, 1815–1859* (Chicago: The University of Chicago Press, 1960), covers the story of pre–Civil War racism supported by the scientific thought of the day; on occasion, these racist notions appeared in the latter half of the nineteenth century.

The inheritance of acquired characters was the dominant theory of heredity in the nineteenth century. Conway Zirkle in his article, "The Early History of the Idea of the Inheritance of Acquired Characters and Of Pangenesis," *Transactions of the American Philosophical Society*, n.s. XXXV, Part II (January 1946), 91–147, traces the theory from its origins in ancient Greek thought to the victorian era. He gives a briefer account in "The Knowledge of Heredity before 1900," *Genetics in the Twentieth Century*, L. C. Dunn, ed. (New York: Macmillan, 1951), pp. 35–58. The essential aspects of pre-Darwinian biological thought are presented in Zirkle's "Species before Darwin," *Proceedings of the American Philosophical Society,* CIII (October 1959), 636–645, and "Natural Selection before 'The Origin of Species,' " *ibid.,* LXXXIV (April 1941), 71–123.

Edward Drinker Cope, paleontologist and biologist, was the leading American expounder of the theory of the inheritance of acquired characteristics. His defense of the theory is in "Catagenesis: Or Creation by Retrograde Metamorphoses of Energy," *Science,* IV (September 12, 1884), 240–243, and in his major publication, *The Primary Factors of Organic Evolution* (Chicago: The Open Court Publishing Co., 1896). Henry F. Osborn has the essential facts of Cope's career in "Biographical Memoir of Edward Drinker Cope, 1840–1897," *National Academy of Sciences of the United States of America, Biographical Memoirs,* XIII (Third Memoir, 1929), 127–317.

Alpheus Hyatt, Cope's contemporary, accepted the inheritance of acquired characteristics. A good example of Hyatt's opinion is his article, "Phylogeny of an Acquired Characteristic," *Proceedings of the American Philosophical Society,* XXXII (May 22–26, 1893), 349–647. Other scientists repeated the major points of the environmentalist interpretation. *The Popular Science Monthly* especially was a major publishing outlet for dissemination of the major pre-Mendelian biological theory. The articles written by different men maintained a high degree of intellectual uniformity. Louis Agassiz, "Evolution and Permanence of Type," *The Atlantic Monthly,* XXXIII (January 1874), 92–101, supported their general conclusions. Edward Lurie places Agassiz in the history of anthropological thought in "Louis Agassiz and the Races of Man," *Isis,* XLV (September 1954), 227–242.

Henry W. Holland, "Heredity," *The Atlantic Monthly,* LII (October 1883), 447–452, and Dr. Andrew Wilson, "What Is Inheritance," *Harper's New Monthly Magazine,* LXXXIII (August 1891), 355–363, provide early qualifications to the orthodoxy of the inheritance of acquired character theory. John M. Tyler combined the theory with Christian idealism in *The Whence and the Whither of Man, A Brief History of His Origin and Development through Conformity to Environment* (New York: Charles Scribner's Sons, 1896). On the other hand, the following writers related the concept of environmentally determined heredity to other problems of life and society: A. J. Morrissey, "Hereditary Influences and Medical Progress," *Arena,* XVII (December 1896), 283–293; George Sergi, "Some Ideas Concerning Biological Heredity," *The Monist,* XII (October 1901), 1–20; Jacques Loeb, "Assimilation and Heredity," *The Monist,* VIII (July 1898), 547–555; Frederick S. Crum, "The Decadence of Native American Stock, A Statistical Study of Genealogical Records," *Publications of the American Statistical Association,* XIV (September 1914), 215–221.

Lester Frank Ward used the "democratic" version of the inheritance of acquired characteristics theory in his various reform plans. The articles, "The Transmission of Culture," *Forum*, XI (May 1891), 312-319, and "Weismann's Concessions," *The Popular Science Monthly*, XLV (June 1894), 175–184, were typical of Ward's use of biological theory in the cause of social reconstruction. Samuel Chugerman presents a laudatory analysis of Ward in *Lester F. Ward, The American Aristotle, A Summary and Interpretation of His Sociology* (Durham, North Carolina: Duke University Press, 1939). John C. Burnham discounts Ward's significance in the history of American reform in *Lester Frank Ward in American Thought* (Washington: Public Affairs Press, 1956). John D. Davies in *Phrenology, Fad and Science, A Nineteenth Century American Crusade* (New Haven: Yale University Press, 1955), related how phrenology utilized the "democratic" version of the environmentalist creed of heredity.

Everett F. Phillips provided a convenient summary in "A Review of Parthenogenesis," *Proceedings of the American Philosophical Society*, XLII (October 16, 1903), 275–345. Thirty years later the *American Philosophical Society* devoted an entire issue of its proceedings to a "Symposium on the Inheritance of Acquired Characters, *ibid.* (April 21, 1923), 270–325.

The Oneida Community was the best-known example of positive eugenics in nineteenth-century United States. John H. Noyes, the founder, discussed his program in *A History of American Socialisms* (Philadelphia: J. B. Lippincott & Co., 1870). Pierrepont B. Noyes, who was conceived and reared under Noyes's direction, praised the system in two books, *My Father's House, An Oneida Boyhood* (New York: Farrar and Rinehart, 1937) and *A Goodly Heritage* (New York: Rinehart and Co., 1958). Anita Newcomb McGee discussed the varied implications of stirpiculture, Noyes's name for eugenics, in "An Experiment in Human Stirpiculture," *The American Anthropologist*, IV (October 1891), 319–325. Twentieth-century eugenists expressed an interest in the experiment as related by Hilda Herrick Noyes and George Wallingford Noyes in "The Oneida Community Experiment in Stirpiculture," published in the *Scientific Papers of the Second International Congress of Eugenics Held at American Museum of Natural History, New York, September 22–28, 1921*, Harry H. Laughlin, ed., I (Baltimore: Williams and Wilkins Co., 1923), 374–386. George Wallingford Noyes edited Noyes's writings under the title, *Religious Experience of John Humphrey Noyes, Founder of the Oneida Community* (New York: Macmillan, 1923), while Robert A. Parker gave a substantial secondary account in *A Yankee Saint, John Humphrey Noyes and the Oneida Community* (New York: G. P. Putnam's Sons, 1935).

Van Wyck Brooks's account of literary Boston in *New England: Indian Summer 1865–1915* (New York: E. P. Dutton and Co., 1940) indicated problems of status among the well-to-do classes of the region. In the same way, Walter Lord, although like Brooks, did not state the status crisis, nevertheless was suggestive in that regard in *The Good Years from 1900 to the First World War* (New York: Harper and Brothers, 1960). A good example of this status crisis among conservative New Englanders is Irving Fisher, "Why Has the Doctrine of Laissez Faire Been Abandoned?" *Proceedings of the American Association for the Advancement of Science,* LVI–LVII (1906–1907), 577–591.

While changes were taking place in the American society, the acceptance of the inheritance of acquired characters declined. Gregor Mendel, the intellectual source of genetics, caused this decline. Conway Zirkle provided an adequate account of the background to Mendel's scientific concepts in "Gregor Mendel and His Precursors," *Isis,* XLII (June 1951), 97–104. In addition to writing the standard biography of Mendel, Hugo Iltis summarizes his account in "Gregor Mendel's Life and Heritage," *Genetics in the Twentieth Century,* L. C. Dunn, ed. (New York: Macmillan, 1951), pp. 25–34. This latter title is a valuable source for showing the growth of genetics and influence of eugenics, particularly William E. Castle's "The Beginning of Mendelism in America," *ibid.,* pp. 59–76, and Theodosius Dobzhansky's "Mendelian Population and Their Evolutions," *ibid.,* pp. 573–590. Bentley Glass explained why Mendel's theories remained unknown until 1901 in "The Long Neglect of a Scientific Discovery: Mendel's Laws of Inheritance," *Studies in Intellectual History* (Baltimore: The Johns Hopkins Press, 1953), pp. 148–160. Mendel's late acceptance made August Weismann "a forerunner, a pioneer" in the attack on older theories of heredity. As editors and translators, Edward B. Poulton, *et al.,* collected Weismann's work under the title *Essays upon Heredity and Kindred Biological Problems,* two volumes. (Oxford, England: Clarendon Press, 1891). A contemporary reaction to his work is found in an unsigned article, "Weismann on Heredity," *The Nation,* L (May 1890), 357–358. Alexander Weinstein gives important biographical information in "Weismann, August," *Encyclopaedia of the Social Sciences,* Edwin R. A. Seligman, ed., XV (New York: Macmillan, 1935), 392. Weinstein's account of "Heredity," in the same source, VII, 328–334, gives historical background material. H. S. Jennings discusses "Eugenics" in the same set of books, V, 617–621.

Beatrice Bateson writes of another critic of the older theories of heredity, *William Bateson FRS* (Cambridge, England: Cambridge University Press, 1928). Bateson provides a major explanation and defense of Mendel's concepts in *Mendel's Principles of Heredity* (Cambridge, England: Cambridge University Press, 1909).

Other writers joined Weismann and Bateson in criticizing the ancient explanation of the inheritance process. Grant Allen, "The New Theory of Heredity," *The Review of Reviews,* I (June 1890), 537–538, provided brief and popular explanation of the changes in hereditary theory. William

K. Brooks instructed the scientists with his contribution, "Heredity and Variation: Logical and Biological," *Proceedings of the American Philosophical Society.* XLV (1960), 70–76. Thomas H. Montgomery contributed two pieces on the validity of the newer biological concepts with "A Study of the Chromosomes of the Germ Cells of Metazoa," *Transactions of the American Philosophical Society,* n.s. XX, Part II (January 18, 1901), 154–236, and "The Main Facts in Regard to the Cellular Basis of Heredity," *Proceedings of the American Philosophical Society,* XLIII (January 15, 1904), 5–14.

Chapter IV

Samuel J. Holmes in 1924 produced *A Bibliography of Eugenics* published as the twenty-fifth volume of the University of California Publications in Zoology by the University of California Press in Berkeley. This work provides innumerable items. During his academic career, Holmes wrote *Studies in Evolution and Eugenics* (New York: Harcourt, Brace and Co., 1923). The same publisher distributed Holmes's *Life and Evolution, An Introduction to General Biology* in 1926, and *The Eugenic Predicament* in 1933. These three books, in comparison with other books dealing with eugenics, are relatively moderate in tone and generally underplay the sensationalism inherent in eugenics.

Charles B. Davenport, on the other hand, is of another type. Morris Steggerda evaluated favorably Davenport's scientific contribution in "Charles Benedict Davenport (1866–1944); The Man and His Contributions to Physical Anthropology," *American Journal of Physical Anthropology,* n.s. II (June 1944), 167–185. Oscar Riddle's "Charles Benedict Davenport, 1866–1944," *National Academy of Science Biographical Memoirs,* XXV (Washington: Government Printing Office, 1946), 75–110, contains a good biographical sketch and a complete bibliography of Davenport's writing. As the Riddle article notes, Davenport was a prolific writer but his work suffered from repetitions and his abiding racial prejudices. For example, the *Proceedings of the American Philosophical Society* from 1917 to 1939 published many of his articles dealing with such topics as child development to the postnatal development of the external nose. In like manner, during the 1920s Davenport wrote for the *Quarterly Publications of the American Statistical Association* on eugenics and the general subject of heredity. His best and complete monograph on eugenics and related field of heredity was published in 1910 by Henry Holt and Co. in New York under the title *Eugenics.* A year later, in 1911, the same company released Davenport's *Heredity in Relation to Eugenics.* In these two popular accounts, a great deal of repetition of conclusions existed. An informative but informal history of the eugenics movement is in Davenport's "The Eugenics Programme and Progress in Its Achievement," *Eugenics: Twelve University Lectures* (New York: Dodd, Mead and Co., 1914), pp. 1–14.

Davenport maintained an amazing consistency in his scientific investigations during his career. The conclusion was always that some groups and races were organically inferior and that their number should be limited in accordance with the principles of eugenics. As coauthor with Morris Steggerda, he wrote a classic statement of this prejudice in *Race Crossing in Jamaica*, Pub. No. 395 (Washington: Carnegie Institution of Washington, 1929). In the years following World War I, Davenport wrote a number of articles for the Carnegie Institution of Washington.

Two examples of Davenport's use of statistical techniques in proving the validity of eugenics creed are *Defects Found in Drafted Men*, Statistical Information (Washington: Government Printing Office for the War Department, 1920), with Albert G. Love as coauthor, and *Statistical Methods in Biology, Medicine and Psychology*, fourth edition (New York: John Wiley and Sons, 1936). Merl P. Ekas served as a fellow author.

While serving as head of the Eugenics Record Office at Cold Spring Harbor, New York, Davenport published in the *Bulletin* of the organization and the first two *Memoirs* in 1912. His defense of Mendelian inheritance in the cause of eugenics is in "Heredity and Mendel's Law," *Proceedings of the Washington Academy of Sciences*, IX (July 1907), 179–187.

As the leading philosopher of American eugenics, Davenport related the creed to other aspects of public policy. He denounced sentimental almsgiving in "Eugenics and Charity," *Proceedings of the National Conference of Charities and Corrections* (Cleveland, 1912), pp. 280–282. In fact, Davenport urged that government base its various policies on eugenics in "The Importance to the State of Eugenic Investigation," *Proceedings of the First National Conference of Race Betterment, January 8–12, 1914* (Battle Creek: Race Betterment Foundation, 1914), pp. 450–456. Emily F. Robbins edited the *Proceedings*. The same theme can be found in "Field Work, An Indispensable Aid to State Care of the Socially Inadequate," *Proceedings of the National Conference of Charities and Corrections at the Forty-Second Session* (Baltimore, 1915), pp. 312–315. Davenport gave progress reports on the eugenics movement in "Research in Eugenics," *Eugenics, Genetics and the Family, Scientific Papers of the Second International Congress of Eugenics*, I (Baltimore: William and Wilkins Co., 1923), 20–28. Harry H. Laughlin edited the volume.

A handy statement of Davenport's belief of the importance of heredity in cultural matters is located in the next two articles. The first, written in conjunction with Lorine A. Nelson, is "Heredity and Culture as Factors in Body Build," *Public Health Reports*, XL (November 21, 1915), 2601–2605. The second article deals with "Crime Heredity and Environment," *The Journal of Heredity*, XIX (July 1928), 307–313. In the above items and through his entire bibliography, Davenport stressed that inheritance—the laws thereof—provided the answer to mankind's cultural problems. "The

Mechanism of Organic Evolution," *Annual Report of the Smithsonian Institution, 1930* (Washington: Government Printing Office, 1931), pp. 417–429, gives a clear statement of that belief in hereditary determinism.

Edward McNall Burns's *David Starr Jordan: Prophet of Freedom* (Stanford: Stanford University Press, 1953) is a scholarly biography, although Burns does not fully develop the importance of eugenics in Jordan's life and thought. Harvey S. Summers's "David Starr Jordan and His Social Philosophy," unpublished master's thesis written in 1956 and located in the University of Texas Library, is totally inadequate. Jordon's autobiography, *The Days of a Man Being Memories of a Naturalist, Teacher and Minor Prophet of Democracy,* two volumes (Yonkers-on-Hudson, New York: World Book Company, 1922) is rather candid and filled with great detail. Alice N. Hays indicates the vastness of Jordan's writings in *David Starr Jordan, A Bibliography of His Writings, 1891–1931* (Stanford: Stanford University Press, 1952). The book is the first volume of the Library Studies of Stanford University.

From 1900 to 1913, the American Unitarian Association of Boston published numerous works of Jordan's. Two typical examples of these materials are *The Blood of the Nation, A Study of the Decay of Races through the Survival of the Unfit* published in 1920, and *The Heredity of Richard Roe, A Discussion of the Principles of Eugenics* released in 1913.

Jordan criticized American higher education in *The Trend of the American University* (Stanford: Stanford University Press, 1929) and *The Higher Foolishness* (Indianapolis: Bobbs-Merrill, 1927). As might be expected, he stressed the racial consequences of popular educational philosophy. Early in his career, Jordan expressed the same view in *The Care and Culture of Men, A Series of Addresses on Higher Education* (San Francisco: The Whitable and Ray Co., 1903).

During his lifetime, Jordan constantly related the importance of eugenics to world peace and anti-imperialism. *The Question of the Philippines, An Address before the Graduate Club of Leland Stanford Junior University on February 14, 1899* (Palo Alto, California: Printed for the Graduate Club by the Courtesy of John J. Valentine, Esq., 1899) provides insights into Jordan's anti-expansion creed. Jordan gives the eugenic reasons for pacifism in "The Human Harvest," *Proceedings of the American Philosophical Society,* XLV (1906), 54–69. With Edward B. Krebbiel, Jordan wrote *Syllabus of Lectures on International Conciliation Given at Leland Stanford Junior University* (Boston: World Peace Foundation, 1912). The same theme of racial destruction may be found in *War and Waste, A Series of Discussions of War Accessories* (Garden City: Doubleday, Page and Co., 1913). A shorter version of the same ideas are found in Jordan's "The Eugenics of War," *Eugenics Review,* V (December, 1913), 197–213. In *War's Aftermath, A Preliminary Study of the Eugenics of War as Illustrated by the Civil War of the United States and the Late Wars in the Balkans* (Boston: Houghton Mifflin, 1914), Jordan attempted to buttress his ideas with historical examples. He later published two full-scale studies in international relations —*Ways to Lasting Peace* (Indianapolis: Bobbs-Merrill Co., 1916), and *Democracy and World Relations* (Yonkers-on-Hudson, New York: World Book Co., 1918).

Jordan's particular version of the inheritance of acquired characteristics is in *The Scientific Aspects of Luther Burbank's Work* (San Francisco: A. M. Robertson, 1909), written in conjunction with Vernon L. Kellogg, and in "Evolution—Its Meaning," *Creation by Evolution* (New York: Macmillan, 1928). Frances Mason edited the composite volume.

Edward East's written contributions to the cause of eugenics lack the dogmatism and verbal extremism of Davenport and Jordan's bibliographies. East was prone, however, like other eugenists, to present the crusade as an either/or situation. His article, "Civilization at the Crossways," *The Birth Control Review*, VII (December 1923), 328–332, is an example of the technique. He stressed the natural goodness of agrarian life in "Population in Relation to Agriculture," *Eugenics in Race and State, Scientific Papers of the Second International Congress of Eugenics Held at American Museum of National History*, II (Baltimore: Williams and Wilkins Co., 1923), 215–232. East's two major works, *Heredity and Human Affairs* (New York: Charles Scribner's Sons, 1927), and *Mankind at the Crossroads* (New York: Charles Scribner's Sons, 1928), are complete statements of his attitudes toward eugenics and related matters. He edited *Biology in Human Affairs* (New York: McGraw-Hill Books, 1931), and he wrote two articles—"Biology and Human Problems" (pp. 1–26) and "Heredity" (pp. 161–196)—in the same volume. These articles generally restate his earlier defense of eugenics. Typically, East sought a connection between mental processes and cultural achievement in "Insanity and Genius," *The Journal of Heredity*, XXXIX (August 1938), 275–279.

Harry Laughlin's bibliographic contribution to the cause of eugenics is discussed in regard to sterilization in Chapter VI.

The balance of the citations in this chapter are random items which have certain values as will be noted. Another excellent discussion of the worth of eugenics as a social philosophy and public policy is William E. Kellicott, *The Social Direction of Human Evolution: An Outline of the Science of Eugenics* (New York: D. Appleton and Co., 1911). Speaking of public policy (no author), "The Bureau of Analysis and Investigation: Its Purpose and Field," *Eugenics and Social Welfare Bulletin #1, State of New York State Board of Charities Department of State and Alien Poor* (Albany: The Capitol, 1912), indicates how New York used the concepts of eugenics in charitable activities. On the other hand, Allen G. Roper discussed the historic and pre-Darwinian roots of eugenics in *Ancient Eugenics* (London: Oxford University Press, 1913).

Madison Grant, noted racist, and Charles Stewart Davison edited *The Alien in Our Midst* (New York: Galton Publishing Co., Inc., 1930), giving a complete explanation of why eugenists advocated immigration restriction. In a larger context, the composite book (no editor given) *Eugenics: Twelve University Lectures* (New York: Dodd, Mead and Co., 1914) demonstrated the widespread interest in eugenics among both social and biographical scientists. The reason, doubtlessly, was the class appeal of the eugenics movement. A. B. Wolfe, "Eugenics and Social Attitudes," *Eugenics in Race and State, Scientific Papers at the Second International Congress of Eugenics Held at the American Museum of Natural History,* II (Baltimore: Williams and Wilkins, 1923), 413–418, reflected the eugenists' class awareness.

Chapter V

Richard Lewinsohn provides an elementary introduction to the relationship between the birth-control movement and the larger aspects of man's sexual behavior in *A History of Sexual Customs,* Alexander Mayce, trans. (New York: Harper and Brothers, 1958). A brief introduction to the historic struggle of the family limitation cause in Victor Robinson, *Pioneer of Birth Control* (New York: Voluntary Parenthood League, n.d.). Richard W. Leopold discussed the full reform philosophy of an early birth-control leader in *Robert Dale Owen, A Biography* (Cambridge: Harvard University Press, 1940). The book is Volume XLV of the *Harvard Historical Studies.* Additional information may be found in Robert S. Riegel, "The American Father of Birth Control," *New England Quarterly,* VI (September 1933), 470–490, which is the story of Charles Knowlton, M.D. Norman Hines noted the Malthusian origin of birth control in "Robert Dale Owen, The Pioneer of American Neo-Malthusianism," *The American Journal of Sociology,* XXXV (January 1930), 529–547.

Four contemporary indications of a widespread interest in population problems of the nineteenth century are James C. Welling, President of Columbia University, "The Law of Malthus," *The American Anthropologist,* I (January 1888), 1–23; (no author cited), "Artificial Selection and the Marriage Problem," *The Review of Reviews,* IV (November 1891), 457–458; E. B. Andrews, "Are There too Many of Us?" *The North American Review,* LCV (November 1892), 596–607; and the Rev. R. F. Clarke, S. J., "Neo-Malthusianism," *ibid.,* CLXIII (September 1896), 345–361. Andrews was president of Brown University and Clarke belonged to the Society of Jesus. The former accepted the existence of overpopulation, while the latter rejected the contention.

The family naturally served as a focus for the birth-control defenders. Arthur W. Calhoun's *A Social History of the American Family from Colonial Times to the Present* was originally published in 1917 and reissued by Barnes and Noble, Inc., of New York in 1945 with the three original volumes bound in one. The book is still a standard source on the history of the family. Interesting comparisons are possible when the Calhoun work is compared with a eugenist's account of family life—William C. D. Whetham, *The Family and the Nation, A Study in Natural Inheritance and Social Responsibility* (London: Longmans, Green and Co., 1909).

Lawrence Lader provided an uncritical evaluation of the titular head of the birth-control enterprise with *The Margaret Sanger Story and the Fight for Birth Control* (Garden City: Doubleday and Co., 1955). For purposes of this book, Margaret Sanger's writings were more important in understanding the birth-control movement during the progressive years, 1900 to 1930. Especially valuable and informative are her *Woman and the New Race* (New York: Brentanos, 1920), and two years later by the same publisher, *The Pivot of Civilization*. The two books expressed clearly Mrs. Sanger's alliance with instinct psychology and her conservative naturalism verbally expressed as avant-garde radicalism. She edited three books which demonstrated fully her concern for the overpopulation menace and allied topics. These books are, *The Case for Birth Control, A Supplement Brief and Statement of Fact to Aid the Court in Its Consideration of the Statute Designed to Prevent the Dissemination of Information for Preventing Conception* (New York: Margaret Sanger, 1917); *Birth Control, The Proceedings of the First American Birth Control Conference Held at the Hotel Plaza, New York, November 11, 12, 1921* (New York: The Birth Control Review, 1921); and *Proceedings of the World Population Conference Held at the Salle Centrale, Geneva, August 29 to September 3, 1927* (London: Edward Arnold and Co., 1927).

Long-time editor of *The Birth Control Review*, Margaret Sanger wrote innumerable articles for the journal. Suffice it to say that *BCR* is a major source in understanding her opinions during the days of an active birth-control movement. Likewise *BCR* contained the writings of many champions of the cause, and at the same time one can trace the worldwide and nationwide progress of the contraception cause in its pages.

During the period discussed in this account, the eugenics agitators and birth-control supporters shared many assumptions and agitation techniques. For example, *BCR* annually published an issue devoted entirely to eugenics, such as the issue of August, 1926, Volume X. In these issues, varied opinions concerning birth control and eugenics relationships were discussed. Responses to an important series indicated however that regardless of a positive or negative response, the vast majority polled stressed the innate connection between the two reforms. The series, "A Question of Policy, Shall the Birth Control Review Be Combined with a Eugenics Magazine?" is found in *BCR*, XII (June 1928), 188; (July 1928), 214; (August 1928), 238; (October 1928), 290–291; (November 1928), 323–329.

Frank Hankins agreed with this belief in his article, "The Interdependence of Eugenics and Birth Control," *BCR*, XV (June 1931), 170–171. He also wrote the "Birth Control" article for the *Encyclopaedia of the Social Sciences*, II, 559–569. Hankins was not, however, a particular supporter of Margaret Sanger as shown by his review of her book, *My Fight for Birth Control* (New York: Farrar and Rinehart, 1931) which is in *BCR*, XV (November 1931), 372–375.

Raymond Pearl, a noted biologist and statistician, expressed concern with the multiplying millions in his articles "The Menace of Population Growth," *BCR*, VII (March 1923), 65–67, and "The Differential Birth-Rate," *ibid.*, IX (October 1925), 278–279, 300–302. Like others of his generation, Pearl saw a logical and valid connection between birth control, sterilization and eugenics—"Sterilization of Degenerates and Criminals Considered from the Standpoint of Genetics," *Eugenics Review*, XI (April 1919), 1–6.

Chapter VI

BCR annually published an issue devoted to sterilization of which the March 1928 issue (Volume XII) provides a good example. C. O. McCormick, M.D., "Eugenic Sterilization," *BCR*, XVI (October 1932), 241–242, is typical of the intellectual relation between eugenics and sterilization.

Stanley P. Davies, *The Mentally Retarded in Society* (New York: Columbia University Press, 1959) is a solid historical account of the role of the social worker dealing with the feebleminded. The Davies volume particularly placed R. L. Dugdale's *The Jukes, A Study in Crime, Pauperism, Disease, and Heredity*, fourth edition (New York: G. P. Putnam's Sons, 1910) in a revealing historical context.

Harry H. Laughlin during his scientific career served as historian, philosopher, and administrator of eugenics and sterilization. As historian he contributed "The Eugenics Record Office at the End of Twenty-Seven Months Work," *Eugenics Record Office Report #1* (Cold Spring Harbor, New York: June 1913); "The Scope of the Committee's Work," *ibid.*, *Bulletin #10A;* and "The Legal, Legislative and Administrative Aspects of Sterilization," *ibid.*, *Bulletin #10B* (Cold Spring Harbor, February 1914). He wrote a summary article of the same material in "Eugenics in America," *Eugenics Review*, XVII (April, 1925), 28–35. His *Eugenical Sterilization in the United States* (Chicago: Psychopathic Laboratory of the Municipal Court of Chicago, 1922) provided a vast collection of historical and statistical data. His commentary on the Bucks Case may be found in *The Legal Status of Eugenical Sterilization: History and Analysis of Litigation under the*

*Virginia Sterilization Statute which Led to a Decision of the Supreme Court
Upholding the Statute* (Chicago: The Municipal Court of Chicago, 1929).

Laughlin's treatment of the Mendelian inheritance theory is the subject
of his article, "The Fundamental Biological and Mathematical Principles
Underlying Chromosomal Descent and Recombination in Human Heredity,"
Research Studies of Crime as Related to Heredity (Chicago Municipal
Court of Chicago, 1925), pp. 75–82. The following three articles outlined
Laughlin's analysis of the importance of eugenics to related topics: "The
Relation of Eugenics to Other Sciences," *Eugenics Review,* XI (June 1919),
53–64; "The Legalization of Voluntary Eugenical Sterilization," *ibid.,* XIX
(April 1927), 12–18; "Eugenists on the Place of Birth Control," *BCR,* X
(January 1926), 7.

Laughlin was an active supporter of a rigid immigration restriction policy.
His findings and opinions were recorded in *A Statement of the Basic Prob-
lem, And of the Main Findings in the Analysis of Pan-American Immigration
Control and Policy* (Washington: Eugenics Record Office of the Carnegie
Institution of Washington, 1936), and *Immigration and Conquest* (New
York: The Chamber of Commerce of the State of New York, 1939).

In addition to his defense of sterilization, Paul Popenoe, with Roswell H.
Johnson as coauthor, wrote *Applied Eugenics* (New York: Macmillan,
1923), which was a standard textbook in the college course of eugenics.
The book is part of the series of Social Science Textbooks, edited by Richard
T. Ely. Popenoe later wrote *Practical Applications of Heredity* (Baltimore:
Williams and Wilkins, 1930) which included the same material and philosophy as his "Birth Control and Eugenics," *BCR,* I (April-May 1917), 6,
and *The Child's Heredity* (Baltimore: Williams and Wilkins, 1929). Popenoe, after the demise of the sterilization and eugenics movement, turned
to full-time work as a marriage advisor. At that time he wrote *Modern
Marriage, A Handbook for Men,* second edition (New York: Macmillan,
1946) and *Marriage Is What You Make It,* published by the same company
in 1950.

During the decade of the Great Depression, however, Popenoe actively
urged sterilization with such articles, for example, as "The Progress of Eugenic Sterilization," *The Journal of Heredity,* XXV (January 1934), 19–26,
and as a leader of the Human Betterment Foundation. With the founder of
this Foundation, E. S. Gosney, Popenoe was coauthor of *Sterilization for
Human Betterment* (New York: Macmillan, 1931). The same men published the results to their efforts for sterilization as *Twenty-Eight Years of
Sterilization in California,* second edition. (Pasedena: Human Betterment
Foundation, 1939).

E. S. Gosney edited a valuable collection of source material under the
title *Collected Papers on Eugenic Sterilization in California* (Pasadena:
The Human Betterment Foundation, 1930). His qualified acceptance of

birth control in "Sterilization and Contraception," *BCR*, XV (July 1931), 202.

Finally, an interesting change in the value of sterilization may be found in comparing J. H. Landman, *Human Sterilization, The History of the Sexual Sterilization Movement* (New York: Macmillan, 1932) with Abraham Myerson, *et al.*, *Eugenical Sterilization, A Reorientation of the Problem* (New York: Macmillan, 1936). The latter volume is highly critical of the movement as a means of realizing racial improvement.

For a present-day evaluation of surgical sterilization, see Andrew and William Ferker, "Vasectomy," *Medical Aspects of Human Sexuality*, II (June 1968), 29–35.

Chapter VII

Otis Pease has edited *The Progressive Years, The Spirit and Achievement of American Reform* (New York: George Braziller, 1962), a collection of contemporary materials introduced with an enlightened preface by the editor. In speaking of basic source material, Walter Lippmann, *Drift and Mastery, An Attempt to Diagnose the Current Unrest,* is essential to a discussion of the progressive mentality. A recent edition was released in 1961 as a Spectrum Book by Prentice-Hall, Inc., of Englewood Cliffs, New Jersey. Marquis Childs and James Reston as editors have collected essays dealing with Lippmann, the man and legend, under the title *Walter Lippmann and His Time* (New York: Harcourt, Brace and Co., 1959). Despite his short-term attraction to socialism, Lippmann is more indicative of the mugwump. Geoffery T. Blodgett, "The Mind of the Boston Mugwump," *The Mississippi Valley Historical Review*, XLVIII (March 1926), 614–634, gives a social-psychological analysis of the political type. Christopher Lasch discussed the same type of individual within foreign policy in "The Anti-Imperialists, the Philippines, and the Inequality of Man," *The Journal of Southern History*, XXIV (August 1958), 319–331. Oscar W. Underwood gave the Southern Democratic response to the mugwump's nativism in "The Restriction of European Immigration," *Proceedings of the American Association for the Advancement of Science*, LV (1906), 482–483.

Edwin Lawrence Godkin's attitudes and comments forecast similar judgments of American progressives between 1900 and 1930. William M. Armstrong traced Godkin's opinions on world events in *E. L. Godkin and American Foreign Policy, 1865–1900* (New York: Bookman Associates, 1957). Alan P. Grimes classified Godkin as an American version of Manchester Liberalism in *The Political Liberalism of the New York Nation, 1865–1932* (Chapel Hill: The University of North Carolina Press, 1953). This book is Volume XXXIV of the *James Sprunt Studies in History and Political Science*. Rollo Ogden edited the *Life and Letters of Edwin Lawrence Godkin* in two volumes (New York: Macmillan, 1907), a standard biography.

The pages of *The Nation*, under Godkin's editorship, discussed the racial basis of human behavior as indicated by these two examples published without a byline, "The Race Question," *The Nation*, XI (July 21, 1870), 39, and "Who Are Our Ancestors?" *ibid.*, XX (June 17, 1875), 405–407. Godkin was firmly in the progressive mold when he discussed "The Problems of Municipal Government," *Annals of the American Academy of Political and Social Science*, IV (May 1894), 857–882. From time to time, Godkin published his writings and speeches under a collective title. The next three titles are such collections—*Reflections and Comments, 1865–1895* (New York: Charles Scribner's Sons, 1895); *Problems of Modern Democracy, Political and Economic Essays*, second edition. (New York: Charles Scribner's Sons, 1897); and *Unforeseen Tendencies of Democracy* (Boston: Houghton Mifflin and Co., 1898).

Historians have conflicting opinions of Herbert Croly. David W. Noble's *The Paradox of Progressive Thought* (Minneapolis: University of Minnesota Press, 1958) states that Croly's ideas were not fully applicable to industrial America. On the other hand, Charles Forcey in *The Crossroads of Liberalism* sees Croly as a major philosopher of modern liberalism. Forcey's book was published by the Oxford University Press in 1961. Regardless of Noble's and Forcey's differences of interpretation, both men have sound observations on progressivism.

Herbert Croly presented his analysis of "reform Hamiltonianism" in the classic progressive work, *The Promise of American Life* (New York: Macmillan, 1914). The book was first published in 1909. It is superior in content to his later *Progressive Democracy* (New York: Macmillan, 1914).

Walter Johnson gives the best biographical account of Kansas editor William Allen White in *William Allen White's America* (New York: Henry Holt and Co., 1947). Everett Rich, *William Allen White, the Man from Emporia* (New York: Farrar and Rinehart, Inc., 1941). and David Henshaw, *A Man from Kansas* (New York: G. P. Putnam's, 1945) are inadequate biographies of the newspaperman.

The Autobiography of William Allen White (New York: Macmillan, 1946) and Walter Johnson's edition, *Selected Letters of William Allen White, 1899–1943* (New York: Henry Holt and Co., 1947), are first-rate sources for understanding White's brand of progressivism. However, Helen Mahin's *The Editor and His People, Editorials by William Allen White Selected from the Emporia Gazette* (New York: Macmillan, 1924) and William A. White, *Forty Years on Main Street* (New York: Farrar and Rinehart, Inc., 1937), compiled by Russell A. Fitzgibbon, are disappointing despite an occasional piece of small-town humor. White was a productive writer-journalist, biographer, historian, writer of fiction, and philosopher. It is the last type of writing that concerns us here. His *The Old Order Changeth, A View of American Democracy* must be ranked with Croly's

The Promise of American Life as a true expression of the progressive creed. White's analysis of *Politics: The Citizen's Business* (New York: Macmillan, 1924) is commonplace. *Some Cycles of Cathay* (Chapel Hill: The University of North Carolina Press, 1925), White's Weil Lectures on American Civilization, contains insights into his philosophy of history. The influence of the New Deal and the Turner thesis existed in the Kansas editor's *The Changing West, an Economic Theory about Our Golden Age* (New York: Macmillan, 1939).

Of all the great mass of material on Theodore Roosevelt, these two books are the best accounts relating his domestic and foreign policies to the larger developments of American history: George E. Mowry, *The Era of Theodore Roosevelt, 1900–1912* (New York: Harper and Brothers, 1958) and Howard K. Beale, *Theodore Roosevelt and the Rise of America to World Power* (Baltimore: The Johns Hopkins Press, 1956). The Mowry book is part of *The New American Nation Series* edited by Henry Steele Commager and Richard B. Morris. Beale's work is taken from the Albert Shaw Lectures on Diplomatic History for 1953. The National Edition of *The Works of Theodore Roosevelt*, twenty volumes. (New York: Charles Scribner's Sons, 1926) is of prime importance in understanding his variety of naturalism. A major source in comprehending Roosevelt's truly conservative and racist philosophy is *The Letters of Theodore Roosevelt*, eight volumes. (Cambridge, Harvard University Press, 1951–1954) edited by Elting Morison. In addition to occasional essays by historians of progressives, the Morison edition has an exceedingly good index. Roosevelt's introduction to Edward A. Ross, *Sin and Society* (Boston: Houghton Mifflin, 1907) is a revealing statement of Roosevelt's mixture of moralism and naturalism. Incidently *Sin and Society* itself must be classified as major bibliographic item of progressivism.

Chapter VIII

Fortunately, psychology has been the subject of a number of historical treatments. John C. Flugel's account of *A Hundred Years of Psychology*, second edition (London: Gerald Duckworth and Co., Ltd., 1953) is good but brief. A. A. Roback briefly discusses *A History of American Psychology* (New York: Library Publishers, 1952). Edwin G. Boring's *A History of Experimental Psychology*, second edition (New York: Appleton-Century-Crofts, 1950) is a fuller discussion and includes more than experimental psychology. Boring also contributed "The Influence of Evolutionary Thought upon American Psychological Thought," *Evolutionary Thought In America* (New York: reprinted by George Braziller, Inc., 1956), edited by Stow Persons. This book was most valuable in tracing the manifestations of Darwin's thought on American ideas. Fay Berger Karpf provides a most intelligent analysis of *American Social Psychology, Its Origin, Development, and European Background* (New York: McGraw-Hill, 1932). In like manner, Jay Wharton Fay indicates the greater clerical influence on *American Psychology Before William James* (New Brunswick, New Jersey: Rutgers University Press, 1939). Merle Curti treats the larger influences on *The Social Ideas of American Educators with a New Chapter on the Last Twenty-Five Years* (Patterson, New Jersey: Pageant Books, Inc., 1959). The edition is, except as noted in the title, a reprint of the classic written for the American Historical Association Commission on the Social Studies. Gardner Murphy's *Historical Introduction to Modern Psychology,* revised edition (New York: Harcourt, Brace, and Co., 1949) is close to a standard history of ideas such as the Curti volume. Robert S. Woodworth, *Contemporary Schools of Psychology,* revised edition (New York: The Ronald Press, 1948) gives an adequate introduction to twentieth-century psychology.

W. B. Pillsbury gives an adequate biography in "Biographical Memoir of James McKeen Cattell, 1860–1944," *National Academy of Sciences Biographical Memoirs,* XXV (1947), 1–16. The Galtonian subject matter and conclusion are quite apparent in Cattell's articles: "The Causes of the Declining Birth Rate," *Proceedings of the First National Conference on Race Betterment* (Battle Creek: Race Betterment Foundation, 1914), 67–72, and "Statistical Study of American Men of Science," *Science,* n.s. XXXIV (November 23, 1906), 699–707; (November 30, 1906), 732–742; (December 7, 1906), 633–648; (November 10, 1910), 672–688. Cattell traced the "The Advance of Psychology" in the *Proceedings of the American Association for the Advancement of Science,* LVII (August 1898), 441–453. He revealed his life-long interest in "Scientific Societies and Associations" for *Monographs on Education in the United States* (Division of Exhibits: Department of Education Universal Exposition, St. Louis, 1940).

Lorine Pruett's *G. Stanley Hall, A Biography of a Mind* (New York: D. Appleton and Co., 1926) is inadequate. Hall's autobiography *Life and Confessions of a Psychologist* (New York: D. Appleton and Co., 1923) is remarkably candid as is his *Recreation of a Psychologist* (New York: D. Appleton and Co., 1920). *Letters of G. Stanley Hall to Jonas Gilman Clark* (Worcester, Mass: Clark University Library, 1948) edited by Orwin N. Rush reveals the formal relationship between Hall and the founder of Clark University. Of a lighter appeal of Hall's personality is his "Boy: Life in a Massachusetts Country Town Forty Years Ago," *Aspects of Child Life and Education* (Boston: Ginn and Co., 1907).

Hall was a productive scholar. His *Adolescence, Its Psychology and Its Relation to Phylogeny, Anthropology, Sociology, Sex, Crime, Religion and Education,* two volumes. (New York: D. Appleton and Co., 1922), and his *Educational Problems* (two volumes published by the same company in 1911) provide a broad discussion of Hall's genetic psychology. The naturalism and eugenics of his psychology are indicated by his articles: "A Study of Fears," *The American Journal of Psychology*, VIII (1897), 147–249; "The Point of View toward Primitive Race," *The Journal of Race Development*, I (July 1910), 5–11; and "Psychological Notes on the War," *ibid.*, VI (April 1916), 357–369. The vast scope of Hall's writing cannot be discussed in detail but G. E. Partridge compiled the *Genetic Philosophy of Education, An Epitome of the Published Educational Writings of President G. Stanley Hall of Clark University* (New York: Sturgis and Walton, 1912), giving a fine comprehension of his philosophy.

Just as Edward L. Thorndike wrote the "Biographical Memoir of Granville Stanley Hall, 1846–1924," *National Academy of Science of the United States of America, Biographical Memoirs*, XII (1925), 135–180, Robert S. Woodworth discussed "Edward Lee Thorndike, 1874–1949," *ibid.*, XXVII (1952), 209–237. These biographies are excellent summations of the two men's scientific activities. The Reverend Walter T. Pax gives a "A Critical Study of Thorndike's Theory and Laws of Learning" in *The Catholic University of America Educational Research Monographs*, XI (January 15, 1938), 7–175.

Thorndike's clearest statement of eugenics is his "Eugenics with Special Reference to Intellect and Character," *Eugenics: Twelve University Lectures* (New York: Dodd, Mead and Co., 1914). Like Hall, a productive writer, Thorndike published essentially the same message. He stressed heredity in human behavior in *The Human Nature Club, An Introduction to the Study of Mental Life* (New York: The Chautauqua Press, 1900) as well as *Individuality* (Boston: Houghton-Mifflin, 1911) and *Educational Psychology* (New York: Teachers College, Columbia University, 1914).

Thorndike's use of statistics in conjunction with other scholars is present in *The Measurement of Intelligence* (New York: Bureau of Publication, Teachers College, Columbia University, 1927). The same method Thorndike employs with Arthur I. Gates as coauthor in Elementary Principles of Education (New York: Macmillan, 1929).

William McDougall was the ideal type of Galtonian eugenist. He—like the American eugenists discussed in this bibliography—was active in writing and yet always repeated the same message of racial reconstruction. Only the bibliographically important items are discussed here.

He saw "The Correlation between Native and Social Status," *Eugenics in Race and State, Scientific Papers of the Second International Congress of Eugenics*, II (Baltimore: Williams and Wilkins Co., 1923), 373–377, as a matter of heredity. In his article "Can Sociology and Social Psychology Dispense with Instincts?" *The American Journal of Sociology*, XXIX (May 1924), 657–670, McDougall endorsed the importance of instincts in human activity. He also applied his instinctual psychology to American society in his two books—*Is America Safe for Democracy?* (New York: Charles Scribner's Sons, 1921) and *The Indestructible Union, Rudiments of Political Science for the American Citizen* (Boston: Little Brown and Co., 1925). McDougall's analysis was in the racist-eugenist tradition. In the same way, the psychologist used his creed of naturalism in solving philosophical problems in *Ethics and Some Modern World Problems* (New York: G. P. Putnam's Sons, 1924). His solution was eugenics within a Social Darwinian public policy. *Character and the Conduct of Life, Practical Psychology for Everyman* (London: Methuen and Co., Ltd., 1921) and *Modern Materialism and Emergent Evolution* (New York: D. Van Nostrand and Co., Inc., 1929) are merely extensions of the same ideas. McDougall saw science as the unifying and saving factor in *World Chaos, The Responsibility of Science* (London: Kegan Paul, Trench, Trubner and Co., Ltd., 1932). Like other Galtonian eugenists, McDougall was a child of the nineteenth century.

L. L. Bernard was McDougall's strongest critic concerning his instinct psychology. Bernard firmly rejected the concepts in *Instinct, A Study in Social Psychology* (New York: Henry Holt and Co., 1924). At the same time, Bernard's *An Introduction to Sociology, A Naturalistic Account of Man's Adjustment to His World* (New York: Thomas Y. Crowell Co., 1942) places him in the behaviorist tradition. With his wife Jessie as co-author, Bernard gives a clear explanation of how many nineteenth-century Americans saw science as an answer to problems of industrial America in the *Origins of American Sociology, The Social Science Movement in the United States* (New York: Thomas Y. Crowell, 1943).

Chapter IX

A brief but good discussion of anthropology is Thomas K. Penniman's *A Hundred Years of Anthropology*, second edition revised (London: Gerald Duckworth and Co., Ltd., 1952). T. Bendyske, "The History of Anthropology," *Memoirs Read before the Anthropological Society of London,* I (1863–64), 335–458, has historic value. Although old, Robert H. Lowie's *The History of Ethnological Theory* (New York: Farrar and Rinehart, 1937) is still valuable. Some key historical facts of anthropology are in *The Story of Human Error* (New York: D. Appleton-Century Co., 1936), edited by Joseph Jastrow. Despite its smug title, the book reveals the state of knowledge in the decade of the Great Depression in its attempt to reject earlier theories.

John C. Greene gives a brief historical sketch of pre-Darwinian theory and anthropology in "Some Early Speculation on the Origin of Human Races," *American Anthropologist,* LVI (February 1954), 31–39. Stanley M. Garn discusses the latest theory on the subject in "Race and Evolution," *ibid.,* LIX (April 1957), 218–223. In discussing *Man's Most Dangerous Myth, The Fallacy of Race,* third edition revised and enlarged (New York:

Harper and Brothers, 1954), Ashley Montagu indicates how, on some occasions, Darwinian thought supported the racist philosophy. Heredity was the answer to the race question and Montagu presents the latest findings in *Human Heredity* (New York: A Mentor Book Published by the New American Library, 1960). The science of measuring the human body, a practice which at one time led to racist conclusions, is clearly explained in Montagu's *A Handbook of Anthropometry* (Springfield, Illinois: Chares C. Thomas, 1960).

The idea of evolution greatly influenced the course of anthropological investigations. Ruth E. Moore presents an informative account in *Man, Time and Fossils, the Story of Evolution* (New York: Alfred A. Knopf, 1953). The essayists in *Evolution and Anthropology: A Centennial Appraisal* (Washington: The Anthropological Society of Washington, 1959), edited by Betty J. Meggers, ably discuss the development of anthropology since Darwin's day. For recent events in physical anthropology, one might read Gabriel W. Lasker, *The Evolution of Man, A Brief Introduction to Physical Anthropology* (New York: Holt, Rinehart and Winston, Inc., 1961).

Abram Kardiner and Edward Preble in their informative book *They Studied Man* (Cleveland: The World Publishing Co., 1961) discuss how social anthropologists discarded the old racist notions found in evolution. H. R. Hays's *From Ape to Angel, An Informal History of Social Anthropology* (New York: Alfred A. Knopf, 1958) is a solid account.

The father of American physical anthropology, Aleš Hrdlička discussed "Physical Anthropology: Its Scope and Aims; Its History and Present Status in America," *American Journal of Physical Anthropology*, I (April-June 1918), 133–183; (July-September 1918), 267–304; and (October-December 1918), 377–414. This journal is a valuable source since its pages discussed eugenics during Hrdlička's long editorship (hereafter cited as *AJPA*). He relates the importance of Mendel's concepts to physical anthropology in "Some Reflections Regarding Human Heredity," *Proceedings of the American Philosophical Society*, LXXV (April 18, 1935), 295–312. His conclusions are not dogmatic, for he also reviews other theories. He stresses the practical importance of his science in *Anthropological Investigations, One Thousand White and Colored Children of Both Sexes, The Inmates of the New York Juvenile Asylum* (New York: Wynkoge Hallenbeck Crawford Co., 1899). Adolph H. Schultz gives a good summary of Hrdlička's career in "Biographical Memoir of Aleš Hrdlička, 1869–1943," *National Academy of Sciences of the United States, Biographical Memoirs*, XXIII (1944), 305–338.

Marcus S. Goldstein, "Franz Boas' Contribution to Physical Anthropology," *AJPA*, n.s. V (June 1948), 145–161, is laudatory of the pioneer cultural anthropologist. A. L. Kroeber and others present a fuller account of his career in "Franz Boas, 1858–1942," *American Anthropologist*, n.s. XLV, (July-September 1943), 5–119. Walter Goldschmidt edits "The Anthropology of Franz Boas, Essays on the Centennial of His Birth," *ibid.*, n.s. LXI (October 1959), 1–163, which indicates the wide scope of Boas's investigations. Robert H. Lowie gives a good summary in "Biographical Memoir of Franz Boas, 1858–1942," *National Academy of Sciences of the United States, Biographical Memoirs*, XXIV (1947), 303–322. Boas' rejection of racial determinism is found in his "Human Faculty as Determined by Race," *Proceedings of the American Association for the Advancement of Science*, XLIII (August 1894), 301–327, and his classic *The Mind of Primitive Man* (New York: Macmillan, 1911).

Eugenists and many anthropologists saw crime as an expression of an individual's heredity. Arthur E. Fink traces the historical development of this idea in *Causes of Crime, Biological Theories in the United States, 1800–1915* (Philadelphia: University of Pennsylvania Press, 1938). R. L. Dugdale accepts hereditary determinism with a great deal of hesitation in "Hereditary Pauperism as Illustrated by the 'Juke' Family," *Proceedings of the Conference of Charities Held in Connection with the General Meeting of the American Social Science Association* (Boston: A. Williams and Co., 1877), pp. 81–99. The Reverend Oscar C. M'Cullock, "The Tribe of Ishmael: A Study in Social Degradation," *Proceedings of the National Conference of Charities and Corrections, 15th Annual Session* (Boston: Press of George H. Ellis, 1888), pp. 154–159, is quite certain that "blood tells." Arthur MacDonald, "Mental Ability in Relation to Head Circumference, Cephalic Index, Sociological Condition, Sex, Age and Nationality," *Publications of the American Statistical Association*, XII (December 1911), 798–804, and Arthur H. Estrabook, *The Jukes in 1915* (Washington, D.C.: Carnegie Institution of Washington, 1916) are two examples of hereditary determinism during the years of progressivism. Robert W. Hebberd, "The Development of State Institutions for the Mentally Defective in the State for the Next Decade," *Eugenics and Social Welfare, #2, Part I, State of New York State Board of Charities Department of State and Alien Poor* (Albany: The Capital, 1912) demonstrates how state agencies used eugenic concepts.

From 1870 to the Great Depression of 1929, magazines carried stories of human degeneration; for a number of reasons, the American population, argued the magazine writers, was becoming weak and racially inefficient. *The Popular Science Monthly* published many of these articles combining racial inadequacy with the causes of crime. Following are three examples of hereditary determinism as an explanation of disease and crime: A. DeQuaterfags, "Physical Characters of the Human Races," *ibid.*, II (March 1873), 541–552; John Reade, "The Intermingling of Races," *ibid.*, XXX (January, 1887), 336–351; and Dr. Nathan Oppenheim, "The Stamping out of Crime," *ibid.*, XLVIII (February 1896), 527–533. The subject of degeneration had a statistical orientation as indicated by Edward Hartwell, "A Preliminary Report on Anthropometry in the United States," *Publications of the American Statistical Association*, III (December 1893), 554–568, and Louis I. Dublin, "The Mortality of Race Stocks in Pennsylvania and New York, 1910," *Quarterly Publication of the American Statistical Association*, XVII (March 1920), 13–44. These articles maintained the distinction of native stock by hereditary means. Daniel G. Brinton claimed the same conclusion in "The Factors of Heredity and Environment in Man," *American Anthropologist*, XI (September 1898), 271–277. Twenty-two years later, Warren S. Thompson, "Race Suicide in the United States," *AJPA*, III (January-March 1920), 97–146, echoed Brinton's sentiment. E. R. Gould, "The Statistical Study of Hereditary Criminality," *Proceedings of the National Conference of Charities and Corrections, Twenty-Second Annual Session* (Boston: Press of George H. Ellis), pp. 134–143, reflects the social worker's concern, while S. Millington Miller, "The Ascent of Man," *Arena*, XII (March 1895), 130–135, demonstrated the concern in a popular journal. Cesare Lombroso, the major philosopher of the born-criminal concept reached the reading middle class with such an article: "The Heredity of Acquired Characteristics," *Forum*, XXIV (September 1897), 200–208. Finally, Milton Gold indicates a link between nineteenth-century theories of racial decay and Toynbee and Spengler's theories of history in "The Continuing Degeneration Controversy," *Bucknell Review*, X (December 1961), 87–101.

Earnest A. Hooton's investigations were based on nineteenth-century racism. A good example of his intellectual origins is found in "Observations and Queries as to the Effect of Race Mixture on Certain Physical Characteristics," *Eugenics in Race and State, Scientific Papers of the Second International Congress of Eugenics*, II (Baltimore: Williams and Wilkins Co., 1923), 64–74. The data and conclusions found in Hooton's articles "Progress in the Study of Race Mixture with Special Reference to Work Carried on at Harvard University," *Proceedings of the American Philosophical Society*, LXV (1926), 312–325, and "Preliminary Remarks on the Anthropology of the American Criminal," *ibid.*, LXXI (April 22, 1932), 349–355, are brought together in *The American Criminal, An Anthropological Study*, which is Volume I of *The Native White Criminal of Native Parentage* (Cambridge: Harvard University Press, 1939), a classic statement of the racial-causation-of-crime thesis. Hooton's *Crime and the Man* (Cambridge: Harvard University Press, 1939) is further evidence of his contention that criminality is hereditary. Hooton was a eugenist. His *Apes, Man* and *Morons* (New York: G. P. Putnam's Sons, 1937) and the *Twilight of Man* (New York: G. P. Putnam's Sons, 1939) are the anthropologist's versions of the eugenic creed. In *Man's Poor Relations* (Garden City: Doubleday,

Doran and Co., Inc., 1942), Hooton discredits modern charity as being dysgenic in nature. His *Up from the Ape*, revised edition (New York: Macmillan, 1946) is a classic statement of his kinship to the naturalist tradition in anthropology.

Chapter X

Although not calling post–Civil War social work "Scientific charity," Clifford S. Griffin gives keen insights into the sociopsychological origins of scientific charity in *Their Brother's Keeper: Moral Stewardship in the United States, 1800–1865* (New Brunswick, N.J.: Rutgers University Press, 1960). Frank J. Bruno covers in an adequate manner developments since 1874 in his book, *Trends in Social Work, 1874–1956, A History Based on the Proceedings of the National Conference of Social Work* (New York: Columbia University Press, 1957). Ralph E. and Muriel W. Pumphrey, *The Heritage of American Social Work* (New York: Columbia University Press, 1961), relates the philosophy of social work to institutional growth. A historian at Ohio State University, Robert H. Bremmer, is a close student of the history of charity. His *American Philanthropy* (Chicago: The University of Chicago Press, 1960), although small, is a handy introduction. This volume is part of the *Chicago History of American Civilization*, Daniel J. Boorstin, editor. Also his "Scientific Philanthropy, 1873–1893," *Social Service Review*, XXX (June 1956), 168–173, and "The Big Flat History of a New York Tenement House," *American Historical Review*, LXIV (October 1958), 54–62, are informative.

Amos Reynolds, M.D., "The Prevention of Pauperism," *Proceedings of the Sixth Annual Conference of Charities Held at Chicago, June, 1879* (Boston: Williams and Wilkins, 1879), pp. 210–216, is a classic statement of how science must "rescue" charity from racially destructive sentimentality. The academic viewpoint is presented by William H. Brewer, "The Relation of Universities to Charity and to Reformatory Work," *Proceedings of the National Conference of Charities and Corrections, Twenty-Second Annual Session* (Boston: Press of George H. Ellis, 1895), pp. 143–149. As late as 1930, and being the fourth edition, the standard textbook on *American Charities and Social Work* (New York: Thomas Y. Crowell Co., 1930), by Amos G. Warner, *et al.*, demonstrated its heritage of nineteenth-century scientific charity and racism.

As usual in his historical investigations, Merle Curti gives the basic outlines and themes of the subject in "Tradition and Innovation in American Philanthropy," *Proceedings of the American Philosophical Society*, CV (April 1961), 146–156. Developments in institutional history of charity since 1900 may be found in F. Emerson, "Growth and Present Status of American Foundations," *Proceedings of the American Philosophical So-*

ciety, CV (April 1961), 157–161. Wilmer S. Rich, *American Foundations and Their Fields,* seventh edition (New York: American Foundation's Information Service, 1955), contains some historical facts about foundations as does earlier editions of this book.

An idea of nature has, historically, provided support to the idea of conservation. Hans Huth traces the developments between the two ideas in *Nature and the American, Three Centuries of Changing Attitudes* (Berkeley: University of California Press, 1957). David C. Coyle, *Conservation, An American Story of Conflict and Accomplishment* (New Brunswick, N.J.: Rutgers University Press, 1957) is a general treatment of the topic. Of a more interpretative and informative nature, Samuel P. Hays, *Conservation and the Gospel of Efficiency, The Progressive Conservation Movement, 1890–1920* (Cambridge: Harvard University Press, 1959), discusses the philosophical basis for conservation. A part of that philosophy of preservation is examined by Gerald K. Marsden in "Philanthropy and the Boston Playground Movement, 1885–1907," *The Social Service Review,* XXXV (March 1961), 48–58.

Publications of the American Statistical Association (hereafter cited as *PASA*) contained many articles dealing with conservation of children, racial health, outdoor life, vs. urban existence and a host of similar topics. E. R. L. Gould, "Park Areas and Open Spaces in Cities," *PASA,* I (June-September 1888), 45–61, is typical of such articles. Laura O. Talbott, "How Shall We Utilize Vagrant Children?" *Proceedings of the American Association for the Advancement of Science,* XXXIX (August 1890), 447–449, indicates the wide intellectual appeal of using "science" in solving social problems. According to W. Townsend Porter's two articles, the relationship between physical and mental composition indicated the educational progress of the individual child: "On the Application to Individual School Children of the Mean Values Derived from Anthropological Measurements by the Generalizing Method," *PASA,* III (December 1893), 576–587, and "The Growth of St. Louis Children," *ibid.,* IV (March-June 1894), 28–34. By the turn of the century, social scientists such as J. E. Baker saw a connection between "City Life and Male Mortality," *ibid.,* XI (June 1908), 133–149. An associate of G. Stanley Hall, Alexander F. Chamberlain, saw many problems resulting from "The 'Antagonism' of City and Country," *Journal of Religion and Psychology, Including Anthropological and Sociological Aspects,* VI (July 1913), 279–293. One problem of urban life was its rapid population increase due to rural migration and immigration. Joseph A. Hill, "Comparative Fecundity of Women of Native and Foreign Parentage in the United States," *PASA,* XIII (December 1913), 583–604, forecast that native women by not producing more children contributed to racial decline. F. Stuart Chapin saw "Immigration as a Source of Urban Increase," *ibid.,* XIV (September 1914), 223–227, and he was displeased. John M. Gillette and George R. Davies concluded in "Measure of Rural Migration and Other Factors of Urban Increase in the United States," *ibid.*, XIV (September 1915), 642–652, that the city absorbed the better rural stock and thereby endangered America's racial future.

Gifford Pinchot, progressive and conservationist, tells his own story in *Breaking New Ground* (New York: Harcourt, Brace and Co., 1947). M. Nelson McGeary, *Gifford Pinchot, Forester, Politician* (Princeton: Princeton University Press, 1960) is the best biography; Martin L. Fausold, *Gifford Pinchot, Bull Moose Progressive* (Syracuse: Syracuse University Press, 1961) is too brief. Pinchot provided insight into his conservation creed with "The Conservation of Natural Resources," *United States Department of Agriculture, Farmer's Bulletin #327* (Washington: Government Printing Office, 1908). In conjunction with Charles O. Gill, Pinchot wrote *The Country Church, The Decline of Its Influence and the Remedy* (New York: Macmillan, 1913), indicating his interest in rural America. Later, Pinchot, aided by the Federal Council of the Churches of Christ in America, wrote *Six Thousand Country Churches* (New York: Macmillan, 1920), tracing the decline of rural religious institutions.

Philip Dorf, *Liberty Hyde Bailey, An Informal Biography* (Ithaca, New York: Cornell University Press, 1956) and Andrew D. Rogers, III, *Liberty Hyde Bailey, A Story of American Plant Science* (Princeton: Princeton University Press, 1949) provide adequate biographical information. Bailey's use of the inheritance of acquired characteristics theory and evolution are present in his "The Factors of Organic Evolution from a Botanical Standpoint," *Annual Report of the Smithsonian Institution* (Washington: Government Printing Office, 1898), pp. 453–475, and *The Survival of the Unlike, A Collection of Evolution Essays Suggested by the Study of Domestic Plants*, fifth edition (New York: Macmillan, 1906).

For a while Bailey was editor of *Country Life in America*, a magazine dedicated to saving the countryside with its values of agrarian aristocracy; the following article is a good example of such a philosophy: "Ellerslie, An American Country Seat, The Estate of Levi P. Morton—A Representative of the Best Ideals in Country Living," *Country Life in America*, I (November 1901), 9–13. On occasion, Bailey was quite poetic in discussing "The Abandoned Farm," *ibid.*, I (November 1901), 3–8. He also edited *Cyclopedia of American Agriculture, A Popular Survey of Agricultural Conditions, Practices and Ideals in the United States and Canada*, four volumes (New York: Macmillan, 1909).

L. H. Bailey was chairman of the Country Life Commission. He gives a clear statement of the neophysiocratic orientation of his philosophy in the *Report of the Country Life Commission* (February 9, 1909), 60th Congress, 2nd Session, Senate Document No. 705. He used this report in his *The Country-Life Movement in the United States* (New York: Macmillan,

1911). Bailey discussed his political views in *The Harvest of the Year to the Tiller of the Soil* (New York: Macmillan, 1927). George W. Fiske supported Bailey's beliefs in *The Challenge of the Country, A Study of Country Life Opportunity* (New York: Association Press, 1916).

Chapter XI

Rene Dubos's *Mirage of Health, Utopias, Progress, and Biological Change* (New York: Harper and Brothers, 1959) is a philosophical discussion about the illusion of perfect health in a universe of disease and death. Conway Zirkle discusses the political implications and uses of biological theories in *Evolution, Marxian Biology and the Social Scene* (Philadelphia: University of Pennsylvania Press, 1959). L. C. Dunn and Theodosius Dobzhansky in their *Heredity, Race and Society,* revised and enlarged edition (New York: Mentor Book Published by the New American Library, 1957), reject racial theories of superiority. *Genetics in the Twentieth Century* (New York: Macmillan, 1957), edited by L. C. Dunn, gives historical and contemporary information on the development of the science of heredity. This book is an excellent source. Dobzhansky discusses *The Biological Basis of Human Freedom* (New York: Columbia University Press, 1956) and thereby rejects the determinism of Galtonian eugenics. Herbert J. Webbes gives the Galtonian analysis in "Eugenics from the Point of View of the Geneticist," *Eugenics: Twelve University Lectures* (New York: Dodd, Mead and Co., 1914). For a discussion of the historical relationship between evolution and heredity, one might read Jay Heslop-Harrison, "Genetics and 'The Origin of Species,'" *Science Survey*, I (New York: Macmillan, 1960). A. W. Haslett and John St. John are editors of the book. A pioneer geneticist, Sewall Wright, provides a convenient review of genetics in "Genetics and Twentieth Century Darwinism, A Review and Discussion," *The American Journal of Human Genetics*, XII (September 1960), 365–372. The best brief historical and scientific statement of genetics is L. C. Dunn, *A Short History of Genetics* (New York: McGraw Hill, 1965).

A. E. E. McKenzie, *The Major Achievement of Science,* two volumes. (Cambridge, England: The Syndics of The Cambridge University Press, 1960), and editors of *Fortune, Great American Scientists, America's Rise to Forefront of World Sciences* (Englewood Cliffs, N.J.: Prentice-Hall, Inc., 1961), are two good sources of the intellectual and biographical developments in the science of genetics. Louis Wirth performs the same task for "The Social Sciences," *American Scholarship in the Twentieth Century* (Cambridge: Harvard University Press, 1953). Merle Curti is editor of the book.

Naturalism, of course, is a large topic, but two books recently published by the University of Texas Press are two examples of contemporary uses of the philosophy. C. Judson Herrick, *The Evolution of Human Nature* (1956) relates naturalism with behaviorism; *Modern Science and Human Freedom* (1959) by David L. Miller is a latter-day version of Darwinian evolution fused with a democratic faith in science. In editing *Man, Race and Darwin* (London: Oxford University Press, 1960), Philip Mason stressed the innately democratic values of evolutionary thought. Hudson Hoagland and Ralph W. Burhoe in editing *Evolution and Man's Progress* (New York: Columbia University Press, 1962) trace developments in scientific research since 1930.

In writing a book review—"Schlesinger: Right Crisis—Wrong Order," *The Nation*, CLXXXIV (March 23, 1957), 257–260—William Appleman Williams analyzes the intellectual crises the progressives experienced during the Great Depression of 1929. Williams's article is brilliantly suggestive.

During their greatest popularity, eugenists and eugenics experienced a great deal of criticism. Two of the most delightful debunkings of the Galtonian faith are G. K. Chesterton, *Eugenics and Other Evils* (New York: Dodd, Mead and Co., 1927), and Harvey Wickham, *The Misbehaviorists, Pseudo-Science and the Modern Temper* (New York: The Dial Press, 1928). Morris Ginsberg's *Essay in Sociology and Social Philosophy*, Volume I of *On The Diversity of Morals* (New York: Macmillan, 1957) is a serious and damaging attack on eugenics. Galtonian eugenists never recovered their intellectual respectability after the attack made by the eminent geneticist, Herbert J. Muller, "The Dominance of Economics, a Paper Delivered at the Third International Eugenics Congress," *BCR*, XVI (October 1932), 236–238.

Since 1930 the environmental and democratic behaviorism of social scientists has influenced the course of eugenics. Frederick Osborn, a eugenist, discusses this "Development of a Eugenic Philosophy," *American Sociological Review*, II (June 1937), 389–397. He claimed that "The American Concept of Eugenics," *The Journal of Heredity* (March 1939), 110, was anti-Galtonian in orientation. Osborn's *Preface to Eugenics*, revised edition (New York: Harper Brothers, 1951) completely rejects Sir Francis Galton's values that shaped American eugenics before the days of the New Deal. Sheldon C. Reed traces the fortunes of "The Local Eugenics Society," *The American Journal of Human Genetics*, IX (March 1957), 1–8, and in so doing reveals why eugenics ceased to have wide public appeal.

As for the future, Herbert J. Muller is moderately optimistic that the genetic composition of individuals will loom larger in public policy in "Progress and Prospects in Human Genetics," *The American Journal of Human Genetics*, I (September 1949), 1–18. C. P. Blacker subscribes to the same general thesis in "Eugenics in an Atomic Age," *The Sixth International Conference on Planned Parenthood* (London: The International

Planned Parenthood Federation, 1959). Finally, a foreign policy note: R. A. McConnell gives an account of a hypothetical positive eugenics program used in biological warfare in "The Absolute Weapon," *The AIBS Bulletin,* XI (June 1961), 14–16. One wonders what Sir Francis Galton would have thought of developments since his formulation of the eugenic creed.

INDEX

of family restoration, 73; natural
female desire, 79–80; natural selection, 74–75; natural social control,
80; neo-Malthusianism, 73; new-
woman movement, 72; questioned by
eugenics, 83–84; racial efficiency, 80;
romantic love, 70–71; Roosevelt's atti-
tude, 126, social control, 73; social
science, 81; sterilization, 95; Walter
Lippmann's attitude, 73–74.
Birth Control Review, 77, 101.
Board of Children's Guardians of St.
Louis, 195–196.
Boas, Franz, 147, 149, 173–174; Galton,
174
Bohemians: nineteenth century, 46
Bowditch, Henry P., 34, 173
Boy Scouts: eugenic implications of, 196
Bremner, Robert, 189–190
Brewer, William, 45; charity laws of,
188–189
Brill, A. A., 153
Brinton, Daniel G., 174–175, 186;
Negro, 175
Bryan, William Jennings, 120
Buck v. *Bell*, 91
Buck, Carrie, 91
Bull Moose Party, 128

Calvinism, 63
Carnegie, Andrew, 51, 116, 189–190
Castle, William E., 34: Mendel's
theories, 49
Castration: not sterilization, 87
Cattell, James McKeen, 146, 147; an-
thropology, 149; biography, 148–151;
human nature, 150; influence of Gal-
ton, 149–150; mental testing, 150–
151; organizational activities, 150
Chandler, Warren A., 16
Changing West, The, 118–119
Charity, 5, 63, eugenics on, 182–184
Civil Conservation Corp, 196
Civil War: changes in U.S. after, 40–41
Civilization: corrupt influence of, 8
Class struggle, 157, examples of, 46
Claverach College, 76
Columbia University, 51
Committee on Immigration and Natural-
ization, 65
Commons, John, 169
Comstock, Anthony, 77
Comte, Auguste, 10; positivism, 11–12
Conference of Governors at the White

House, 194
Congress, 66
Conservation, 182; child welfare move-
ment, 193; Davenport's policy, 195;
human beings, 192; immigration
restriction, 195–196; natural laws of,
191–192; "popular front" aspect,
194.
Conservatives: birth control, 81
Cook, O. F., 197
Cooley, Charles, 161, 176
Cope, Edward Drinker, 38
Correns, K., 48
Country Life Commission, 198–199
Country-life movement, 182, 197
Crania Americana, 165
Croly, Herbert, 20, 31, 32, 102, 103,
138, 158; biography, 109–114; class
analysis, 110–111; closing of the fron-
tier, 113; defense of war, 113–114;
efficiency, 112; Alexander Hamilton,
111–112, influence by Comte, 110;
instinct psychology, 114; Thomas
Jefferson, 111; nationalist, 112; Negro,
112; philosophic influences on, 110,
Roosevelt, 111; trade unions, 112–
113.
Crum, Frederick, 178
Cultural anthropology, 177
Culture: social thought, 186

Darwin, Charles, 18, 60; anthropology,
influence on, 166; psychology, 145–
146
Darwinism: Hegelian relationship, 15
Davenport, Charles B., 4, 10, 42, 48,
52, 53, 55, 64, 65, 172, 176, 179,
212; anti–natural rights, 92; biography, 56–57 class struggle, 59; conservation, 195; crime, 59; distrust of
cities, 59; eugenics, defense of, 206;
genetics, 207–208; racist beliefs, 57–
58; relationship with Galton, 34, 214;
role in Eugenics Record Office, 51;
Roosevelt, 121; Sanger, 83; scientific
charity, 58–59; sterilization, 94–95;
support of birth control, 58; support
of immigration restriction, 58; use of
Mendel's theories, 50
Declaration of Independence, 13
Democracy: racial basis, 74
Department of Genetics, 57
Descent of Man, The, 163